The
Teacher-Friendly
Guide™

to Climate Change

Edited by Ingrid H. H. Zabel, Don Duggan-Haas, & Robert M. Ross

Paleontological Research Institution
2017

ISBN 978-0-87710-519-0
Library of Congress no. 2017940300

PRI Special Publication no. 53

© 2017 Paleontological Research Institution
1259 Trumansburg Road
Ithaca, New York 14850 USA
priweb.org

First printing May 2017

This material is based upon work supported by the National Science Foundation under grant 1049033. Any opinions, findings, and conclusions or recommendations are those of the author(s) and do not necessarily reflect the views of the National Science Foundation.

Layout and design by Jonathan R. Hendricks. The interactive online version of this *Teacher-Friendly Guide™* (including downloadable pdfs) can be found at http://teacherfriendlyguide.org. Web version by Brian Gollands.

The *Teacher-Friendly Guide™* series was originally conceived by Robert M. Ross and Warren D. Allmon.

The *Teacher-Friendly Guide™* is a trademark of the Paleontological Research Institution.

Cite this book as:
Zabel, I. H. H., D. Duggan-Haas, and R. M. Ross (eds.), 2017, *The Teacher-Friendly Guide to Climate Change*. Paleontological Research Institution, Ithaca, New York, 284 pp.

Cite one chapter as (example):
Duggan-Haas, D., 2017, Why Teach about Climate Change? Pages 1–8, in: Zabel, I. H. H., D. Duggan-Haas, and R. M. Ross (eds.), 2016, *The Teacher-Friendly Guide to Climate Change*. Paleontological Research Institution, Ithaca, New York.

On the front cover: the "Blue Marble." Composite images produced by NASA in 2001-2002.

On the back cover: Atmospheric CO_2 concentration at Mauna Loa Observatory from 1958 to 2014 (NOAA).

Preface

The subject of climate change has become so socially and politically polarizing that it may be awkward to bring it up in polite conversation if one is not already sure of where others stand on the issue. But climate change is happening, and it's essential for all to have an accurate understanding of the findings and implications of climate science: climate change is one of the most critical issues of the 21ˢᵗ century. Indeed, in the context of school curricula, it is difficult to imagine a subject that is *not* in some way affected by climate change or the processes of mitigating or adapting to it, so there are potentially myriad connections of this subject to just about everything that goes on in the classroom.

Despite this importance, even the basic science of climate change has until recently appeared much less in K-12 education than might be expected. Its presence is now accelerating, however, facilitated in part by its integration into the Next Generation Science Standards, and there are many existing books on climate change and some excellent online resources for teachers to help with integration of climate change into curricula. Yet there exist few user-friendly books on climate change, written *for teachers*, that include both the basics of climate change science *and* perspectives on teaching communities of learners across the polarized spectrum. That is a need we seek to help fill with this volume.

This book was written for teachers who could benefit from a "teacher-friendly" resource on climate change. Our focus audience is high school Earth science and environmental science teachers, but we expect that a much wider audience will find it useful, including educators of other grade levels, subjects, and contexts, as well as non-teachers who find the approach helpful. Ultimately schools may find it an effective strategy to incorporate climate change across disciplinary boundaries, including all STEM subjects, social studies, and other humanities. Climate change is a scientific issue, but it is also a historical, social, psychological, and economic issue that can only be deeply understood through mathematics, language and art. Like any book about a topic as complex and growing as climate change, this one is just a starting point, thus we have listed sets of resources at the end of each chapter.

Over the past decade, we (educators at the Paleontological Research Institution) have been involved in providing educational outreach on a number of topics that are sociopolitically controversial, including not only climate change, but energy choices (in particular, hydraulic fracturing), as well as the long-standing issues of biological evolution and deep geologic time. While each of these topics has its own unique set of characteristics, what all have in common is polarized attitudes often more closely tied to social identity in peer groups than to scientific understandings. Since these cognitive issues have implications for teaching, this book explores such factors, with the goal of improving empathy for how our students and communities (and we ourselves) have come to believe what we do.

This book focuses on scientific aspects of climate change: how climate works and why scientists think it's changing, and the science and engineering behind the steps that would mitigate climate change and enable humans to adapt to climate changes that do occur. These scientific conclusions, and the content of this book, aren't intended to translate into support for specific political policies; that is a matter of societal values, politics, and voter choices. The book does take as a fundamental point of departure throughout, however, that *the net impact on many people of unbridled climate change is expected to be strongly negative, and that certain kinds of education and actions (such as using less energy) would be necessary to slow it down.*

We focus especially on why scientists think human-induced climate change is happening, yet we do not present the existence of climate change as a debate. While all scientific hypotheses are, in principle, provisional, there is such a substantial set of independent evidence that climate change is happening now, built across decades by thousands of climate scientists internationally, that we treat the broad phenomenon of human-induced climate change as effectively "true." There is, however, scientific uncertainty about countless details such as the rates of change and interactions among components of the climate system; this is the nature of research on all complex systems, and is important to understand as an aspect of scientific practices.

This volume is a sister to a series of seven *Teacher-Friendly Guides*™ to regional Earth science, covering all 50 states. PRI also has two *Teacher-Friendly Guides*™ to evolution using model organisms, one focused on bivalve mollusks (clams and their kin) and one on maize. This volume and the others are all available at http://teacherfriendlyguide.org as interactive websites and downloadable pdfs, and in grayscale printed hard-copies.

We welcome your feedback on *The Teacher-Friendly Guide to Climate Change* and hope you find it useful.

Robert M. Ross, Associate Director for Outreach
Don Duggan-Haas, Director of Teacher Programs
Ingrid H.H. Zabel, Climate Change Education Manager

Paleontological Research Institution
April 2017

Table of Contents

Contributors

From the Paleontological Research Institution, Ithaca, NY:

Don Duggan-Haas
Alexandra F. Moore
Robert M. Ross
Ingrid H. H. Zabel

From the Center for Global Change Science, Massachusetts Institute of Technology, Cambridge, MA:

Benjamin Brown-Steiner

Chapter 1:
Why Teach About Climate Change?

Weather tells you what clothes to wear and climate tells you what clothes to own.[1] In most places, a look out the window can provide good insights into the local climate (*Box 1.1*). The Earth's climate is changing, and the changes are primarily the result of human activities. **Climate change**[2] is a real and serious problem for our environment and for humanity, and we can take actions that will make the problems less serious. These issues, which are expected to influence the lives of our students for decades to come, make climate change an important topic for the classroom.

As a teacher, your starting point in planning to teach about climate change depends upon a mixture of very local and personal factors. Questions to ask yourself as you move forward include:

- What do I know about climate?
- What do the learners I'm working with know about climate?
- What relevant misconceptions do my students and I hold?
- What district, state, and national standards do I need to attend to?
- How has climate shaped my community, my region, my country, and the world?
- How is climate change likely to affect things in the coming decades?
- How do I navigate the interconnected scientific, political, economic, and psychological factors connected to this incredibly complex problem?
- What are the most important facts and ideas for my students to know and understand about climate change?

This book will help you begin to answer these questions. Some of the questions, however, are richly complex and areas of ongoing research and affected by ongoing societal change, and thus will involve a lifetime of learning.

climate change • *the current increase in the average surface temperature worldwide, caused by the buildup of greenhouse gases in the atmosphere, and the related changes to other aspects of climate such as precipitation patterns and storm strength. See also GLOBAL WARMING.*

---

[1] In practice, climate scientists define climate based on weather averaged over a span of 30 years or more.

[2] In this volume we generally use the term "climate change" rather than the approximate synonym "global warming," since the climate change the Earth experiences involves more than just temperature increase. Technical scientific literature tends to use "climate change."

CHAPTER AUTHOR

Don Duggan-Haas

Why Teach Climate Change?

Weather is the face of climate. Look out the nearest window to look it in the eye. How has the climate shaped what you see? What do the plant life, the types of buildings, the weather right now, the vehicles that you see, and the clothes people wear indicate about the climate?

Climate's fingerprints likely cover much of the view out your window. Animals, plants, people, and infrastructure are all adapted to the climate. Anytime of year, the area around Buffalo, New York looks very different from the area around Phoenix, Arizona. It doesn't need to be a winter day to be able to tell that a place probably gets below freezing in the winter. Even if it's raining, you might be able to identify a place that doesn't get much rain. What are climate's telltale signs?

(A) Deciduous forest (near Buffalo, NY). (B) A desert setting (near Phoenix, AZ). What visual clues tell you these places differ in their climates, even though the weather on the days these photographs were taken may have been fairly similar?

See Chapter 3: What is Climate? for a more detailed explanation of weather and climate.

1. Why Teaching About Climate Change Matters

"We basically have three choices: mitigation, adaptation, or suffering. We're going to do some of each. The question is what the mix is going to be. The more mitigation we do, the less adaptation will be required and the less suffering there will be."

- John Holdren, 2007

John Holdren was president of the American Association for the Advancement of Science when he made these remarks. His summation of the problem of climate change concisely describes the choices we face and does so without the level of pessimism sometimes included in such pronouncements. When it comes to climate change there *is* reason for pessimism, but there is also reason for hope. We have the capacity to act, and many of the actions we might take have benefits beyond climate. They also have the potential to save money in both the short and long term and to improve health and other measures of quality of life.

Why Teach Climate Change?

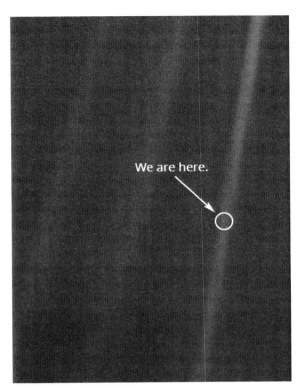

Figure 1.1: View of Earth from outside the Solar System, at a distance of about 6 billion kilometers, from the Voyager 1 spacecraft. The image was taken at the request of astronomer and educator Carl Sagan.

Scientific study of the size and age of the universe, and of the geological and fossil record on Earth, have helped us to understand that humanity is a blip in time on a speck in space[3] (*Figure 1.1*). Because everyone we know and love is encapsulated in this blip and speck, we treasure it deeply and want to preserve its richness, its diversity, and its life-supporting aspects. We are profoundly lucky to live *right here* and *right now*. We have a duty to preserve our luck for future generations. This does not speak to the absence or presence of forces beyond nature, but it does speak to the awesomeness and wonder of nature. Understanding the science of Earth systems may deepen our sense of wonder and of our responsibility for sharing it forward.

We educators are lucky to do what we do.

2. Science Learning, Its Application, and Politics

Effective and up-to-date teaching of the *science* of climate change is of paramount importance to good science education, but simply sharing scientifically accurate content is not the same as good teaching, and is not sufficient to build meaningful understandings. The science does make clear that the biggest challenges we will face in the coming decades will be related to climate, energy, water, and soil, which are inextricably linked with each other.

---

[3] In 1994 Carl Sagan and Ann Druyan published the book Pale Blue Dot: A Vision of the Human Future in Space. It focused on perspectives of Earth given our understanding of space.

1

Biases

Why Teach Climate Change?

Society depends upon a fairly stable climate, clean water, energy to power our way of life, and soil to provide the food we need.[4]

This book addresses the science of climate change, how to teach it, and climate change's interdisciplinary nature. And much more than that. All readers of this book are also well aware that climate change is a deeply socially and politically contentious issue, thus effective climate change teaching also requires an understanding of how people decide what is true and worth acting on. This means we must delve into the fields of sociology and psychology, to come to a deeper understanding of how our students think, why they think the way they do, and how to consider our own influences and biases.

There is an important philosophical distinction between educating about the science of climate change, and educating about the sorts of actions people can take to mitigate or adapt to climate change. The latter, in focusing on personal actions, may be perceived as encroaching upon political advocacy[5]. Effective science education, however, should be relevant to learners' lives, and climate change is a defining aspect of our current world. No matter what their political leaning, students will need to make lifestyle choices, make sense of the news, and vote; a scientifically literate citizenry will make better, more informed choices about science issues.

While teaching climate change we must, of course, be careful not to tread into political advocacy. Effective discourse and learning requires that students consider the classroom a safe place where their (and their families') world views will be respected. Working with other teachers may permit, however, exploring change from different social and economic perspectives. For example, students might explore how the implications of climate change will vary among professions (farmers, insurance brokers, military strategists, social workers, environmentalists, investors, or bankers), regions of the US, demographic setting (urban versus rural), and so on.

And we must communicate to our students that climate change is politically but *not scientifically* controversial. More than 97% of climate scientists agree that climate change is caused by human activity. Many in the general public believe scientists are divided, and that science teaching ought to address this (perceived) divide. There is uncertainty and disagreement about many of the finer details of climate change, but the overarching question of whether human-induced climate change is occurring is not questioned by a large percentage of climate scientists.

---

[4] Co-founder of Earth Day, Senator Gaylord Nelson noted, "The economy is a wholly owned subsidiary of the environment." An opportunity for cross-curriculum discussion with social studies, history, and economics could include mapping out how these environmental variables have influenced US and world history, and how they might influence the future.

[5] You can read a more in-depth review of these issues in Christopher Schlottmann's article "Climate Change and Education" in the book Canned Heat: Ethics and Politics of Global Climate Change (Ethics, Human Rights and Global Political Thought) (eds. Marcello Di Paola and Gianfranco Pellegrino), August 2014.

Why Teach Climate Change?

3. We All Have Biases

This book also gives attention to why many people have a difficult time accepting the scientific consensus behind climate change specifically, and, more generally, why perhaps everyone believes some refutable ideas. There are a wide range of reasons why people believe things that aren't true due to various kinds of **cognitive biases** and **logical fallacies**. Among the most important with respect to climate change are the closely related ideas of "**identity protective cognition**" and "motivated reasoning." These are the unintentional thought practices that help us preserve how we see the world and how we stay in good graces with people who think like we do—our "tribe."

There are obvious advantages to both fitting in with those we affiliate with and to maintaining internal consistency among our ways of thinking (worldview) about our community, the broader world, and ourselves. When new evidence threatens our worldview, we may find clever ways to discount the data to maintain our conceptions. When we cannot create explanations for data that seem to conflict with our views, we may instead compartmentalize our beliefs and thereby hold onto perceptions of the way the world works that are in conflict with one another.

Ultimately, we are likely to trust information from our own tribe, including solutions for maintaining our view in conflict with ample evidence. Determining the difference between reliable and unreliable information is a struggle that has persisted throughout human history and the amount of misinformation available related to both climate and energy is substantial. Problematic arguments (in climate change and elsewhere) stem from both sincere but incorrect information and explanations, and from intent to misinform; though we may blame people with different worldviews for the latter, the former is much more common. Responding to intentional falsehoods—lies—may require a different kind of response than falsehoods that are believed by the person making the argument.

See Chapter 10: Obstacles to Addressing Climate Change, for a more extensive discussion of cognitive issues.

4. Systems and Scales

To understand climate change deeply requires a systems perspective. You, the climate, and the Earth are all systems of systems. Understanding **systems**—the connections among individual components—is as important as understanding those components in isolation. Seeing things from a systems perspective requires some understanding of **feedback loops**, **tipping points**, the history of the system, and the ability to think across multiple scales (*Figure 1.2*). In terms of decision-making, it includes attention to the notion that advocating against a particular course of action often unintentionally carries advocacy for a course of action not considered.

The abstractions related to understanding very large and very small scales weakens our abilities to make sense of the science and mathematics of climate change and energy. For example, it is cognitively extremely challenging to

cognitive bias • *a holding on to incorrect thinking even in the presence of contrary information, because of beliefs or points of view one has.*

logical fallacy • *incorrect reasoning due to faulty logic.*

identity protective cognition • *a way of thinking that drives us to select the evidence that is consistent with the worldview of our social groups, sometimes leading us to believe certain things that are demonstrably false.*

system • *a combination of interacting parts whose interaction creates behaviors that might not occur if each part were isolated.*

feedback loop • *a repeating process where some of the output of a system becomes input as well.*

tipping point • *an event after which the behavior of a system changes or a phenomenon occurs. See also THRESHOLD.*

Why Teach Climate Change?

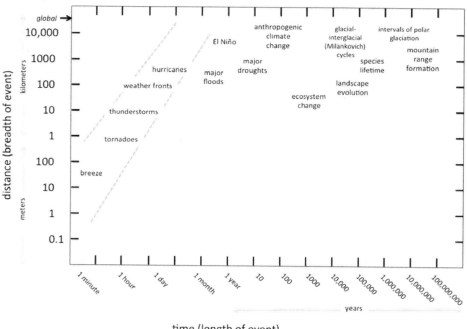

Figure 1.2: Weather and climate events in time and space, with other Earth system events for comparison, using logarithmic scales. On this plot events in time occur over a span of 15 orders of magnitude and in space over 7 orders of magnitude.

conceive of and compare large numbers such as a thousand, million, billion, and trillion. Time and space scales smaller and larger than common individual human experiences make it difficult to understand intuitively the importance of atmospheric greenhouse gases and the collective global impact of billions of individuals each influencing the environment in minor ways over decades. We ask our students and the general public to trust the idea that molecules they cannot see are real, that small percentages of the atmospheric composition nonetheless represent billions of trillions of molecules per liter, and that changes in the amount of these molecules over timescales stretching thousands to billions of years have influenced the history of Earth's climate.

Because systems and scales are inherently difficult concepts, we must find models and activities to help students past these hurdles. For these reasons and others we will need different approaches to education than traditional didactic and discipline-focused approaches.

5. Love and Beauty Will Persist

Engaging in the important work of climate and energy education can be profoundly depressing. Understanding the environmental challenges we face means confronting challenges that are on a scale perhaps never faced by humanity. Civilization and agriculture arose and came to thrive in a relatively stable climate, and it was the general stability of the climate that allowed the rise of civilizations. The climate is no longer as stable as it was, and is changing in some ways that will be difficult to adapt to and some that are difficult to predict. Teaching about it is also, however, an opportunity for full engagement in a purposeful life.

Why Teach Climate Change?

Figure 1.3: Aerial photograph taken in 1938 of land near Ithaca, NY and satellite photograph of the same area taken in recent years. This regrowth of forests is typical of many parts of the Northeastern US.

And though climate is changing, and we will almost certainly lose some wonderful environments, species, and human settlements, we won't lose it all, and to at least some degree new ones will also emerge. If the work gets you down, consider, for example, spending time in a natural environment. Many places that we consider of great beauty and value have been impacted by humans, such as in the widespread forests of the Northeastern US. Regrettably, almost none of this forest is original "old growth"—that was lost a few generations ago to humanity's hunger for fuel, building materials, and other land use. But in certain respects there is more nature in these areas than there was a century ago (*Figure 1.3*). And some of the lakes and rivers in the region are much cleaner than they were fifty years ago, as is the air of many cities. These are just a few examples of many stories in which increased scientific awareness, understanding, and change that people worked together to make have made a positive difference.

Why Teach Climate Change?

Resources

Books

Children's book author Lynne Cherry and photojournalist Gary Braasch offer an excellent introduction to climate change for middle grade students. Scientist detectives uncover mysteries of the Earth's climate history through mud cores, ice cores and tree rings and much more. The book is solution-focused and includes ways that kids can reduce their carbon footprints and emissions within their communities. Cherry, Lynne & Braasch, Gary. How We Know What We Know about Our Changing Climate: Scientists and Kids Explore Global Warming. Nevada City, CA: Dawn Publications, 2008.

Award-winning climate scientist Michael Mann and Pulitzer-Prize winning cartoonist Tom Toles offer rich insights into the science of climate change and how to communicate it with a sense of humor. Mann, Michael E., and Tom Toles. The Madhouse Effect: How Climate Change Denial Is Threatening Our Planet, Destroying Our Politics, and Driving Us Crazy. Columbia University Press, 2016.

Online Resources

The Skeptical Science website, https://www.skepticalscience.com/, offers a wide range of resources to investigate skepticism of climate skepticism.

The Debunking Handbook, https://skepticalscience.com/docs/Debunking_Handbook.pdf, is offered through Skeptical Science and carefully lays out strategies to avoid the backfire effect and more generally how to engage with people who disagree with the scientific consensus about human contributions to climate change.

Climate Change Evidence and Causes, The Royal Society and The National Academy of Sciences (2014), provides answers to frequently asked questions about climate change science: https://royalsociety.org/~/media/Royal_Society_Content/policy/projects/climate-evidence-causes/climate-change-evidence-causes.pdf.

Chapter 2:
What Should Everyone Understand About Climate Change and Energy?

1. What Do You Think?

In this chapter, we approach the question in the chapter's title in three different ways:

- We provide responses from experts we surveyed—scientists both from the natural and social sciences, journalists, and educators—on what they think is most important for everyone to understand, and to boil it down to about 100 words or less.
- We review consensus documents written through collaborations of scientists and educators. These ideas were developed with input from many individuals.
- We share a framework of key ideas developed for this book, but drawn from a series of Earth Science Overarching Questions and Bigger Ideas we have used in our programming for many years.

Before sharing the specifics of any of these ideas, we ask that readers consider the question themselves. If you are going through the trouble of reading the book, it's a question you've at least wondered about.

The ideas that we are asking you to consider here and those that are discussed throughout this chapter are metaphorically at the 30,000-foot level. It is the core ideas that should persist throughout one's life. Don Weinshank[1] summarized a great deal of educational research rather succinctly: Ninety percent of your students will forget 90% of the content of your course within 90 days of finishing the course. This statement carries with it at least two important implications. We need to rework the nature of education so it no longer holds true, and we need to think very carefully about what that 10% of the content that is retained is composed of. This chapter is about that 10%. It is also about crafting a coherent conceptual framework for instruction that will hopefully lead to more than 10% ultimately being retained.

Now please pause and consider the question in the chapter's title. Then we'll share the answers we received from a set of selected experts. You should write your ideas down, since going by memory alone can be misleading: by writing it down, you decrease the odds of fooling yourself and have a much more reliable record of changes in thinking.

CHAPTER AUTHOR

---

[1] Donald Weinshank was a Michigan State University professor. The 90% isn't based on research, but educators and learners alike widely agree on the spirit of the idea.

Don Duggan-Haas

Expert Opinions

---

climate change • the current increase in the average surface temperature worldwide, caused by the buildup of greenhouse gases in the atmosphere, and the related changes to other aspects of climate such as precipitation patterns and storm strength. See also GLOBAL WARMING.

---

fossil fuel • a non-renewable, carbon-based fuel source like OIL, NATURAL GAS, or COAL, developed from the preserved organic remains of fossil organisms.

---

system • a combination of interacting parts whose interaction creates behaviors that might not occur if each part were isolated.

What Should Everyone Understand?

The idea for this exercise came from Richard Feynman's similar question:

> *"If, in some cataclysm, all of scientific knowledge were to be destroyed, and only one sentence passed on to the next generations of creatures, what statement would contain the most information in the fewest words?"*[2]

2. Collecting Expert Opinions

We reached out to selected experts who work as climate scientists, as social scientists, as science educators, or as journalists with interests related to **climate change** communication. Feynman's answer about the most important scientific knowledge, and the invitation to contribute to our survey, are in an appendix at the end of this chapter.

2.1 What the Responses Say

Responses are arranged by author in alphabetical order.

Richard B. Alley, PhD, Evan Pugh University Professor, Department of Geosciences, and Earth and Environmental Systems Institute, The Pennsylvania State University:

> *"Wise policies that respect the solid scholarship on climate and energy will be helpful economically as well as environmentally and ethically."*

Or, Alley suggested, if we want an answer with more motivation, though a longer sentence, here's another option.

> *"We have a history of facing scarcity and unintended consequences after burning through energy sources such as trees, whales, and now **fossil fuels** far faster than nature makes more, but we are the first generation that knows how to build an energy **system** that can power everyone almost forever and that is economically beneficial, environmentally sound, and ethical."*

Don Duggan-Haas, PhD, Director of Teacher Programs, The Paleontological Research Institution:

> *"Fossil fuels both made modern society possible and endanger modern society. We know substantially reducing energy use is among the most straightforward ways to reduce the threats of climate change, yet we struggle to do so. Why? Largely because abandoning the status quo and forfeiting investments of time, money, and other resources is challenging psychologically even if the scientific evidence supporting such changes clearly shows wide ranging substantial benefits. These challenges are compounded by challenges related to: understanding perspectives of those who see the world differently than we do; thinking with a systems perspective; and, quite simply, being scared."*

---

[2] Feynman, R.P. 1963. The Feynman Lectures on Physics. Reading, MA., Addison-Wesley Publishing Company.

What Should Everyone Understand?

Alan Gould, PhD, specialist in Global Systems Science, University of California, Berkeley and The Lawrence Hall of Science:

"At first we might think that understanding climate change and making societies' energy systems sustainable are scientific and engineering endeavors respectively. But all too soon we realize they entail studies of economics, politics, sociology, psychology, religion, ethics, short-sightedness vs. long-term planning, greed vs. community spirit, and wholistic ecology vs. human-centeredness. They are wonderfully interdisciplinary and intricately interwoven."

Gabriele Hegerl, PhD, Fellow of the Research Society of Edinburgh, Chair of Climate System Science, GeoScience, University of Edinburgh:

*"The mean surface temperature of the planet is governed by **energy balance** between **solar** and **thermal fluxes**. If the balance changes, powerful feedbacks kick in to strengthen and change the climate response. They affect the global water cycle, the **cryosphere**, the **carbon cycle**, even the dynamics of the **atmosphere** and **oceans**. While some changes occur quickly, it takes centuries for climate to arrive at a new **equilibrium**, because the entire ocean needs to warm or cool, and **ice sheets** to change. Increasing **greenhouse gases** in the atmosphere changes the energy balance, and therefore starts these major changes."*

Joseph A. Henderson, PhD, is a research scientist at the University of Delaware where he specializes in climate change education.

"Climate change is a human construction. Millions of individuals have created a wicked collective action problem, and some bear more responsibility than others. Individual actions, while important, are insufficient to effect at scale. Educators must begin to teach collective solutions. Such a project is inherently political and cultural, and we should not shy away from this dimension of the challenge."

George Lakoff, PhD, Emeritus Professor of Linguistics, University of California at Berkeley:

"Systemic causation takes more than 100 words."

Lakoff advocates for use of the term "systemic causation" (in contrast to direct causation) for explaining such impacts of climate change as increased frequency in extreme weather events, noting that it is complex and hard to explain briefly.[3]

energy balance • *a state in which the energy coming in to a system equals the energy going out.*

solar flux • *the rate of flow of solar energy across an area such as the surface of the Earth.*

thermal flux • *the rate of flow of thermal energy across an area such as the surface of the Earth.*

cryosphere • *the part of Earth's surface where water exists in solid form. This includes all major forms of ice, such as SEA ICE, GLACIERS, ICE SHEETS and permafrost.*

carbon cycle • *the exchange and recycling of carbon between the geosphere, hydrosphere, atmosphere, and biosphere.*

atmosphere • *the layer of gases that surrounds a planet.*

ocean • *the large, saline body of water that covers most of the Earth's surface.*

equilibrium • *a state of balance in opposing forces, amounts, or rates.*

---

[3] See, e.g., Global Warming Systemically Caused Hurricane Sandy by G. Lakoff, 2012, The Huffington Post (http://www.huffingtonpost.com/george-lakoff/sandy-climate-change_b_2042871.html).

What Should Everyone Understand?

ice sheet · *a mass of glacial ice that covers part of a continent and has an area greater than 50,000 square kilometers (19,000 square miles).*

greenhouse gas · *a gas that absorbs and re-radiates energy in the form of heat; carbon dioxide, water vapor, and methane are examples.*

potential energy · *the energy stored within an object or system, due to its position (gravitational potential energy), charge (electric potential), or other characteristics.*

Sankey Diagram · *a diagram that depicts flows of any kind, where the width of each flow pictured is based on its quantity.*

R. G. (Bob) Landolt, Emeritus Professor of Chemistry, Texas Wesleyan University & currently, director of a Climate Science Toolkit Challenge Grant Project for the DFW Local Section of the American Chemical Society:

*"Twin major consequences impact the climate arising from using the high quality, **potential energy** stored in fossil fuels. Significant heat energy is wasted or "rejected" at every step in the energy flow, especially in the production and transmission of electricity, and carbon dioxide resulting from combustion and related processes has been generated in such quantities since the industrial revolution as to pose a threat to sustainable coexistence of many species, including humanity. The qualitative and quantitative aspects of these energy/mass flows are very complex and comprehension may be graphically demonstrated for past, present, and projected future through **Sankey Diagrams**.[4]"*

Tamara Shapiro Ledley, PhD, Senior Scientist, TERC:

"The Earth is a system of interacting components (air, water, land, life), each impacting the others and together shaping the Earth's climate. These components interact through the movement of energy (light and heat) and matter (water, gases, and minerals), determining the distribution of hot and cold temperatures and wet and dry conditions throughout the Earth system and influencing where and if life flourishes or declines."

Catherine Middlecamp, PhD, Professor, Nelson Institute for Environmental Studies, Madison, WI:

"Carbon is found in many places on our planet. It moves around. Where it ends up matters."

Joshua Sneideman, Einstein Fellow, Department of Energy, and middle school teacher, Irvine, CA:

"You can talk about energy without talking about climate change but you can't—shouldn't—talk about climate change without talking about energy."

Robert Ross, PhD, Associate Director for Outreach, Paleontological Research Institution:

"The climate system is complex, but the basic principles of human-induced climate change are not: the chemical properties of carbon dioxide have been long known, and we see the warming influence of CO_2 plainly from studies of other planets and Earth's history. Specific atmospheric CO_2 concentrations are not inherently good or bad. But current rapid rates of change in CO_2 and therefore climate are both faster and different than most natural changes in the geologic past. Such rapid changes will have impacts on humans and other life that, in many places, will lead to suffering and loss that cannot be undone."

---

[4] The 2016 Sankey Diagram for U.S. energy use can be viewed here: http://www.vox.com/energy-and-environment/2017/4/13/15268604/american-energy-one-diagram.

What Should Everyone Understand?

William S. Spitzer, PhD, Vice President - Programs, Exhibits, and Planning, New England Aquarium:

"We need to shift the climate change conversation from 'doom and gloom' to 'hope, innovation, and change.' We need to go beyond describing the impacts, to help people understand how our systems for energy and transportation need to shift away from burning fossil fuels. Environmental education used to focus on the small things we can do to make a difference. Given the scope of the problems we face, we need to do big things and make a big difference. We need to act as a community, realizing our potential as citizens, not just as consumers."

Laura Faye Tenenbaum, Senior Science Editor, NASA Jet Propulsion Laboratory:

*"We can move from powerlessness to powerful. Our choices are important and we can make a difference. Yes, **anthropogenic** climate change is the greatest challenge of our time, but it's also our greatest opportunity. Remember, without struggle and challenge, nothing ever improves. So decide to welcome climate change as an exciting impetus. It's an opportunity to come together; to connect with each other and the world around us, and to re-evaluate what's important so we can build a cleaner way of living using new technologies. Go on, take responsibility for whatever you can and work together to make a difference."*

Kevin E. Trenberth, PhD, Distinguished Senior Scientist, National Center for Atmospheric Research:

"Carbon dioxide is a product of burning fossil fuels and thus human activity. It has a remarkably long lifetime in the atmosphere: centuries. That is why concentrations continue to sky-rocket and values are over 40% above pre-industrial: more than half the increase is since 1980. Many politicians and the public seem to think that global warming can easily be stopped if and when they decide it is time. It is not true. There is huge inertia that requires long-term planning."

Jim White, PhD, Director, Institute of Arctic and Alpine Research, Professor, Geological Sciences and Environmental Studies, University of Colorado, Boulder:

*"One of the most faithful relationships in nature is that between global temperature and **sea level**; when air and water warm, land ice melts and sea level rises, and when the earth cools, land ice forms taking water out of the ocean. The physics are simple. What is profoundly surprising and not well known is that small changes in temperature lead to large changes in sea level; on average 1 degree C change corresponds to 15 to 20 meters of sea level change. Think about that as world leaders work to limit warming to a 2 degree C change."*

What Should Everyone Understand?

Ingrid Zabel, PhD, Climate Change Education Manager, The Paleontological Research Institution:

Two responses, one with an education perspective.

"1. Carbon emissions from the fossils fuels we burn to heat our buildings, generate electricity, and power our transportation are leading directly to a warming planet. We won't go back to a time before electricity, but we can be smarter about how we make and use energy. People are already taking action to limit climate change, and we need to join in to support their work, build on it, and innovate."

"2. How do we learn to read, to cook food, to use math to solve problems, to understand our past? Through education, with many different teachers to guide us. How are we going to reduce our carbon emissions so we can limit climate warming and secure our future? We start with education and then follow with action, so people understand that the goal is to find better ways to make and use energy, and that we can innovate and work toward this goal."

The collection of what we could call "big ideas" is impressively varied. We have purposefully not grouped them: you may wish to do this with your students. Do these ideas resonate with your own? Can you find common themes?

This section drew on individual responses. The next section discusses consensus documents of experts.

3. Consensus Documents

Several other documents already exist arising from initiatives to create a consensus among scientists and science educators of what everyone should know about climate change and energy. A fundamentally important document for those working to build understandings of climate is *Climate Literacy: The Essential Principles of Climate Science*.[5] This carefully crafted set of ideas was the result of a collaboration of many climate scientists and educators (including the author of this chapter). Its guiding principle might be considered a consensus statement of the most important thing everyone should understand about climate: "Humans can take actions to reduce climate change and its impacts." Seven more Climate Literacy Principles follow the guiding principle, each with several supporting concepts (see *Table 2.1*).

Another of those literacy documents that is important for anyone teaching about climate is *Energy Literacy: Essential Principles and Fundamental Concepts for Energy Education*[6] (see *Table 2.1*). Pundit Chris Hayes notes, "Teaching about climate change without teaching about energy is like teaching about lung cancer without teaching about smoking." Thus, those who teach about climate change should be at least somewhat familiar with both sets of principles.

---

[5] Climate Literacy: The Essential Principles of Climate Science, http://oceanservice.noaa.gov/education/literacy/climate_literacy.pdf.

[6] Energy Literacy: Essential Principles & Fundamental Concepts for Energy Education, https://energy.gov/eere/education/energy-literacy-essential-principles-and-fundamental-concepts-energy-education.

Table 2.1: The climate and energy literacy principles.[5, 6] For both sets of principles, each individual principle is supported by between five and eight fundamental concepts.

Climate Literacy Principles	Energy Literacy Principles
Guiding Principle: Humans can take actions to reduce climate change and its impacts. 1. The sun is the primary source of energy for Earth's climate system. 2. Climate is regulated by complex interactions among components of the Earth system. 3. Life on Earth depends on, has been shaped by, and affects climate. 4. Climate varies over space and time through both natural and man-made processes. 5. Our understanding of the climate system is improved through observation, theoretical studies and modeling. 6. Human activities are impacting the climate system. 7. Climate change will have consequences for the Earth system and human lives.	1. Energy is a physical quantity that follows precise natural laws. 2. Physical processes on Earth are the result of energy flow through the Earth system. 3. Biological processes depend on energy flow through the Earth system. 4. Various sources of energy can be used to power human activities, and often this energy must be transferred from source to destination. 5. Energy decisions are influenced by economic, political, environmental, and social factors. 6. The amount of energy used by human society depends on many factors. 7. The quality of life of individuals and societies is affected by energy choices.

In addition to the climate and energy literacy consensus documents, there are several literacy documents for other areas of Earth science (ocean science, atmospheric science, and (approximately) solid Earth science), each of which contain content relevant to climate change and energy. All of these documents are briefly described in Box 2, "Essential Earth system science ideas for science literacy."

4. Striving for a Coherent Conceptual Framework

While there is value in consensus documents that summarize the most important ideas within each discipline, taken together they also pose a serious challenge to educators in how or if to effectively cover them all. Collectively, they include 38 "big ideas" (easily half of which can be related to climate

Box 2: Essential Earth system science ideas for science literacy

Over the course of about eight years from 2004–2012, a series of consensus documents was written that compiled the most important ideas of several of the fundament spheres (subsystems) of Earth system science. Each document had a slightly different impetus for its creation, but each was influenced in general structure by the documents that came before it.[7] These documents collectively cover most of Earth system science, and all have parts relevant to climate change and energy.

- The Ocean Literacy Network created the publication Ocean Literacy, the Essential Principles for the Ocean Sciences K12 (http://oceanliteracy.wp2. coexploration.org/ocean-literacy-framework). The document summarizes principles in ocean literacy and maps them to the National Science Education Standards.[8]

- The construction of the Atmospheric Science Literacy Framework (https:// scied.ucar.edu/atmospheric-science-literacy-framework) involved creation of a set of essential principles for literacy in atmospheric science and climate broadly.

- The Climate Literacy Network created the guide Climate Literacy: The Essential Principles of Climate Science (http://cleanet.org/cln), a framework for understanding and communicating about climate science specifically, with special attention to climate change. The Climate Literacy Network is hosted by the Climate Literacy & Energy Awareness Network (CLEAN) (http://cleanet.org), which features an extensive set of educational resources.

- The booklet Energy Literacy: Essential Principles and Fundamental Concepts Framework (https://energy.gov/eere/education/energy-literacy-essential-principles-and-fundamental-concepts-energy-education) presents energy concepts to help individuals and communities make informed energy decisions.

- The Earth Science Literacy Principles (http://www.earthscienceliteracy. org) covers the most fundament concepts of the solid Earth geosciences, including interactions with hydrosphere and biosphere.[9]

- The approach of the Next Generation Science Standards (https://www. nextgenscience.org/) is to reimagine science education, with less attention to specific content areas ("Disciplinary Content Ideas") than previous sets of standards, replaced by more focus on the "Crosscutting Ideas" and "Science and Engineering Practices." The NGSS are based on the Framework K–12 Science Education (https://www.nap.edu/catalog/13165/a-framework-for-k-12-science-education-practices-crosscutting-concepts) created by the National Research Council.[10]

---

[7] The Earth Science Literacy Initiative is described at http://www.earthscienceliteracy.org/index.html, and brief descriptions of four other relative Earth system science initiatives are described under the tab "Complementary Projects."

change in some way) and 247 supporting concepts. There is, of course, some redundancy in big ideas among documents, and an ambitious teacher might try to boil the big ideas into a smaller set, but this isn't simple. Add to this the Next Generation Science Standards: eight science and engineering practices, seven crosscutting concepts, and thirteen disciplinary core ideas.

There are no examples of creating large sets of ideas everyone should understand about any topic that has led to broad understanding the target content, in spite of countless attempts to do just that throughout history. Without a coherent framework to connect them one to another, it isn't likely that learners will understand or remember them. We need a *smaller set* of *bigger* ideas – a small set that cut across all of the big ideas from the various Earth science disciplines.

Once again, pause and consider a slightly different version of our original question (What should everyone understand about climate and energy?). If there were just a *few key ideas* that everyone understood about climate and energy, what should those few ideas be? To share an example from another discipline, E.O. Wilson suggests that if we taught biology as stemming from two key ideas, we'd be more effective in our efforts. Wilson identifies two "laws" for biology:

1. All organic processes are ultimately obedient to the laws of physics and chemistry.
2. All living systems and processes evolved by natural selection.

If you were to identify a *small set of big ideas* for energy and climate change, what would those ideas be? Come up with a list of somewhere between two and seven ideas. Here are suggested guidelines for framing those ideas.

- Each idea cuts across the curriculum area (in this case, climate and energy).
- Understanding of each idea is attainable by students and the understanding holds promise for retention.
- Each idea is essential to understanding a variety of topics.
- Each idea requires uncoverage; it has a bottomless quality.

Furthermore, the entirety of climate change and energy's role in the curriculum should be represented by this (small) set of ideas. (Again, writing down your ideas is helpful.)

Our big questions and ideas about climate change might serve to frame a climate change course, but we expect that most readers of this book will instead be working within the context of other courses, with broader foci than climate change (or energy) alone. These climate change and energy ideas offer

---

[8] The National Science Education Standards (NSES: https://www.nap.edu/catalog/4962/national-science-education-standards), published by the National Research Council in 1996, are a set of guidelines for K-12 science education in the US. One way the NSES were notable was including Earth science as a major subject with biology, physics, and chemistry. The NSES were superseded with the release of the Next Generation Science Standards.

[9] A co-author of this Guide, Ross, was on the Earth Science Literacy Initiative organizing committee.

[10] The author of this chapter was on the Earth science team for development of the Framework K–12 Science Education.

What Should Everyone Understand?

a coherent conceptual framework that can be nested within larger frameworks that serve courses, or across different grades and disciplines.

In our programming[11] with teachers from around the country, we have long used a set of five fundamental Earth system science big ideas that are "one size up," that is, more generalized than our climate change big ideas. These Earth System Science Bigger Ideas and Overarching Questions can serve to frame a course or to provide guidance across a series of courses with Earth and environmental science content, and their design can be used as a model for assembling and creating lists of big ideas for courses in other disciplines. The following section describes these ideas and questions.

4.1 Our Five Bigger Ideas and Two Bigger Questions about Climate Change

Our questions and ideas draw from a range of sources. One of them is the guiding principle from "Climate Literacy: The Essential Principles of Climate Science" described above. That idea, "Humans can take actions to reduce climate change and its impacts," stands alone among all of the ideas because it potentially has the most significant outcome. Perhaps it ranks as the biggest idea. We worked to craft a set of ideas of roughly that scale, that collectively meet the criteria described in the preceding section.

The pedagogical idea of whittling the list of ideas down to a small number (such as five) is grounded in research on how people learn and the related implications for curriculum and instruction. It is widely known that the US has not fared well in international comparisons of achievement in science and mathematics. In secondary mathematics and science courses in the US, dozens of key concepts are addressed in a single year. In Japan, the typical course covers about seven major concepts, and they consistently outperform the US in international science tests. One explanation for the better performance is that students appear to learn more deeply with a smaller set of chosen concepts.

A number of researchers have suggested that quality instruction benefits from covering fewer topics in depth, emphasizing a small number of big ideas.[12] Identifying such big ideas can help teachers and students to build a conceptual framework that ties the ideas of the discipline together in a meaningful way, one that facilitates the retrieval and application of that organized knowledge (Donovan et al., 1999). These big ideas are obviously not the full set of understandings every high school graduate should have, but rather should serve as a foundation for all of those ideas. This was part of the thinking behind the development of the various sets of literacy principles, but because there are sets of ideas for each of the sub-disciplines that are typically taught within the same one-year middle or high school course, the problem of too many concepts re-emerges.

---

[11] By "our" we mean education programs of the Paleontological Research Institution (PRI).

[12] The book Understanding by Design by Grant Wiggins and Jay McTighe (2005) provides a good overview on why focusing instructional attention on a small set of big ideas is more likely to yield deeper and more durable understandings than traditional approaches. The National Academy of Science's Committee on How People Learn issued a series of reports on key findings on learning research, including the importance of coherent conceptual frameworks.

What Should Everyone Understand?

4.1.1 The First Three Bigger Ideas

The answers to the above question varies to some degree related to the context in which you teach, but there are common ideas and principles that apply across a wide range of settings. Some bottom-line ideas that summarize what people such as those we surveyed think can and should be understood by most anyone from grade school to grad school (and beyond) are the following.

1. *Climate change is a real and serious problem facing global society in the coming decades and centuries.*
2. *Climate change in recent decades is primarily caused by human activities, especially as related to energy use.*
3. *Humans can take actions to reduce climate change and its impacts.*

These ideas are simultaneously simple and complex. While each can be stated in a single, clear sentence, they also possess a bottomless quality that allows for continued productive investigation for learners in most any setting, and at most any level. Their bottomless nature means that there is always more to learn about each of them even though they can be understood in a meaningful way by most anyone. That bottomless nature also points to two more important ideas that are necessary for deep understandings of climate change.

4.1.2 Models and Maps: The Fourth Bigger Idea

A fourth idea that highlights the need for mathematical thinking as related to understanding climate, energy, and the broader Earth system:

4. *To understand (deep) time and the scale of space, models and maps are necessary.*

The Earth's climate has been changing throughout its 4.5 billion year history, but for the last 10,000 years, the climate has been relatively stable. Agriculture originated about 10,000 years ago, and civilization, which depends upon agriculture, has grown to what it is today within the confines of that relatively stable climate. In the last two and a half centuries, the concentration of carbon dioxide in the atmosphere has grown substantially from about 280 parts per million in pre-industrial times to more than 400 parts per million (and still increasing) today. This is an increase of more than 40% and that increase in CO_2 is driving a rapid (on geologic time scales) increase in global temperature.

Maps and models aid in the understanding of things that are not possible to observe directly, and in the comprehension of time and space at both immense and sub-microscopic scales.[13] Models are also essential for making predictions. Given that climate change plays out over numerous spatial scales from local and global, maps of various kinds will be among the most commonly used models in this kind of work. Graphs are also an important type of model, and *Figure 2.1* shows an especially relevant example.

---

[13] A discussion of scale, and of big ideas in Earth system science generally, can be found in the first chapter of each of the regional Teacher-Friendly Guides to Earth Science: http://geology.teacher-friendlyguide.org.

What Should Everyone Understand?

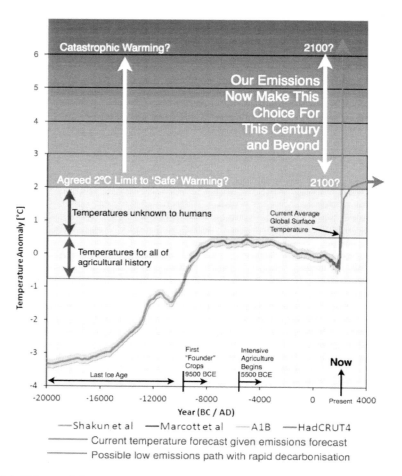

Figure 2.1: This graph is a model of climate change over the last 20,000 years and extending 4000 years into the future. Note that models are always limited in some ways. This shows only global average temperature over time. Climate is more than temperature. Since Homo sapiens *emerged as a species 200,000 years ago, the year 2016 experienced the warmest global temperature during that interval. (See Teacher-Friendly Guide website for a full color version.)*

Understanding geologic time entails understanding that humans as they are today have been around for only a remarkably small sliver of the history of the universe and occupy only the tiniest portion of the enormity of space. The graph in *Figure 2.1* shows only a tiny portion of geologic history: 24,000 years out of 4,540,000,000 years, or 0.0000053% of Earth history. Numbers and percentages are models as well.

4.1.3 Systems of Systems: The Fifth Bigger Idea

The fifth idea in this list of five is perhaps the most important, as all the others depend upon it. It highlights the importance of not only understanding the basics of climate and its component sciences, but also the many other topics with which it connects.

> 5.   *The Earth is a system of complex systems.*

Highlighting the importance of both simplicity and complexity is a recurring theme in climate change education, as it should be throughout all education. Issues surrounding climate and energy are profoundly complex. Neither complexity

Conceptual Framework

cognitive bias • *a holding on to incorrect thinking even in the presence of contrary information, because of beliefs or points of view one has.*

logical fallacy • *incorrect reasoning due to faulty logic.*

nor the nature of systems have been prominent in school curricula historically. However, these issues are central to some newer reform initiatives, including the Next Generation Science Standards. Like journalists and politicians, educators often strive to simplify the seemingly complex, and that clearly has its place. The world, however, is indeed a complex place, and the desire to simplify too much can become an obstacle to effective teaching. At such times, educators need to complexify the seemingly simple.

Complex systems, including the Earth itself and its climate system:
- are evolving;
- involve the interplay of different disciplines;
- are composed of multiple nested subsystems (indicating an importance for understandings of scale);
- are better understood from perspectives that include contextualization in space and time (perspectives that include the history of the system);
- are partially defined by feedback; and
- are not necessarily greater than, but qualitatively different from, the sum of their parts.

The list, of course, is not exhaustive (see *Figure 2.2*).

One fundamental aspect of complexifying as related to climate change is recognizing that deciding not to do something often brings with it a decision to do something else that has not been carefully considered. For example, unless we use less energy, choosing not to use one energy source is indirectly a choice to use other available (possibly *status quo*) sources.

Another fundamental aspect of complexifying is that it is confusing. There is no way around that—if science wasn't confusing, we wouldn't need careful methods to study it.

4.1.4 Two Big (Overarching) Questions

Introduction of these big ideas also invites discussion of the nature of science. As curricula are designed and implemented, the traditional topics of science should be complemented with ideas on how we have come to know what we know about the natural world. Within our big ideas framework, we draw attention to the nature of science with two overarching questions:

1. How do we know what we know?
2. How does what we know inform our decision-making?

These questions, when addressed in concert with the big ideas, provide a gateway into the nature and utility of the range of scientific ideas.

A very important complicating factor in understanding both questions is recognizing that we all "know" things that just aren't true and for which there exists contradictory evidence. Our minds can play tricks on us in ways that make it very challenging to see or accept evidence that runs counter to our expectations. **Cognitive biases** and **logical fallacies** are types of

For more information about cognitive biases, see Chapter 10: Obstacles to Addressing Climate Change.

errors in reasoning that stand in the way of what others might call rational decisions. Of course, our decisions seem rational to us—and they are rational within the context of how we interpret the world.

Taken individually, these big ideas and overarching questions represent important aspects of Earth system science, but together they are more significant. Keeping these ideas in mind—and considering how they arose through scientific methods and investigation—is invaluable as one proceeds throughout his or her curriculum, and it can provide a conceptual framework upon which to build an enduring understanding of the discipline.

4.2 Even Bigger Ideas

The five *even bigger* Earth system science big ideas and overarching questions in the "Rainbow Chart" (named for color-coding the chart and other content according to the five big ideas) shown in *Figure 2.2* have been refined with extensive input from scientists and educators. You can see their close relation to the climate change big ideas—in fact the first and last of the Bigger Ideas also appear in our list of climate change ideas.

Here the Bigger Ideas are stated at different depths—a "nickname" of a single word, at the sentence level, and in a short paragraph.[14] Stating them as a single word in the form of an idea's nickname is intended to make them easier to remember. A simple exercise is to have learners describe how a specific activity demonstrates (or is otherwise connected to) one or more of the Bigger Ideas, and to draw connections between ideas and the topic or field site under study.[15]

Any course in the natural sciences can be viewed through the lens of these five biggest ideas, as can any part of a curriculum that includes climate change and energy.

---

[14] Each big idea is described in more detail in the first chapter of each of the regional Teacher Friendly Guides to Earth Science: http://geology.teacherfriendlyguide.org.

[15] To explore more about Bigger Ideas and the "rainbow" chart of Figure 2.2, see the Prezi by Don Duggan-Haas "Bigger Ideas in Earth System Science" at http://virtualfieldwork.org/Big_Ideas.html.

What Should Everyone Understand?

	Overarching Questions: How do we know what we know? How does what we know inform our decision-making?				
	Systems	Energy	Life	Change	Models
Earth System Science Bigger Ideas	The Earth is a System of Systems.	The Flow of Energy Drives the Cycling of Matter.	Life, including human life, influences and is influenced by the environment.	Physical and chemical principles are unchanging and drive both gradual and rapid changes in the Earth system.	To Understand (Deep) Time and the Scale of Space, Models and Maps are Necessary.
	The Earth System is composed of and part of a multitude of systems, which cycle and interact resulting in dynamic equilibrium (though the system evolves). The Earth is also nested in larger systems including the solar system and the universe. However there is an inherent unpredictability in systems, which are composed of an (effectively) infinite number of interacting parts that follow simple rules. Each system is qualitatively different from, but not necessarily greater than the sum of its parts.	The Earth is an open system – it is the constant flow of solar radiation that powers most surface Earth processes and drives the cycling of most matter at or near the Earth's surface. Earth's internal heat is a driving force below the surface. Energy flows and cycles through the Earth system. Matter cycles within it. Convection drives weather and climate, ocean currents, the rock cycle and plate tectonics.	Photosynthetic bacteria reformulated the atmosphere making Earth habitable. Humans have changed the lay of the land, altered the distribution of flora and fauna and are changing atmospheric chemistry in ways that alter the climate. Earth system processes affect where and how humans live. For example, many people live in the shadow of volcanoes because of the fertile farmland found there, however they must keep a constant vigil to maintain their safety. The human impact on the environment is growing as population increases and the use of technology expands.	Earth processes (erosion, evolution or plate tectonics, for example) operating today are the same as those operating since they arose in Earth history and they are obedient to the laws of chemistry and physics. While the processes constantly changing the Earth are essentially fixed, their rates are not. Tipping points are reached that can result in rapid changes cascading through Earth systems.	The use of models is fundamental to all of the Earth Sciences. Maps and models aid in the understanding of aspects of the Earth system for which direct observation is not possible. Models assist in the comprehension of time and space at both immense and sub-microscopic scales. When compared to the size and age of the universe, humanity is a speck in space and a blip in time.

Figure 2.2: The "Rainbow Chart" of big ideas. (See Teacher-Friendly Guide website for a full color version.)

Resources

Books

This book is a good introduction to the series of reports from the National Academy of Science on how people learn. It's available as a free pdf or for sale in hardcopy. Donovan, M. Suzanne, and John D Bransford, eds. How Students Learn: History, Mathematics, and Science in the Classroom. National Academy Press, Committee on How People Learn, A Targeted Report for Teachers, Center for Studies on Behavior and Development, National Research Council, 2005. https://www.nap.edu/catalog/10126/how-students-learn-history-mathematics-and-science-in-the-classroom.

Wiggins and McTighe describe the "backward design" process for instructional design. Their book clearly steps through an approach where big ideas and essential questions are the starting point for developing curriculum. Its two key ideas are contained in the book's title: 1) focus on teaching and assessing for understanding and learning transfer, and 2) design curriculum "backward" from those ends. Wiggins, Grant P, and Jay McTighe. Understanding by Design. Expanded 2nd edition. Alexandria, VA: Association for Supervision and Curriculum Development, 2005.

Online Resources

See Box 2 for links to the different Earth science literacy initiative documents. Big Ideas that synthesize these different efforts are discussed in both the chapters of that name in each of the Teacher Friendly Guides to the Earth Science of the United States (http://geology.teacherfriendlyguide.org/) and in Ross, R. M, and D. Duggan-Haas. "Big Ideas in Earth System Science." American Paleontologist 18, no. 1 (2010): 24. http://virtualfieldwork.org/downloadabledocs/AP_18_1%20Ross_Duggan-Haas.pdf.

Famed biologists E.O. Wilson and James Watson discussed the "laws of biology" as part of a longer discussion about Charles Darwin on Charlie Rose's PBS program. See the full program here: https://charlierose.com/videos/18174. E.O. Wilson describes his ideas about biological laws just before the six minute mark.

Appendix

We asked a set of experts in the science and communication of climate change for statements on the most important thing to know about climate and energy. The request included a deadline and an email address to submit responses. It was sent to 44 individuals. Following is the letter:

"If you could help everyone understand one key concept about climate and energy, what would that concept be?"

What we're asking: We're asking selected distinguished natural and social scientists, educators, and journalists who work on issues related to climate change and energy to contribute 50 to 100 word responses to the question above. All of the statements will be included, with authors' permissions, on the website for book, The Teacher-Friendly Guide to Climate Change. The best answers will be included in the book, authored by myself and my colleagues, Ingrid Zabel, and Rob Ross. This is part of the broader impacts outreach for Natalie Mahowald's NSF grant Improved Regional and Decadal Predictions of the Carbon Cycle (NSF 1049033). The book is also part of our series of Teacher-Friendly Guides.

We hope that contributors will find this to be an interesting exercise that may be helpful in their own work.

The inspiration comes from Richard Feynman's similar question:

"If, in some cataclysm, all of scientific knowledge were to be destroyed, and only one sentence passed on to the next generations of creatures, what statement would contain the most information in the fewest words?"
- Feynman, 1963

While it would be wonderful if we could identify some sort of gateway or keystone ideas that trigger a cascade of understanding, our goal is honestly less ambitious. We want to learn and share what important thinkers think is most fundamental to understand about climate, energy, or the nature of learning related to climate and energy.

Feynman's answer to his own question was 51 words:

"I believe it is the atomic hypothesis (or the atomic fact, or whatever you wish to call it) that all things are made of atoms—little particles that move around in perpetual motion, attracting each other when they are a little distance apart, but repelling upon being squeezed into one another."

He continued, *"In that one sentence, you will see, there is an enormous amount of information about the world, if just a little imagination and thinking are applied"* (Feynman, 1963). We're allowing twice the length of Feynman, though you might wish to match his concision.

We've also worked on similar projects about big ideas in different areas in the past. You may wish to look to this work for examples, but you may wish to first consider the question without being influenced by this work. We have

What Should Everyone Understand?

---

contributed to the literacy principles efforts in Climate, Energy, and Earth Science, and have created a synthesis set of big ideas that encompasses these different efforts. We are glad to talk about the nature of your contribution if you would like.

The book will address important aspects of the physical science that underlie climate change, but it is intended to be about much more than just that physical science. Climate change and energy are scientific issues, but they are also much more than that. While we expect the lion's share of the readership to be middle and high school science teachers, we are hoping to engage educators from across the disciplines and from informal settings as well as K-12 schools and colleges. We are also explicitly addressing social and psychological issues that make teaching and learning controversial issues challenging. That's why this request is going to social and cognitive scientists, and selected journalists as well scientists and science educators.

Sincerely,

Don Duggan-Haas, PhD, Director of Teacher Programs, the Paleontological Research Institution

Chapter 3:
What is Climate?

1. Climate is a System

One can describe **climate** as a symphony of weather, taking into account the entire range of weather conditions in a region, the extremes as well as the average.[1] Climatologists technically define climates through the calculation of "climate normals": thirty-year averages of variables such as daily temperature, rainfall, snowfall, and frost and freeze dates that can be compared with thirty-year averages of these variables from other time periods. Fluctuations in these variables that last hours, days, or up to two weeks are called **weather**.

Weather is what we all feel when we step outside: if you want to know what today's weather is, just go outside! No one ever actually experiences the climate in the present, because no one can ever step outside and feel that day's climate.[2] One practical way to think about the difference between climate and weather is that knowing the weather tells you what clothing to wear on a given day, whereas knowing the climate tells you what clothing you need to own.

Life is possible on Earth because the climate is favorable for it to flourish. In particular, the average range of surface temperatures on Earth allows for abundant liquid water, which is essential for life as we know it. Earth's average surface temperature has changed over time; for example, average global temperature may have been as much as 11°C (20°F) higher than today during parts of the **Mesozoic** Era, the time of the dinosaurs. But for most of Earth history it has fluctuated within a range that allows for liquid water in the oceans and in land water bodies. Temperature on our planet is controlled, in part, by the fact that we have a thin atmosphere of gases surrounding us; this thin layer acts to hold in some of the energy that the Earth radiates after being warmed by sunlight.

> See Chapter 4: Past Climates for more detail on climate change through Earth's history.

Our two closest neighbor planets, Mars and Venus, have very different atmospheres from Earth, and hence, very different surface temperatures. Venus is similar to the Earth but is closer to the sun, and the additional heat has caused what we call a "runaway greenhouse effect" in which increased temperatures increased the levels of greenhouse gases, which further increased the temperature, which further increased greenhouse gases, and so on. The end

---

[1] Climate as a "symphony of weather" is a term used by Dr. Arthur T. DeGaetano, Professor of Earth and Atmospheric Sciences at Cornell University.

[2] Interesting blog posts on this concept and more—including climate models— have been written by Dr. Ben Brown-Steiner and can be found on the Climate Change 101 Blog (see http://climatechange101.blogspot.com/2014/10/whats-climate-like-outside-today.html and other entries from 2014 and 2015).

climate • a description of both the average weather conditions (temperature, precipitation, wind, etc.) and the extremes that a region experiences.

weather • fluctuations in variables such as temperature, rainfall, snowfall, and wind that last hours, days, or up to two weeks.

Mesozoic • a geologic time era that spans from 252 to 66 million years ago. This era is also called the "age of reptiles" since dinosaurs and other reptiles dominated both marine and terrestrial ecosystems. During this time, the last of the Earth's major supercontinents, PANGAEA, formed and later broke up, producing the Earth's current geography.

CHAPTER AUTHORS

Ingrid H. H. Zabel

and authors of

A Very Short Guide to Climate Change

3 What is Climate?

Climate System

system • *a combination of interacting parts whose interaction creates behaviors that might not occur if each part were isolated.*

atmosphere • *the layer of gases that surrounds a planet.*

hydrosphere • *all of the water on Earth.*

geosphere • *the solid portion of the Earth.*

biosphere • *all plants, animals, and people, both living and non-living, on Earth.*

methane • *CH_4, a greenhouse gas formed from organic matter under heat and pressure from burial and from fermentation of organic matter by bacteria in low oxygen settings, including the digestion of animals.*

trace gases • *gases whose volume makes up less than 1% of the Earth's atmosphere.*

ozone • *a molecule (O_3) found in the STRATOSPHERE which absorbs ultraviolet light. When found near the surface of the Earth, ozone is considered a pollutant because it is a component of smog and can cause lung irritation.*

currents • *directional movements of a fluid mass.*

result is that the temperatures on Venus now can exceed 450° C (842° F) and the atmosphere is nearly 100 times denser than the Earth's atmosphere. The atmosphere surrounding Venus is 96% carbon dioxide (CO_2) (*Box 3.1*). Mars, farther than Earth from the sun, has an atmosphere similar to Venus, with 95% CO_2, but the total atmosphere is much less dense than that on Earth, about 50 times less dense than the air at the top of Mount Everest. With such a thin "blanket," little total heat is trapped, thus the average surface temperature on Mars is -53°C (-63°F). The relationship between Venus, Earth, and Mars is an example of what has been called the **Goldilocks Principle**—the temperature on Earth is not too hot and not too cold, but "just right" for life to exist.

The Earth's climate is a **system** (*Box 3.2*). This means that it has many parts that interact with each other to create behaviors that might not occur if each part were isolated. The Earth's climate is a *complex* system, meaning that it has many parts with many interactions. Complexity reduces (or at least makes more difficult) the predictability of the overall behavior of the system. Yet, scientists have enough understanding of the physical and chemical laws that govern Earth's climate system that they can build computer models which can accurately replicate historical climate data. These same models can be run to predict future climates under different scenarios.

The Earth's climate system consists of air, water, land, and life (or, as they are often called, the **atmosphere**, **hydrosphere, geosphere**, and **biosphere**). Phenomena outside of the Earth (mainly the sun, but also cosmic dust and meteorite impacts) also affect its climate. All of these components interact over time to create the climate conditions that we observe. Life on Earth evolves partly in response to changes in climate, but living systems also influence climate through absorption or emission of greenhouse gases such as CO_2 and **methane** (CH_4).

See Section 3 in this chapter on the greenhouse effect.

The **atmosphere**—the blanket of gas surrounding the Earth (commonly called "air")—is where most of what we think of as weather and climate happen. Other planets, such as Mars and Venus, also have atmospheres, but they are very different from that on Earth. Our atmosphere consists mostly (approximately 80%) of nitrogen, with oxygen making up most of the rest. Other gases exist in much smaller quantities (*Table 3.1*) and are called **trace gases**. Despite their small quantities in terms of percentage of the atmosphere, some of these other gases—such as water vapor, carbon dioxide, methane, and **ozone**—control the Earth's climate system because of their influence on temperature.

The **hydrosphere** includes all the liquid and frozen water at the Earth's surface. The oceans contain approximately 97% of the water on Earth. Because water holds heat for longer than land, the oceans play a very important role in storing and circulating heat around the globe. The **currents** in the oceans, in fact, are driven primarily by differences in density, influenced by temperature and also by the salt content. The surface of the ocean receives heat from the sun. This warm water is less dense than colder water found deeper in the oceans. Atmospheric winds and forces that result from the rotation of the Earth create ocean currents

Box 3.1: Why all the fuss about carbon dioxide?

Carbon dioxide (CO_2) is a molecule made of one atom of carbon and two atoms of oxygen. Within the range of temperatures found on Earth, CO_2 usually takes the form of a gas. It is a natural component of Earth's atmosphere, exhaled by **aerobic** organisms such as plants, animals, fungi, protists, and many bacteria, and used by plants in the process of photosynthesis. Thus, concentrations of CO_2 in the atmosphere vary seasonally as a result of **deciduous plants** in the northern hemisphere that, in the summer, absorb more CO_2 than they release.

CO_2 is part of the **carbon cycle** (see *Figure 3.7*), which includes carbon found in living things, the atmosphere, oceans, and Earth's crust—in **limestone**, and in **oil**, **natural gas**, and **coal** deposits. Because carbon usually cycles slowly through the ocean (thousands of years) and the crust (millions or billions of years), these are called "**carbon sinks**." Without human intervention the carbon cycle is generally in **equilibrium**, with approximately as much carbon being released into the atmosphere each year as is absorbed by sinks worldwide.

Large forests are carbon sinks, storing carbon in their biomass until they die and decay. Some large forests, such as the Amazon rainforest, are shrinking because of human activities such as deforestation. As the forests are destroyed they release their carbon back into the atmosphere and switch from carbon sinks to carbon sources.

Human burning of **fossil fuels**, such as oil, natural gas, and coal, releases the carbon stored in the ancient **organic matter** as CO_2 gas. Because these sinks have been long-term repositories for carbon, their rapid release into the atmosphere has caused an imbalance which results in increasing levels of CO_2 in our atmosphere and oceans.

This additional emission of CO_2 into the environment, and the reduction of some carbon sinks, tips the equilibrium of the carbon cycle, so that each year the concentration of CO_2 in the atmosphere grows by about 1%. This is believed to be the primary cause of current climate change.

Once emitted into the atmosphere, CO_2 can stay there for hundreds of years, causing imbalances that can last thousands of years, so increased levels of CO_2 resulting from human activities can impact the climate for thousands of years.

that allow cold bottom water to well up to the surface. In the tropics, most of the warm water at the surface is pushed by wind to the centers of large rotating masses of water called **gyres** (*Figure 3.1*). Some of the water, such as the **Gulf Stream**, moves toward the poles. When warm water approaches the poles, it mixes with colder water. Evaporation and formation of sea ice leave behind slightly saltier surface water. This cold, salty sea water, which forms especially in the North Atlantic and near Antarctica, is relatively dense and sinks. It then begins to move under the surface back toward the equator, sliding underneath the warmer and less dense surface waters. This is the primary driver of deep ocean circulation, which can take hundreds or thousands of years to complete one cycle.

aerobic • *involving free oxygen.*

deciduous plants • *plants which lose their leaves, typically in autumn, and regrow them the following spring.*

carbon cycle • *the exchange and recycling of carbon between the geosphere, hydrosphere, atmosphere, and biosphere.*

limestone • *a sedimentary rock composed of calcium carbonate ($CaCO_3$). Most limestones are formed by the deposition and consolidation of the skeletons of marine invertebrates; a few originate in chemical precipitation from solution.*

oil • *a naturally occurring, flammable liquid found in geologic formations beneath the Earth's surface and consisting primarily of hydrocarbons. Oil, also called PETROLEUM, is a fossil fuel, formed when large masses of dead organisms (usually algae or plankton) are buried underneath sediments and subjected to intense heat and pressure.*

natural gas • *a hydrocarbon gas mixture composed primarily of methane (CH4), but also small quantites of hydrocarbons such as ethane and propane. See also FOSSIL FUEL.*

3 What is Climate?

Climate System

coal · *a rock formed from ancient plant matter that can be burned as fuel. Since coal is formed from fossilized plant remains it is considered a FOSSIL FUEL..*

carbon sink · *a system or part of a system which absorbs carbon.*

equilibrium · *a state of balance in opposing forces, amounts, or rates.*

fossil fuel · *a non-renewable, carbon-based fuel source like OIL, NATURAL GAS, or COAL, developed from the preserved organic remains of fossil organisms.*

organic matter · *decomposed remains of plants, animals, and their wastes.*

gyres · *large- (i.e., global-) scale rotating masses of ocean water.*

Gulf Stream · *a current in the Atlantic Ocean which transports warm water from the Gulf of Mexico along North America's East Coast, then across the Atlantic in two streams, one traveling to Northern Europe and one to West Africa.*

Box 3.2: How systems work

A **system** is a collection of parts that interact with each other. Earth's climate system is made up of all of the objects and processes that have a global impact on climate. To begin to understand a system as complicated as the Earth's climate system, scientists observe and analyze the components and their interactions and how a change in one component (a forcing) impacts the other components (a response).

The term **forcing** refers to factors that cause change; **responses** are the changes that result. Forcings can produce responses at various rates. These rates can be directly proportional to the magnitude of the forcing, in which case they are called **linear**. For example, pushing a merry-go-round harder will result in a linear increase in the speed of the merry-go-round. Or they can be produced in some more complex, **non-linear** pattern. For example, a small push to a ball at the top of a hill can cause a much larger change if the ball rolls down the hill. A forcing might induce a response immediately after it is applied, or only after some period of time has passed (**lag**). For instance, when grass seed is planted, there is a lag before your yard is covered by grass, and that amount of time is determined by rainfall, exposure to the sun, and other factors. Forcing can be applied at a variety of **magnitudes** (strong or weak) and **durations** (long or short).

A very important behavior of all systems is **feedback** between components. Feedbacks can either amplify a behavior (positive or reinforcing feedback) or suppress it (negative or balancing feedback).[3]

An example of a positive or reinforcing feedback cycle in the climate system is melting of sea ice. Sea ice forms when seawater freezes at the surface of the ocean, and it is much brighter (more reflective) than the water around it. Since it is bright it reflects much of the incoming sunlight back to the atmosphere. If a little bit of sea ice melts, more ocean water is available to soak up the heat from the sun, and this warmer water melts more of the nearby ice. This process can amplify until the ice is completely melted. At this point the system of sea ice and seawater has crossed a **threshold**, that is, it has changed dramatically.

An example of negative or balancing feedback is the impact of clouds on global warming. Warm air contains more water vapor than cold air and more water vapor leads to more clouds, so a warmer Earth will have more clouds. However, clouds are white and reflect sunlight, so more clouds will result in less sunlight reaching the Earth, cooling the climate. Clouds have the potential to counteract global warming, although we do not know exactly by how much.

---

[3] Dr. Kim Kastens, in her 2010 article "Going Negative on Negative Feedback," discusses the confusion often generated by the colloquial meaning of the words "positive" and "negative" and the use of these words in describing feedback in systems. She suggests alternative terms of "reinforcing" and "balancing" feedback. Her article can be found at http://serc.carleton.edu/earthandmind/posts/negativefeedbac.html.

Table 3.1: Composition of Earth's atmosphere.

Gas	% in Atmosphere
Nitrogen (N_2)	78
Oxygen (O_2)	21
Water vapor (H_2O)	1 to 4*
Argon (Ar)	0.93
Carbon dioxide (CO_2)	0.041**
Neon (Ne)	0.0018
Helium (He)	0.00052
Methane (CH_4)	0.00017
Krypton (Kr)	0.00011
Hydrogen (H_2)	0.000055
Nitrous oxide (N_2O)	0.00003
Carbon monoxide (CO)	0.00001
Xenon (Xe)	0.000009
Ozone (O_3)	0.000007
Nitrogen dioxide (NO_s)	0.000002

* The concentration of water vapor in the atmosphere varies from about 1% to 4%, depending on the temperature. If temperatures warm, more water vapor can be held in the air, increasing the greenhouse effect from water.

** The concentration of CO2 is rising (407 parts per million as of March 2017); see the most recent data at: https://www.esrl.noaa.gov/gmd/ccgg/trends/index.html.

The movement of ocean currents, carrying heat energy to different parts of the globe and transferring energy to the atmosphere, plays an extremely large role in global climate. Therefore, the configuration of the continents, around which the ocean currents flow, also plays a large role in their respective regional climates.

Ice at the Earth's surface includes **sea ice**, **glaciers**, and continental **ice sheets**, which altogether hold approximately 2% of the water on Earth. Scientists refer to this system as the **cryosphere**. Sea ice forms when seawater freezes at -1.9°C (29°F), which is lower than "freezing" (0°C or 32°F) because of the salt content. Like all ice, frozen seawater is less dense than liquid water, and floats atop it. Sea ice acts as an insulating barrier that prevents the ocean from interacting with the atmosphere. When ice is present, heat from the ocean is not lost to the atmosphere, and the water can remain much warmer than the air. Glacial ice occurs as **mountain glaciers** or continental ice sheets. Mountain glaciers can occur anywhere in the world, but in the tropics they cannot form below 5 kilometers (about 16,400 feet) altitude, where it is too warm.

There are currently two continental ice sheets on Earth, covering most of Greenland and Antarctica. These large continental glaciers lock up great quantities of water that would otherwise be in the ocean, resulting in lower

Climate System

system • a combination of interacting parts whose interaction creates behaviors that might not occur if each part were isolated.

linear • a mathematical relationship where a variable is directly proportional to another variable.

non-linear • a mathematical relationship where a variable is not directly proportional to another variable.

lag • a period of time between events, such as between the incidence of solar radiation and a certain amount of warming of the Earth.

magnitude • the size of a quantity.

duration • the length of time an event or activity lasts.

feedback • the response of a system to some change that either balances/opposes or reinforces/enhances the change that is applied to a system. Balancing feedback (sometimes called negative feedback) tends to push a system toward stability; reinforcing feedback (sometimes called positive feedback) tends to push a system towards extremes.

What is Climate?

Climate System

threshold · *a magnitude of a quantity beyond which the behavior of a system changes or a phenomenon occurs. See also TIPPING POINT.*

sea ice · *frozen seawater at the surface of the ocean.*

glacier · *a very large piece of ice that sits at least partially on land and moves under the force of gravity.*

ice sheet · *a mass of glacial ice that covers part of a continent and has an area greater than 50,000 square kilometers (19,000 square miles).*

cryosphere · *the part of Earth's surface where water exists in solid form. This includes all major forms of ice, such as SEA ICE, GLACIERS, ICE SHEETS and permafrost.*

mountain glacier · *a glacier found in high mountains, often spanning across multiple peaks.*

sea level · *global sea level is the average height of Earth's oceans. Local sea level is the height of the ocean as measured along the coast relative to a specific point on land.*

albedo · *the fraction of solar energy that a surface reflects back into space.*

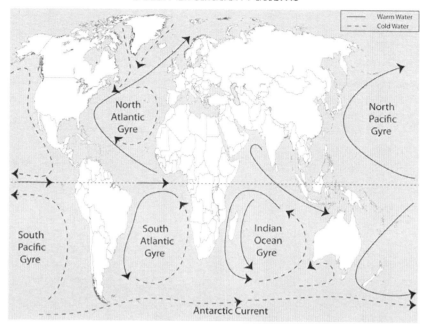

Figure 3.1: *Modern ocean surface circulation. Ocean currents play a huge role in transporting heat energy from equatorial regions to temperate and polar regions. Surface circulation of a relatively thin layer of water is driven by the wind and by the Coriolis force, an effect of rotation of the Earth, which drives gyres in the Atlantic and Pacific Ocean. Subsurface circulation, which is not shown, is driven by cold salty water that sinks near the poles, especially in the North Atlantic. When the warm water begins to cool at higher latitudes, such as around northern Europe, its heat is lost to the atmosphere, contributing significantly to warming the air. Land near water in these regions is therefore usually warmer than land far from the coast. For instance, the average yearly temperature in London is 14°C (57°F). At the same latitude across the Atlantic in Calgary, Alberta, Canada, the average yearly temperature is 4°C (39°F). This is because the Gulf Stream carries warm water from near the equator in the Atlantic Ocean northeast to London, but Calgary is in the middle of North America, far away from the moderating influence of ocean currents.*

sea levels. If these ice sheets were to melt entirely, global sea level could rise as much as 70 meters (approximately 230 feet). Ice also affects climate itself through its **albedo**. Albedo is the reflectivity of a surface; high albedo means that a surface is very reflective of light energy, and low albedo means that it absorbs light energy. Ice has high albedo compared with the ocean or land; it reflects back a high percentage of sunlight into the atmosphere, cooling the surface. Continental glaciers can be thousands of feet thick, and can therefore also actually block or redirect air flow, causing warm air to deflect away from the area covered by the ice sheet, and preventing or slowing the warming process. The geosphere is the solid Earth, from the surface to the core. We might not often think of rocks as being connected to the atmosphere, but they very much are, especially over long stretches of time. For example, even though oxygen makes up 20% of the atmosphere, there is about 200 times more oxygen in the crustal rocks below the surface of the Earth. Exposed rock reacts with atmospheric oxygen by absorbing it, removing oxygen from the atmosphere. The solid Earth affects the climate in many ways. Volcanic eruptions can put large amounts of gas and particles into the atmosphere. Particulates temporarily suspended in the atmosphere can affect how much of the sun's heat reaches the surface and how much of that is retained; after a large volcanic eruption,

What is Climate?

the global climate may cool by a few degrees for several years. The different land surfaces have different albedos, variously absorbing and reflecting energy from the sun. Further, **sediments** and rocks hold a large amount of the Earth's carbon, impacting the concentration of CO_2 in the atmosphere (see Section 4.2 for more discussion).

The biosphere includes all of the life on Earth. Life on Earth is more than just a green layer sitting passively on the surface of a rocky ball: life is an integral part of the geology and climate of the planet. Living things have enormous effects on many atmospheric, oceanic, and geological processes. For example, **soil** is a byproduct of life; without organic matter, soil would be no more than rock dust (like on the moon). Life also profoundly affects the atmosphere. It is only because of the photosynthetic activity of green plants, along with small organisms like **protists** and **bacteria**, that the Earth's atmosphere contains so much oxygen. These organisms can also act as sinks for the carbon that they contain when they die and are buried in sediment that may become rock.

A wide range of organisms help to cycle carbon back to the atmosphere. Plants stabilize the land and limit **physical weathering** (erosion) from wind and water and simultaneously contribute to **chemical weathering** of rocks by changing the acidity of the soil. Animals (not to mention humans) alter the landscape in a wide variety of ways, from churning up seafloors and soils to building major structures like coral reefs, beaver ponds, and termite mounds. The remains of dead plants, animals, and microbes form vast deposits of sediment that become layers of rock in the Earth's crust. All of the coal, oil, and natural gas and most of the limestone in the world, for example, were formed by the accumulated body parts of once-living things.

2. Measuring Climate

The main indicators of a region's climate are temperature and precipitation. The most basic way to measure precipitation is with a standard **rain gauge**: a graduated cylinder, 4 centimeters in diameter, fed by a funnel and inside a larger cylinder that can catch any spillover (see *Box 3.3*). The amount of rain that falls in a certain time period, typically 24 hours, is measured in inches or centimeters of water height captured by the gauge. If the precipitation fell as snow then the standard measurement is the liquid water equivalent of ice, measured by melting the snow captured by the gauge and then reading the height of the melted liquid in the gauge.

Rain gauge measurements have their limits. For example, they may not capture accurate measurements of rainfall during storms with high winds because winds may direct the rain horizontally and out of reach of the gauge. They also only give point measurements at the location of the gauge. The National Weather Service's rain gauges are spaced about 20 miles apart on average. The gaps in this network of measurements may be filled in by citizen scientists, particularly by members of the Community Collaborative Rain, Hail, and Snow Network (cocorahs.org) (see *Box 3.3*).

For broader coverage of precipitation measurements we now can rely on satellite data. Early satellite instruments could only measure precipitation in the

Measuring Climate

sediments • *grains of broken rock, crystals, skeletal fragments, and ORGANIC MATTER.*

soil • *the accumulation of natural materials that collect on Earth's surface above the bedrock.*

protists • *a diverse group of single-celled eukaryotes (organisms with complex cells containing a nucleus and organelles).*

bacteria • *single-celled microorganisms with cell membranes but without organelles or a nucleus.*

physical weathering • *the breaking down of rock through physical processes such as wind and water erosion and cracking from expansion of freezing water.*

chemical weathering • *the breaking down of rock through chemical processes.*

rain gauge • *an instrument used to measure precipitation by collecting rainfall.*

33

near-surface • *near the surface of the Earth; typically within a few meters above the surface.*

What is Climate?

Box 3.3: CoCoRaHS

The Community Collaborative Rain, Hail, and Snow Network, or CoCo-RaHS, is a great way to get students involved in making climate measurements. All one needs is a standard rain gauge and a relatively open place to put it. Students can enter their measurements online at cocorahs.org and immediately see a map of measurements contributed by citizen scientists across the country. The CoCoRaHS website contains tutorials about how to obtain, place, and set up a rain gauge and how to make measurements.

Standard rain gauge. Measurements of rainfall from this gauge are sent to the Community Collaborative Rain, Hail, and Snow Network's database.

tropics and could not detect light rain or snow. In February 2014, NASA and JAXA, Japan's space agency, launched the Global Precipitation Measurement (GPM) Core Observatory, with sensors that can detect a range of precipitation from light rain to heavy snow, and that provide data from the tropics to near the poles.

The temperatures that we hear or read about in the local daily weather report are almost always measurements of air temperature obtained by thermometers in particular locations close to the ground (referred to as **near-surface**) at particular moments (e.g., taken at a nearby airport at 8:00 a.m., or taken at a station on the roof of a local school). These individual measurements are likely to be similar to one another, but rarely are they identical, and they can be averaged to produce assessments of temperatures over some geographic area or a length of time (e.g., this morning's mean temperature for the Northeastern US, or Florida's daily high from yesterday). Extreme values are smoothed away if the data are averaged over large areas over long periods of time, and the site-to-site and day-to-day variability converges to an area or time average.

What is Climate?

There are also differences from year to year. We all know that July is going to be hotter than January, but the high temperature on July 15th of this year is going to be different than the high temperature of last July 15th, or the July 15th from ten years ago. These differences are caused by natural cycles in our Earth climate system. **El Niño**, for example, is a well-known example of an interannual cycle, in which the temperature or rainfall of a region can be higher or lower than average depending on the strength of El Niño that year. There are also differences on decadal time scales. For example, in the 1930s a severe drought together with land use changes (millions of acres plowed for farming) caused the famous "Dustbowl" conditions in the American West and Midwest. More recently, California experienced a prolonged and exceptionally severe drought from 2012 to 2016 (*Figure 3.2*).

Satellite-based sensors also provide surface temperature measurements, and climate scientists have developed sophisticated models to provide temperature and precipitation data over geographic grids and to obtain coverage between point weather stations. These models, such as the Parameter-elevation Regressions on Independent Slopes Model (PRISM)[4], have been shown to be very accurate and are widely accepted by the scientific community, government agencies, and businesses that need these data.

The average global surface temperature (the average of near-surface air temperature over land and sea surface temperature) on Earth during the 20th century was approximately 14.8°C (58.6°F).[5] It is important to note that there were very few moments when the actual temperature in any given location was exactly that temperature. This value is a long-term global average. As of 2016, the average global surface temperature has increased since 1880 by about

> *El Niño* • *also called the El Niño – Southern Oscillation (ENSO); is represented by fluctuating temperatures and air pressures in the tropical Pacific Ocean. During an El Niño event, the eastern Pacific experiences warmer water and higher air pressure than the western Pacific, changing rainfall patterns, eastern Pacific upwelling, and weather variables globally. ENSO events typically occur every 3 to 7 years.*

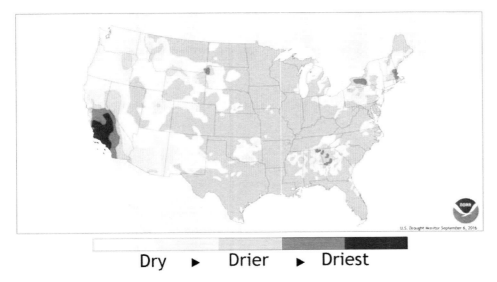

Dry ▶ Drier ▶ Driest

Figure 3.2: Drought conditions across the continental US as of September 6, 2016. A large part of southern California was experiencing Exceptional Drought, the most severe category. (See Teacher-Friendly Guide website for a full color version.)

---

[4] This model has been developed by the PRISM Climate Group at Oregon State University, http://prism.oregonstate.edu/.

[5] This measurement and many climate datasets are available from the NOAA National Centers for Environmental Information, https://www.ncdc.noaa.gov/sotc/.

Measuring Climate

heat island • *an urban area which experiences higher temperatures than do surrounding rural areas as a result of pollution, pavement, and the surfaces of buildings magnifying localized heating.*

rain shadow • *an area on one side of a mountain that experiences little rainfall.*

lake effect snow • *snowfall caused by the movement of cold weather systems over a relatively warm lake, in which an air mass picks up water from the lake and deposits it in the form of snow across an adjacent land mass.*

Box 3.4: Regional weather and climate patterns

Just as weather and climate are affected globally by the placement of continents and oceans, smaller features such as topography and local human land use can affect regional weather and climate patterns, frequently making it difficult to predict what effect climate change will have in a given area. It is also difficult to extrapolate from such regional patterns to global patterns. These regional features create regional and local effects, such as **heat islands**, **rain shadows**, and **lake effect snow**.

Heat islands occur in urban areas, with the result that such areas are often warmer than nearby rural areas. The building materials used to create metropolitan structures absorb heat in the day and then release it at night. This can cause some urban areas in extreme circumstances to be up to 9°C (16°F) warmer than their rural counterparts.

Rain shadows refer to the areas adjacent to a mountain range that receive little rain. The mountains separate the area in a rain shadow from a significant water source, like an ocean. As warm air moves over the ocean it collects water in the form of water vapor, which can run into a mountain range where it is forced upward. When air is forced upwards, it expands and cools. Warm air can contain more water vapor than cool air, so as this air cools water vapor condenses out to form clouds and rain. The rain falls on the windward side of the mountains closer to the water source, leaving the opposite side (leeward) of the mountains and adjacent areas very dry, in a rain shadow.

Lake effect snow refers to a type of snowfall pattern in which cold air flows over the warmer water of a large lake. As water evaporates from the lake it interacts with the cold air, forming clouds over the lake. These then get carried to shore by the winds,

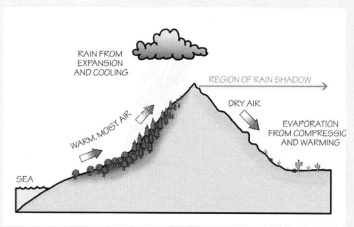

Key characteristics of a rain shadow. (See Teacher-Friendly Guide website for a full color version.)

which deposit snow (sometimes a lot of snow) on land in the path of the winds. Regions along the eastern shores of large lakes, such as the eastern shores of Lake Michigan (Traverse City and Grand Rapids), Lake Erie (south of Buffalo) and Lake Ontario (Syracuse and Watertown), can have significantly different snowfall patterns than areas farther from the lakes.

See Chapter 6 for a review of climate change in different regions of the U.S.

0.8°C (1.4°F). The temperature that you feel when you step outside today will be different from this average value due to many factors such as land use, elevation, topography, and proximity to bodies of water (*Box 3.4*).

3. Greenhouse Gases and Global Temperature

The Earth's surface temperature is controlled by the only major source of energy in our solar system: the sun. **Radiation** from the sun reaches the Earth throughout the year, but the Earth's temperature depends on the complex interaction of different components of the solar radiation with the atmosphere and with the Earth's surface (*Figure 3.3*). Sunlight consists of radiation at a variety of wavelengths. The shortest wavelengths (**ultraviolet light**) are rapidly absorbed and filtered by the atmosphere and do not reach the Earth's surface. The same is true for the longest wavelengths (**infrared light** or **thermal radiation**). The middle wavelengths (**visible light**) pass through the atmosphere largely unobstructed and allow us to see the world around us.

When visible light from the sun is absorbed by the Earth's surface, its energy is transformed to heat energy that increases the temperature of the surface. Some of this energy is re-emitted back into the atmosphere as infrared light. Since the atmosphere absorbs infrared light, some of this light is captured by the atmosphere and then reemitted both up into space and back down to the surface again, effectively trapping heat. This phenomenon is called the **greenhouse effect** (*Box 3.5*) and depends on the levels of **greenhouse gases** (*Table 3.2*)—carbon dioxide, methane, water vapor, and others—that make up only a tiny fraction of the gases in our atmosphere.

The surface of the Earth, therefore, is heated both by direct radiation from the sun, but also by this trapped and retransmitted radiation. This greenhouse effect is very important for life on Earth. Without it, the average surface temperature would be below the freezing point of water, and there would be little or no liquid water, and therefore possibly no life on Earth!

While greenhouse gases keep the Earth's surface warmer than it would be otherwise, other factors also affect the Earth's surface temperature. Since the equator gets more direct solar radiation than either of the poles, and thus more energy per square meter, the temperature in the tropics is warmer than in the polar regions. Warm air at the equator rises and flows toward the poles, then cools, sinks, and flows back toward the equator. This process is called **convection** and a zone where the convection process occurs is called a **convection cell**. The Earth's rotation forces the poleward-moving air sideways (a phenomenon called the **Coriolis effect**), so the poleward moving air doesn't make it as far as the pole, but rather descends in a high pressure band around 30 degrees latitude in each of the northern and southern hemispheres. For related reasons, two additional convection cells, at mid latitudes and high latitudes, form in each hemisphere. These latitudinal convection cells are host, from equator to pole, of the **trade winds**, westerlies, and polar easterlies. Overall, the global movement

Greenhouse Gases

Radiation • emission of electromagnetic energy from an object.

ultraviolet light • electromagnetic radiation in the part of the spectrum with wavelengths from 10 to 400 nanometers.

infrared light • electromagnetic radiation in the part of the spectrum with wavelengths from 750 nanometers to 1 millimeter. People sense infrared radiation as heat.

thermal radiation • the emission of electromagnetic radiation from all materials, from the motion of charged particles.

visible light • electromagnetic radiation in the part of the spectrum with wavelengths from about 400 to 750 nanometers.

greenhouse effect • the influence of GREENHOUSE GAS molecules in the Earth's atmosphere to retain heat (infrared radiation) radiating from the Earth's surface that would otherwise escape into space.

greenhouse gas • a gas that absorbs and re-radiates energy in the form of heat; carbon dioxide, water vapor, and methane are examples.

Greenhouse Gases

convection • *movement of a fluid, such as air or water, resulting from gravitational force on the fluid. Warmer, less dense matter rises and cooler, more dense matter sinks, producing heat transfer.*

convection cell • *a zone where warm, less dense air or water rises and cool, more dense air or water sinks, creating a repetitive pattern of motion.*

Coriolis effect • *the apparent deflection of air masses in the atmosphere, which are moving relative to the rotating reference frame of the Earth.*

trade winds • *persistent, large-scale winds in the tropical oceans which blow from the northeast in the Northern Hemisphere and from the southeast in the Southern hemisphere.*

What is Climate?

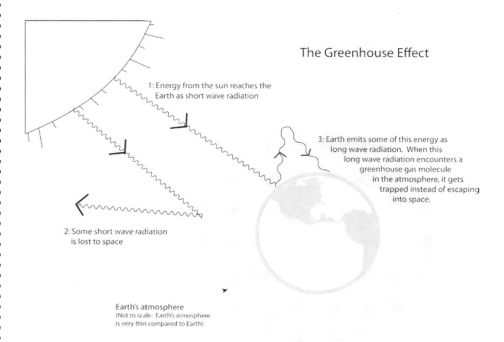

Figure 3.3: The greenhouse effect. Incoming solar radiation passes through the Earth's atmosphere, with some being reflected back before entering. The Earth absorbs visible (shortwave) sunlight and re-radiates infrared, longwave light (heat). The atmosphere acts somewhat like a blanket, trapping some of re-radiated heat and keeping Earth warm enough to sustain life. It does this through atmospheric greenhouse gases such as CO_2 which absorb infrared light and re-radiate it both out to space and back to Earth. The thicker the blanket, that is, the more greenhouse gases in the atmosphere, the more heat is trapped.

of air distributes heat from the equator to the poles and keeps the surface temperature within the bounds currently experienced on Earth.

Among greenhouse gases, water vapor actually has the greatest capacity to absorb longer-wavelength radiation. In studying changes in the Earth's surface temperature over time scales of more than a few weeks, however, more attention is usually given to CO_2 because water vapor concentration in the atmosphere changes much more quickly than does CO_2. For example, a molecule of water vapor, such as might evaporate from the ocean, will remain in the atmosphere for approximately two weeks, whereas an average molecule of CO_2, such as you might exhale, will remain in the atmosphere for hundreds of years.

The average annual concentration of CO_2 in the atmosphere prior to the Industrial Revolution (when large quantities of fossil fuels began to be burned by humans) was approximately 280 ppm (see *Box 3.6* for information about the unit of ppm). This has been determined by measuring CO_2 trapped in air bubbles in ice sheets. By the mid-twentieth century, atmospheric CO_2 concentrations were well above this, around 310 ppm, and now they have reached over 400 ppm (see *Figure 3.4*). Scientists suspected as early as the late 1890s that CO_2 concentrations might influence the temperature of the Earth, but it was not until the 1950s that scientists began to systematically measure the concentration of CO_2 in the atmosphere with high degrees of accuracy and on a regular basis.

CO_2 concentration in the modern atmosphere varies seasonally over a range of 5-6 ppm, as seen in the cyclical pattern in the trend line in *Figure 3.4*. This

What is Climate?

Box 3.5: The greenhouse effect and the greenhouse metaphor

A greenhouse works by letting energy from the sun in through its windows, and then trapping warmed air from escaping with the same windows. In the atmosphere, what is commonly referred to as the "Greenhouse Effect" is more complex.

Step 1: Earth absorbs energy from the sun in the form of shortwave radiation (visible light), which heats the planet's surface.

Step 2: Earth emits some of this heat in the form of long-wave (infrared) radiation.

Step 3: Some of the longwave radiation being given off by the planet strikes molecules of greenhouse gases in the atmosphere and is absorbed. These gases re-radiate infrared light, warming the air.

Step 4: Because of the chemistry of greenhouse gases, longwave radiation is more easily trapped than shortwave radiation. As a result, much of the heat given off by Earth is retained by the atmosphere instead of being allowed to pass through.

The greenhouse metaphor is not a perfect one. Greenhouse windows let light into a building, which heats the air. The windows then protect that heat from being dissipated or carried away by winds, locally providing heat to the plants inside. Earth's atmosphere, on the other hand, is open, so air is not being trapped. Rather, greenhouse gas molecules in the atmosphere are radiating heat back towards the Earth.

Table 3.2: Common greenhouse gases.

Gas	Formula
Water vapor	H_2O
Carbon dioxide	CO_2
Methane	CH_4
Ozone	O_3
Nitrous oxide	N_2O
Chlorofluorocarbons (CFC's)	Composition varies, but commonly include C, Cl, F, and H

is because of the growth of forests in the Northern Hemisphere. Forests take in more CO_2 (through photosynthesis) than they give off (in respiration) in the spring and summer, and mostly release CO_2 (through respiration) in the fall and winter. The cycle is reversed in the Southern Hemisphere, but there is much less land area and so fewer forests in the Southern Hemisphere; therefore the Southern Hemisphere effect is much smaller and seasons in the Northern Hemisphere dominate the annual CO_2 cycle.

Greenhouse Gases

cloud · *a visible aggregation of condensed water vapor in the atmosphere.*

What is Climate?

Box 3.6: Measuring gases in the atmosphere

The concentration of a gas in the atmosphere is commonly measured in parts per million (ppm). A value of 1 ppm means that one molecule is present in every million molecules of air. One molecule in a million does not sound like a lot of molecules, but one cubic centimeter of air at the Earth's surface contains approximately 2.7×10^{19} molecules, so a 1 ppm concentration of a gas has 2.7×10^{13} molecules in the same small volume. That's 27 trillion molecules of CO_2 in the space of a sugar cube!

The emission of CO_2 into the atmosphere is commonly expressed in tons. A single ton (2,000 pounds) of carbon corresponds to 3.67 tons of CO_2 because of the additional weight of the oxygen. To raise the atmospheric concentration of CO_2 by 1 ppm requires 7.8×10^9 (7.8 billion or 7,800,000,000) tons of CO_2, which is approximately 1 ton of CO_2 per person on Earth. Human burning of fossil fuels currently adds approximately 9×10^9 (9 billion or 9,000,000,000) tons of carbon to the atmosphere annually.

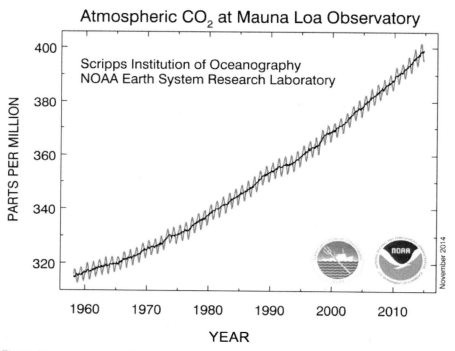

Figure 3.4: Atmospheric CO_2 concentration at Mauna Loa Observatory from 1958 to 2014.

Greenhouse gases are not the only components of the atmosphere that affect global temperature. **Clouds** (masses of tiny water droplets) influence climate in a variety of ways and on a variety of spatial and temporal scales. Clouds can cool the Earth by reflecting sunlight back into space. They can also warm the Earth by reflecting infrared radiation back to Earth through the greenhouse gas effect described above. The amount of water vapor (and thus of clouds) in the atmosphere is sensitive to temperature: the warmer it is, the more water evaporates, and the more water that the air can hold—approximately 6% more water vapor for every °C of additional heat. This creates a reinforcing feedback in the climate system: the warmer it gets, the more water vapor there will be in the atmosphere, and this will cause still more warming.

Other important compounds in our atmosphere that influence the Earth's climate are **aerosols**, which are solid, liquid, or mixtures of solid and liquid particles suspended in the air—from volcanic eruptions, storms, or anthropogenic emissions. Aerosols can cool the Earth by both reflecting incoming sunlight and also serving as "seeds," or **condensation nuclei**, for clouds. The number and size of aerosol particles determines whether the water in clouds condenses into a few large droplets or many small ones, and this strongly affects the amount of sunlight that clouds reflect and the amount of radiation that they absorb. The increased reflection of sunlight into space by aerosols usually outweighs their greenhouse effect, but because aerosols remain in the atmosphere for only a few weeks the impact of greenhouse gases in the long run is much more significant.

4. Natural Causes of Climate Change

In this section we address climate changes caused not by human activities, but by natural forces within and outside of Earth's climate system.

4.1 Scale

As we ask and answer the question of why climate changes, we must simultaneously consider the temporal scale of our discussion, that is, the extent of time over which changes occur (*Table 3.3*). Earth has been in existence for 4.6 billion years, and life has been visibly thriving on it, in one form or another, for most of that time. Thus, what has happened in the last 100 years is only a tiny part of the history of Earth and its life and climate. Some causes of climate change have tremendous influence, but are only apparent over a million years or more. Others are smaller, but their impacts are seen more readily over shorter time scales, in decades or hundreds of years.

On the scale of millions of years, climates change because of plate tectonic activity. Plate tectonics, the mechanism that moves the continents across the globe and forms new ocean floor, has many effects on global climate. Plate tectonic activity, for example, causes volcanism, and extended periods of high volcanic activity can release large amounts of greenhouse gases into the atmosphere. Volcanism also creates new rock, as magma is expelled from the interior of the Earth and cools on the surface. In underwater volcanic activity, new rock can displace ocean water and increase global sea level, which changes the way the oceans distribute heat, and further impacts global climate. For example, the Cretaceous Period, from 145 million to 66 million years ago, was a particularly warm period in Earth's history, in part due to the high amounts of greenhouse gas emission from volcanism, and was also a time of higher global sea level.

For information about how human activity is shaping our climate, see Chapter 5: Evidence and Causes of Recent Climate Change.

Natural Causes

aerosol · *the suspension of very fine solid or liquid particles in a gas.*

condensaton nuclei · *suspended particles in the air which can serve as "seeds" for water molecules to attach to, in the first step in the formation of clouds. See also NUCLEATION SITES.*

3 What is Climate?

Milankovitch cycles • *cyclical changes in the amount of heat received from the sun, associated with how the Earth's orbit, tilt, and wobble alter its position with respect to the sun. These changes affect the global climate, most notably alterations of glacial and interglacial intervals.*

Heinrich events • *periods during the last 100,000 years when large volumes of freshwater entered the ocean from icebergs which broke off glaciers and ice sheets in the Arctic and floated into the North Atlantic Ocean. This release of freshwater changed ocean circulation because freshwater and seawater have different densities.*

iceberg • *a large chunk of ice, generally ranging in height from 1 to 75 meters (3 to 246 feet) above sea level, that has broken off of an ice sheet or glacier and floats freely in open water.*

Table 3.3: Some common causes of climate change in Earth's history and their temporal scale.

Climate Change Cause	Scale of Change
Position in the solar system	billions of years
Heat generated by the sun	billions of years
Evolution of photosynthesis, other biological impacts	millions to billions of years
CO_2 input from volcanism	millions of years
CO_2 removal from weathering	millions of years
Movement of tectonic plates	millions of years
Shape of Earth's orbit around the sun (eccentricity)	hundreds of thousands of years
Tilt of Earth's axis relative to the sun (obliquity)	tens of thousands of years
"Wobble" of Earth's axis (precession)	tens of thousands of years

Plate tectonics also impacts climate on the scale of millions of years due to the changing location of the continents. Climate on land is heavily influenced by ocean currents, so global climate is significantly different when the continents are close together (as in the supercontinent Pangea, which came together approximately 250 million years ago) versus when they are more widely separated, as in modern times. Also, land masses in the equatorial regions have a different impact on climate than continents in higher latitudes because of how heat is distributed from equatorial regions north- and southward around land masses. Therefore, the position of plates over time has had significant impacts on past global climate.

On the scale of hundreds of thousands of years, climates change because of periodic oscillations of the Earth's orbit around the sun, called astronomical or **Milankovitch cycles** (see *Box 3.7, Figure 3.5*). These oscillations primarily affect the subtly varying amount of sunlight received over the course of the year and the distribution of that sunlight across latitudes. Glacial intervals can occur when, in part as a result of these orbital variations, high latitudes receive less summer sunlight, so that their cover of ice and snow does not melt as much. Thus, the Pleistocene Ice Age record of dramatic warming followed by slow, steady cooling (seen in *Figure 3.6*) reflects repeated glaciations every 100,000 years or so, caused in part by Milankovitch cycles. Understanding these cycles has turned out to be critical to understanding natural variation in the Earth's climate system over the past several million years and beyond.

On the scale of millennia (thousands of years), climates during the last glacial-interglacial cycle have been influenced by cyclic events such as **Heinrich events**. Heinrich events occurred approximately every 7,000-13,000 years and are evidenced by sediment layers on the northern Atlantic Ocean floor, deposited by the melting of huge ice sheets with small rocks and debris contained in them. Scientists believe that these were caused by large **icebergs** that were released from Canada that, after floating into warmer waters, melted and released large quantities of freshwater into the North Atlantic. This changed ocean circulation because the large, quick releases of freshwater are less dense than the seawater, decreasing the density of the ocean surface and diminishing the sinking of dense water that drives ocean circulation. These large, abrupt releases of freshwater caused a switch from glacial to interglacial types of ocean current patterns.

On the scale of human experience and history (centuries to decades), climates change for a number of reasons. Some are cyclic, and others are the culmination of small changes in topography, land use, and other factors that occur in this relatively short span of time. Two examples of changes on this scale are the **Younger Dryas** event and the **Little Ice Age**. The Younger Dryas event was a 1,200-year interval of colder temperatures that punctuated a warming trend that began approximately 13,000 years ago. Scientists have ascertained that a shift from warming to cooling happened over the course of only a few decades, and brought back glacial climate characteristics such as mountain glaciers in New Zealand and intense windstorms in Asia. One hypothesis suggests that the Younger Dryas was triggered by an ice dam breaking and sending large amounts of freshwater into the northern Atlantic Ocean, reducing flow of warm Gulf Stream water into the area. Other hypotheses have been offered to explain the Younger Dryas, including one postulating icebergs breaking off of an Arctic ice sheet and floating southward, again sending large amounts of freshwater into the North Atlantic. One thing seems certain—the Younger Dryas is an example of how a single event can reverse or significantly change global climate within a matter of decades.

The Little Ice Age occurred between approximately the years 1200 and 1800 CE and followed a time in history called the **Medieval Warm Period**, which peaked approximately 1,000 years ago. The difference in temperature between the Medieval Warm Period, which allowed the Viking people to inhabit Greenland, and the Little Ice Age, which kept Icelandic fishermen frozen in port for up to three months per year from the 1600s through 1930, was only approximately 1°C (1.8°F) globally.

Many factors affect weather and climate on the scale of a few years, and some of these can be cyclic or nearly so. One of the most important of these is **El Niño**. El Niño is a climate pattern that occurs across the tropical Pacific Ocean every 3-7 years, characterized by warming ocean surface temperatures and accompanying major shifts in precipitation in the Americas and ocean circulation in the eastern Pacific.

The sun also plays a role in a short-term climate cycle through its frequency of **solar flares**, or **sunspots**, which increase and decrease on an 11-year cycle. When solar flares occur more frequently, the sun has a larger number of "spots" on its surface and emits more solar energy, which increases the intensity of energy (**irradiance**) that the Earth receives from the sun. Direct measurements of solar output since 1978 show a rise and fall over the 11-year **sunspot cycle**, but there is no overall up- or downward trend in the strength of solar irradiance that might correlate with the temperature increase that Earth has experienced. Similarly, there is no trend in direct measurements of the sun's ultraviolet output or in cosmic rays. Thus, even though solar irradiance is the primary energy that heats our planet, because sunspots have shown no major directional increases or decreases in their recorded history, they do not appear to be related to the current, directional change in global climate.

Natural Causes

Younger Dryas • an abrupt shift in the Northern Hemisphere from a warm to a cold climate and then an abrupt shift back again, occurring over about 1,200 years starting around 13,000 years ago. The shift back to a warmer climate occurred with a 10°C (18°F) rise in temperature over only a decade.

Little Ice Age • a relatively modest cooling (less than 1° C) of the Northern Hemisphere in the 16th – 19th centuries.

Medieval Warm Period • a period of warm climate in the North Atlantic region during approximately the years 950 to 1100.

solar flare • a sudden release of energy near the Sun's surface which appears very bright from the Earth.

sunspots • dark areas on the surface of the Sun that are cooler than surrounding regions. Sunspots typically last from a few days to a few months. SOLAR FLARES can erupt from sunspots.

irradiance • the intensity of radiated energy received, for example, by the Earth from the sun.

Natural Causes

sunspot cycle • *an 11-year cycle over which the number of SUNSPOTS varies, associated with a cyclical variation in the Sun's magnetic field.*

insolation • *the amount of solar radiation reaching the Earth.*

Box 3.7: Milankovitch Cycles: the sun and orbital variations

The sun is the source of most incoming energy on Earth; it is this solar energy over a given area and time known as **insolation** that controls the energy that drives Earth's climate. Climate models indicate that a relatively small change in the amount of heat retained from the sun can have a lasting impact on Earth's temperature.

Because nearly all of Earth's atmospheric energy is ultimately derived from the sun, it makes sense that the planet's position and orientation relative to the sun would have an effect on climate. The Earth's orbit around the sun is not a perfect circle, but an ellipse. The distance from the Earth to the sun changes as the Earth travels its yearly path (see *Figure 3.5*). In addition, the axis of the Earth (running from pole to pole) is not vertical with respect to the sun, but is currently tilted approximately 23.5°. Earth's tilt is responsible for the seasons, which various parts of the world experience differently. It is summer in the Northern Hemisphere during the part of the year that it is tilted toward the sun and receives the sun's rays more directly; conversely, when Earth is on the other side of its orbit and the Southern Hemisphere is tilted toward the sun, it is summer in the Southern Hemisphere.

Earth's orbit also changes on a longer time scale. Milankovitch Cycles (see *Figure 3.5*) describe how the position of Earth changes over time in predictable patterns of alternations of the proximity and angle of Earth to the sun, and therefore have an impact on global climate. These are:

- **Eccentricity**, the change of Earth's orbit from a round orbit to an elliptical one, which occurs on a 100,000-year cycle. When Earth's orbit varies between more circular and more elliptical (i.e. more extreme eccentricity), the length of the seasons change.

- **Obliquity**, the tilt of the Earth on its orbital axis, which can range from 22-24° from vertical, and occurs on a roughly 40,000-year cycle. The tilt of the Earth impacts how much insolation is absorbed by the planet at different latitudes.

- **Precession**, commonly called "wobble," because it is the small variation in the direction of Earth's axis as it points relative to the fixed stars in the galaxy. Because of precession, the point in Earth's orbit when the Northern Hemisphere is angled toward the sun changes over a cycle of approximately 20,000 years.

These three variables interact with each other in ways that can be very complex, but are predictable mathematically. For example, the influence of the shape of the orbit on Earth's climate depends very much on the angle of tilt that Earth is experiencing at the time. The orbital variations described by Milankovitch Cycles are predictable based on the known laws of planetary motion. Confirmation of their climatic effects, however, comes from the geological record, where, in deep-sea sediment cores stretching back further than 5,000,000 years, scientists have found indications of temperature fluctuating in ways similar to what Milankovitch Cycles would predict.

What is Climate?

Milankovitch Cycles

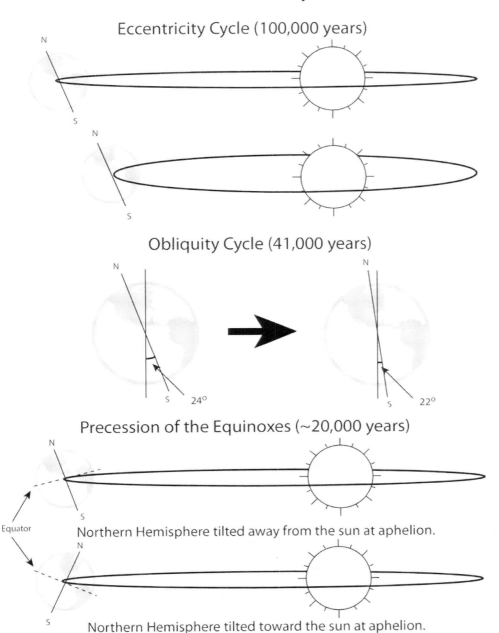

Eccentricity Cycle (100,000 years)

Obliquity Cycle (41,000 years)

24° → 22°

Precession of the Equinoxes (~20,000 years)

Northern Hemisphere tilted away from the sun at aphelion.

Northern Hemisphere tilted toward the sun at aphelion.

Figure 3.5: Milankovitch Cycles. The Earth's orbital variation around the sun experiences cyclic changes in shape. Eccentricity, caused by gravitational forces from other planets in our solar system, changes the shape of the orbit on a 100,000-year cycle from a circular to a more elliptical shape. Obliquity is the change of the angle of Earth's axis, which ranges from 22° to 24° from normal, and occurs on a 40,000-year cycle. Precession, commonly called the "wobble" of Earth's axis, affects the positions in Earth's orbit at which the Northern and Southern Hemispheres experience summer and winter. Precession changes on an approximately 20,000-year cycle.

Natural Causes

What is Climate?

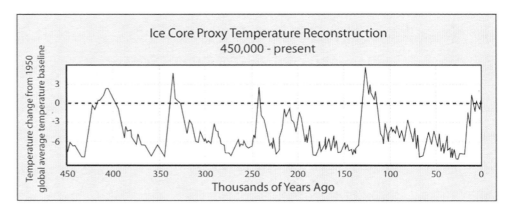

Figure 3.6: 100,000-year temperature cycles. Ice age temperature changes for the last 450,000 years in this diagram are represented as differences of temperature (in °C) from a modern baseline. These differences are called temperature anomalies. The graph shows abrupt temperature spikes approximately every 100,000 years, each followed by slower cooling. The highest temperatures occurred just after the global climate changed from glacial to interglacial intervals. These temperature changes correlate with changes in the shape of Earth's orbit (due to Milankovitch Cycles). According to this pattern, Earth should now (during this interglacial period) be experiencing slow cooling, not warming.

4.2 The Carbon Cycle

The element carbon plays a crucial role in the way that the Earth works. Because of its ability to readily form up to four bonds with other elements and other particular chemical properties, carbon constitutes the basic building block of living things as well as major constituents of the atmosphere, crust, and oceans. Individual carbon atoms combine with other elements in a variety of ways as they move between these various Earth systems in a series of steps known as the carbon cycle (*Figure 3.7*). Understanding the role of CO_2 in the Earth's climate starts with understanding how carbon behaves in this cycle.

CO_2 that enters the atmosphere from volcanoes is approximately balanced (in the absence of humans) by removal of CO_2 from the atmosphere by two processes. One is long-term burial of organic matter—that is, the products of photosynthesis not recycled. This occurs when, for example, dead phytoplankton sink to the bottom of the ocean and are covered by sediment. The other is chemical weathering, or the breakdown of rocks at the surface by chemical change. During chemical weathering, water reacts with minerals in rocks and CO_2 from the atmosphere. The CO_2 is thus removed from the air and transferred into other compounds, which eventually become stored in the sediments that accumulate in the ocean and ultimately become part of sedimentary rocks (*Figure 3.7*).

Evolutionary changes in organisms throughout geologic time have had a strong effect on the global carbon cycle. The evolution of organisms capable of photosynthesis, over 3 billion years ago, drew *CO_2* out of the atmosphere and created the first significant amounts of atmospheric oxygen. The first appearance of large animals in the early Cambrian, 540 million years ago, and the evolution of land plants in the Devonian, approximately 380 million years ago, accelerated the cycling of carbon and its burial in sediments. It is widely believed that the evolution of land plants led to a significant drop in CO_2 concentrations in the

What is Climate?

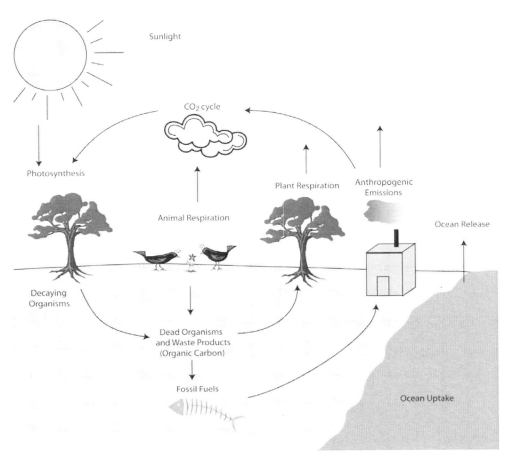

Figure 3.7: The carbon cycle (a very simplified view). Every living thing contains carbon. When animals exhale, CO_2 is emitted into the atmosphere. It is absorbed by plants through the process of photosynthesis and gets incorporated into their structures. When plants and animals die, the carbon in their bodies gets incorporated into sediments, which might eventually become rocks in the Earth's crust, where it usually remains for millions of years. The extraction and burning of this carbon in the form of fossil fuels emits CO_2 into the atmosphere, and some of it becomes incorporated into carbon sinks like oceans and forests. Omitted from this figure are biological processes in the oceans, volcanoes, weathering of rocks, and the formation of limestone.

atmosphere and caused the widespread glaciation of the Carboniferous Period (360 to 295 million years ago).

See Chapter 4: Past Climates for further information about the history of Earth's climate and the evolution of life.

The carbon cycle functions on a variety of time scales. A single atom of carbon that you exhale (as part of a molecule of CO_2) will on average remain in the atmosphere for hundreds of years, before being absorbed by a plant or other photosynthesizing organism. When the plant dies, that carbon atom could in a few weeks or months be taken up by another plant, or oxidize back into CO_2 and re-enter the atmosphere, or it might be buried in the Earth's crust and remain there for millions of years. When we burn fossil fuels—oil, natural gas, and coal extracted from the Earth—we very quickly release carbon into the atmosphere from sources that took millions of years to form.

3

What is Climate?

Summary

tectonic plate · *a section of the Earth's lithosphere that moves along the surface of the Earth. The scientific theory of plate tectonics is that Earth's crust consists of a series of 7 or 8 large plates and numerous small ones. Plate tectonics are responsible for the distribution of the Earth's continents, for the uplift and position of mountain ranges, and for many other features of the Earth's surface.*

seafloor spreading · *the formation of new crust around an oceanic ridge when two adjacent oceanic plates move in opposite directions and lava erupts from between them, hardens, and then the new material moves apart.*

magma · *molten rock located below the surface of the Earth.*

Box 3.8: The faint young sun paradox

On the scale of billions of years, the Earth's climate has been controlled by the balance between its distance from the sun and the composition of its atmosphere. If we compare Earth to its planetary neighbors, Mars and Venus, we see what might have happened on Earth, but didn't. Earth's original atmosphere came from volcanism that emitted gases from the planet's interior. The high concentration of CO_2 and methane (CH_4) in this early atmosphere kept the Earth warm when the sun was younger and fainter. Some of the first life on Earth put oxygen into the atmosphere by the process of photosynthesis, and drew down CO_2. Lower levels of greenhouse gases in the atmosphere helped to compensate for the brightening sun, which otherwise would have warmed Earth too much for living organisms, or even liquid water, to be present. Thus, the greenhouse effect allowed life to exist on Earth when it might not have otherwise.

4.3 Plate Tectonics

The Earth's surface is like a jigsaw puzzle. It is made up of many huge pieces, or plates, which slide around the globe very slowly, at about the rate that your fingernails grow. The continents are embedded in these **tectonic plates** (*Figure 3.8*). Where these plates come together or move apart, earthquakes, mountain building, and many other geologic processes can occur. Plate movement is thought to be driven by the Earth's internal heat, as convection currents from the lower mantle heat the rock above, lowering its density and pushing it upward.

Plate movement can significantly affect climate over millions of years, in several ways. The position of a plate on the globe, and of any continents that might be on top of it, is one determinant of whether that continent will experience glaciation or tropical temperatures. For example, if the plate that now holds North America and Greenland were shifted a bit to the north, North America might now be covered in a continental ice sheet. Instead, only Greenland is covered in ice because it is positioned farther north today. Plate movement also affects climate because when two plates come together, volcanoes often result, adding CO_2 to the atmosphere when they erupt. When plates move apart, in a process known as **seafloor spreading**, hot **magma** is often released directly into the ocean, bringing CO_2 with it.

5. Summary

Climate is a system, driven by solar radiation and interactions of the atmosphere, hydrosphere, geosphere, and biosphere. A number of natural phenomena contribute to Earth's climate. These phenomena—plate tectonics and weathering, evolution of new life, and others—have interacted via the carbon cycle to change the amount of CO_2 in the atmosphere and cause temperatures to change throughout geologic time.

Humans are now influencing Earth's climate in a dramatic way (see Chapter 5). To understand the scope of this influence, it is useful to first look at the history of climate change in the past (Chapter 4).

What is Climate?

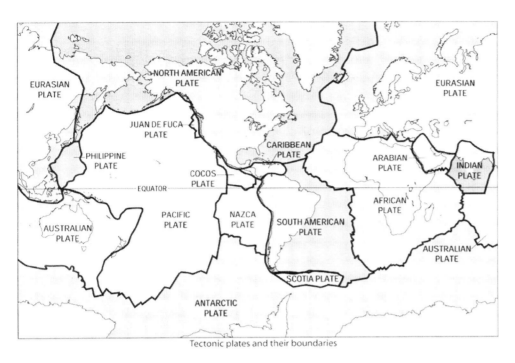

Tectonic plates and their boundaries

Figure 3.8: Plate tectonics. A world map with all of the individual tectonic plate boundaries highlighted. The plates move around like puzzle pieces over the globe.

What is Climate?

Online Resources

The Greenhouse Effect

1. An interactive simulation in which one can vary the concentration of greenhouse gases in the atmosphere and see the changes in infrared radiation in the atmosphere and the effect on Earth's temperature: https://phet.colorado.edu/en/simulation/greenhouse.

2. A brief (approximately 2 minute) video by Cornell University Professor Toby Ault which explains the greenhouse effect and illustrates the roles of visible and infrared light using simple props and an infrared camera: https://www.youtube.com/watch?v=7perebgdXAQ.

3. A brief (approximately 2 minute) video from National Academy of Sciences *Lines of Evidence* series, explaining the greenhouse effect: https://www.youtube.com/watch?v=3JX-ioSmNW8&feature=youtu.be.

Climate Measurements

1. An article about satellite measurements of precipitation and the Global Precipitation Measurement Core Observatory: https://pmm.nasa.gov/education/videos/for-good-measure.

2. A website with information about the Community Collaborative Rain, Hail, and Snow Network, a citizen scientist project that generates measurements of precipitation all over the US. The site contains maps, data, and information about how to join the project and make measurements. http://www.cocorahs.org/Login.aspx.

Climate Change Over Geologic Time

Paleomap Project: a set of detailed maps of the world showing the past positions of the continents and describing Earth's past climates, going back to the Cambrian period: http://www.scotese.com/climate.htm .

Recent Climate Change: Data and Visualizations

1. NASA Vital Signs of the Planet website, an excellent overview of key climate change data: http://climate.nasa.gov . This site also contains many links to articles, information about solutions, images, videos, interactives, education resources, and information about NASA missions.

2. An animation of global temperature change from 1884 to 2014: http://climate.nasa.gov/climate_resources/25/.

3. A source of time-series graphs of global climate indicators such as temperature, CO_2, sea ice, sea level, and more: https://www.climate.gov/maps-data#global-climate-dashboard.

What is Climate?

4. NOAA Climate Data Snapshots: maps of monthly US climate data including temperature, precipitation, drought, and severe weather. The time records of the datasets vary, but the earliest go back to 2000. https://www.climate.gov/maps-data/data-snapshots/start.

5. Climate Change Indicators in the United States: a website with access to maps and graphs of many different climate change indicators as well as a summary report. https://www.epa.gov/climate-indicators.

6. The Third National Climate Assessment: a comprehensive overview of climate change in the US and its impacts: http://nca2014.globalchange.gov/ . The National Climate Assessment is updated every few years.

General Climate Change Teaching Resources

1. Teaching resources associated with the Third National Climate Assessment (2014), which give examples of how to use key figures in the National Climate Assessment to illustrate points about climate change in the US. Resources are organized by geographic region. https://www.climate.gov/teaching/national-climate-assessment-resources-educators/2014-national-climate-assessment-resources.

2. A reviewed collection of teaching resources: Climate Literacy and Energy Awareness Network (CLEAN); http://cleanet.org/index.html.

Carbon Cycle

1. An interactive carbon budget tool which allows users to explore altering sources and sinks and see the effects on atmospheric CO_2: http://carboncycle.aos.wisc.edu/carbon-budget-tool/.

2. A set of clearly written and illustrated articles on the carbon cycle: http://earthobservatory.nasa.gov/Features/CarbonCycle/.

Contributions (Natural and Anthropogenic) to Climate Change

1. An infographic on potential causes of climate change from 1880-2005 and their effects, based on datasets from NASA: http://www.bloomberg.com/graphics/2015-whats-warming-the-world/.

2. Charts of US greenhouse gas emissions by type of gas, fuel source, and sector: https://www.eia.gov/environment/emissions/ghg_report/ghg_overview.cfm.

3 What is Climate?

Weather Simulation

Weather in a Tank: http://paoc.mit.edu/labguide/, https://www.youtube.com/watch?v=uWdKVpQ94Ns, and https://vimeo.com/user14026932/videos. These sites contain information about and videos of a system for running rotating fluid laboratory experiments, allowing one to simulate dynamics of the atmosphere and ocean.

Chapter 4:
Climate Change Through Earth History

1. Why Past Climate Change Matters

A frequent question to geologists who talk about climate change is why current climate change matters if change has been occurring throughout Earth's history. The practical answer to that question is that current change is rapid and significant enough to matter to *people* and it matters to other living things, which are also valued by people. But why should we care about climate change that has occurred in the Earth's history?

One answer is pedagogical: Though understanding ancient climates is not likely to be the most important thing for students to know about current climate change, it may help students see that climates *can* change, put the kinds of changes we see today into a historical perspective, and help students understand how researchers use paleoclimates to study our currently changing climate. The idea that the Earth's climate could potentially change is an abstract concept that is outside the range of our personal experiences and was, until a couple hundred years ago, a radical idea. Accepting the idea that the Earth does change has profound implications for how we see the Earth and its future. Seeing direct evidence of Earth change in one's own region—such as through rocks or fossils normally associated with much colder or warmer, or drier or wetter, environments than occur now—communicates the idea that the Earth *does* change. It also connects climate to aspects of Earth systems such as the rock and fossil record.

Another answer is scientific and practical: Past climates help scientists understand how the Earth *could* change by understanding how the Earth *has* changed. Climate scientists' predictions for temperature and precipitation changes associated with current climate change frequently rely on sophisticated computer models. But there is no practical way to physically test hypotheses derived from such models about the long-term rates of glacial retreat, changes in oceanic circulation, influences on organisms, and so on—we can't recreate a global laboratory except in a computer simulation. Climate change events in Earth's history, however, have performed some of the experiments for us. The lessons learned from ancient climates may be difficult to apply to modern climate change because the circumstances (land positions, atmospheric chemistry, vegetation, and so on) become increasingly different the further back we go in time, but even very ancient climate changes in a world that seems quite foreign provide sometimes surprising lessons about how the Earth system operates, and how fast and to what extremes it can change.

CHAPTER AUTHORS

Robert M. Ross

and authors of

A Very Short Guide to Climate Change

53

Climate and Earth History

Observing Climate

phytoplankton • *one-celled photosynthetic algae that float near the surface of bodies of both marine and freshwater.*

Paleozoic • *a geologic time era that extends from 541 to 252 million years ago. Fossil evidence shows that during this time period, life evolved in the oceans and gradually colonized the land.*

In simplest terms, detecting climate change of the past requires only a sequence of sediments. For those of us with an outcrop of sedimentary rocks in our area, the results of climate change are within view nearly any time we see two or more layers that look different. Little specialized knowledge is necessary: the fact that the rocks vary in color, resistance to weathering, or bedding patterns indicates that the character of the sediments changed, and that means we are seeing the results of past environmental change. There is a good chance that this environmental change was associated with, if not caused by, changes in climate. Add in understanding of a few principles about how sediments vary among environments, and you and your students can hypothesize about climate changes in the geologic past wherever you may find sedimentary rocks.

It's also interesting to ponder that the rocks we see that are a record of climate change frequently played a role in creating that change: the carbon stored in sediments and rocks is part of the global carbon cycle that affects atmospheric CO_2 concentrations. Large amounts of Earth's carbon are tied up in limestones ($CaCO_3$) and organic carbon in sedimentary rocks, particularly shales and coal, which you may be able to see at the surface in your region. In many areas of the country we can also observe such deposits in the making: organic-rich sediment in modern environments around us, e.g., dark muds along ponds and lakes, and accumulation of peat in swampy areas. These are effectively the same substances that became, after the pressure and heat of deep burial, fossil fuels. Mass production of energy through the burning of fossil fuels is burning the accumulation of hundreds of thousands or millions of years of forests and **phytoplankton**. It may be easier for students to put into perspective how rapid must be the rate of change of CO_2 in the atmosphere today we when think about how long it took for the accumulation of organic carbon that became fossil fuels.

2. Observing Climate Through Time in the Rock Record

When we use the term "climate change" we are referring to a global average— "global warming"—while also referring to other environmental shifts in specific geographic regions. Though we hear particularly about warming, we know that for some places the most significant trends impacting living things may be changes in storm intensity or precipitation in addition to or instead of temperature changes. Some places in the world may experience cooling (at least for some years) even while most places are experiencing warming. The same is true of trends in climate history: the rock records in different parts of the United States reflect environmental changes in those regions, which may or may not clearly reflect global changes occurring at the time the rocks were deposited.

Another consideration is that the history of climate at any specific place over geologic intervals of hundreds of millions of years will involve changes in latitudinal position of the continent. To make sense of why a place had the climate it did at some time in the past we must distinguish between the roles of moving tectonic plates from the role of changing global climates. Rocks and fossils from the **Paleozoic** era (*Figure 4.1*) in the United States primarily indicate warm environments, but this can be explained from independent evidence that North America was at low latitudes, even right over the equator, during

Climate and Earth History

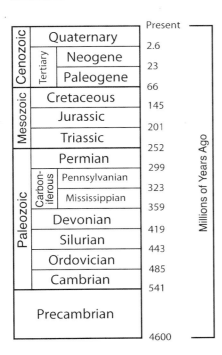

			Present
Cenozoic		Quaternary	
	Tertiary	Neogene	2.6
		Paleogene	23
			66
Mesozoic		Cretaceous	
		Jurassic	145
		Triassic	201
			252
Paleozoic		Permian	
	Carboniferous	Pennsylvanian	299
		Mississippian	323
			359
		Devonian	
		Silurian	419
		Ordovician	443
		Cambrian	485
			541
		Precambrian	
			4600

Millions of Years Ago

About the time scale

The time scale in The Teacher-Friendly Guides™ follows that of the International Commission on Stratigraphy (ICS). The Tertiary period, though it was officially phased out in 2008 by the ICS, remains on the scale in the Guides, since "Tertiary" is found extensively in past literature. In contrast, the Carboniferous and Pennsylvanian & Mississippian periods all enjoy official status, with the latter pair being more commonly used in the US.

Figure 4.1: The geologic time scale (spacing of units not to scale).

proxy • an alternative to direct measurements of climate variables; data from sources like tree rings, lichens, and pollen are used to infer climate information.

much of that time. We use evidence from other continents that were at higher latitudes during the Paleozoic to ascertain that some geologic time intervals were relatively warm at a global scale, but other time intervals were relatively cool with polar glaciers (such as the end-Ordovician and the Carboniferous periods).

These complications notwithstanding, the ancient environments we can see in the rock record of the United States, in particular those in one's own region, may provide useful discussion points about how the Earth's climate changes and what those changes mean for current climate change.

2.1. Inferring Ancient Climates

How do we know what ancient climates were like? To know the average temperature of the world 10,000 years ago, since we cannot look at a thermometer, we need a substitute—a **proxy**—that indirectly recorded that information.

Wherever Earth's atmosphere contacts water and sediment (stirring it, heating and cooling it) and helps or hinders the growth of organisms, climate records are left behind. Earth scientists reconstruct ancient climates by using traces left in the rocks, fossils, and sediments available on the Earth's surface. Even after thousands or millions of years, many of these materials contain information about the environmental conditions that existed at the time that they were laid down as soils or preserved in sediments in bodies of water. This climatic information can be found in unconsolidated sediments (for example, in mud at the bottom of a pond), in rocks and fossils, in glacial ice sheets, or even in a living tree or coral colony. Each of these systems records something about the world in which they formed. See *Boxes 4.1* (proxies from rocks), *4.3* (fossils), *4.4* (oxygen isotopes), *4.7* (ice cores), and *4.8* (living organisms) for more detailed information.

4 Climate and Earth History

Precambrian

Precambrian • *a geologic time interval that spans from the formation of Earth (4.6 billion years ago) to the beginning of the CAMBRIAN (541 million years ago). Relatively little is known about this time period since very few fossils or unaltered rocks have survived. What few clues exist indicate that life first appeared on the planet as long as 3.9 billion years ago in the form of single-celled organisms.*

bacteria • *single-celled microorganisms with cell membranes but without organelles or a nucleus.*

protists • *a diverse group of single-celled eukaryotes (organisms with complex cells containing a nucleus and organelles).*

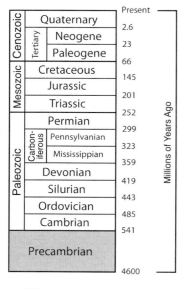

Of course, not all of these proxy materials are present everywhere, and in fact many places have few or none. Not unlike human history, we have to piece together geological history from different times and different places, to make a general storyline across broad regions or globally.

3. History of the Earth's Climate

Though a minor amount of Earth's internal heat is released at the surface, nearly all heat that influences climate comes from the sun. The heat of the sun on the Earth's surface varies through geologic time because of variations in the sun itself and predictable variations in the way the Earth tilts, rotates, and revolves around the sun. Just as important as heat received at the Earth's surface, however, is the relative proportion in which that heat is reflected away, absorbed but quickly lost back to space, or "trapped" by the atmosphere. Broadly speaking, factors affecting retaining or losing heat from the sun has been the driver of most global climate change over the history of the Earth.

Changes in concentrations of the greenhouse gases CO_2 and CH_4 had an impact on Earth's climate from early in Earth history, and reciprocal variations in CO_2 and O_2 have characterized some of the largest events in the history of both Earth and life. Changes to the Earth's surface have also had a big effect on the amount of heat the Earth and ultimately the atmosphere absorb. Surface phenomena such as moving continents, changing rocks at the surface, evolution of plant life onto land, and changes in distribution of ice explain why Earth's climate has changed over geologic time in the way that it has. The insights this gives climate scientists regarding **forcings**, **feedbacks**, interactions, and sensitivities of the climate system can be applied to understanding current and future human-induced climate changes.

3.1. The Early Evolution of the Atmosphere

The first four billion years (about 85%) of Earth history, collectively known as the **Precambrian**, might be described as the interval during which Earth systems came to be (relatively speaking) the way they are today: for example, plate tectonics, atmospheric chemistry and structure, and ecosystem processes developed over the course of that interval. The Precambrian became, sometime within its first third, occupied by a great diversity of **bacteria**, with **protists** diversifying in the final third.

The early evolution of Earth's atmospheres signals the major influence CO_2 and CH_4 would go on to play in the evolution of climate and life through Earth history. Most people may not stop to consider whether an atmosphere like the one we have is inevitable. Every planet in our solar system, or any planetary system for that matter, will have its own unique chemical composition. If circumstances are such that a planet retains an atmosphere, it will likely have started with gasses made of some combination of the elements hydrogen, helium, carbon, nitrogen, and oxygen. Smaller planets, like Mars, as well as moons in our own solar system, have a very thin atmosphere: at one time there were greater quantities of gases on these planetary bodies, but the gravity of the planet did not retain the same mass of air as the Earth has.

Climate and Earth History

Not long after the Earth first formed, more than 4.5 billion years ago, its atmosphere was composed mostly of hydrogen and helium, which, because of the Earth's modest size and gravity field, was mostly lost to space. Volcanic activity ("degassing") and to a much lesser extent, collisions with meteorites and comets added water vapor, carbon dioxide, and nitrogen to the atmosphere. As the Earth cooled enough for liquid water to form, the vapor formed clouds from which torrential rains poured for millions of years, absorbing salt and other minerals from the earth as the rainwater coursed to the lowest areas, forming Earth's oceans and seas.

The Earth still could have lost its atmosphere, in spite of its gravity: **ionizing radiation**—"solar wind"—from the sun might have, over time, knocked most gas molecules out of the atmosphere. The Earth, however, has a **magnetic field** associated with convection in its core and this magnetic field, originating sometime in Earth's first billion years, has since acted to block most of the effects of ionizing radiation.

Within the first billion years of Earth's history, as the early atmosphere was evolving, the surface of the Earth was cooling to form a solid crust of rock (there are mineral crystals indicating that this process may have started as early as 4.4 billion years ago). Regardless of precisely when this took place, it represented the formation of continental terranes that were the precursor to the processes of plate tectonics that have continued ever since. The motion of these plates through different latitudinal climate zones, and the size and arrangement of the continents, have greatly impacted heat retention and patterns of circulation and precipitation. The amount and types of minerals at the Earth's surface exposed to the atmosphere (or covered by water or glaciers) played a huge role in atmospheric chemistry. For example, rock that is enriched in **organic matter** will release abundant amounts of carbon dioxide as it weathers, while rock rich in **feldspar** and mica will remove carbon dioxide during the chemical process of weathering.

UV light caused much of the atmospheric gas in the form of methane (CH_4) and ammonia (NH_3) to dissociate, leaving N_2, CO_2, and H_2, the latter of which was lost to space. Molecular oxygen (O_2) did not exist, and thus was not available to oxidize surviving molecules such as CH_4. It is widely accepted that energy from the sun very early in Earth history was about 30% less than it is today and, all else being equal, one would expect Earth to have been about 30 °C colder, which should have led to widespread and long-term ice formation. Geological evidence (such as record of liquid water) suggests, however, that this was not the case, thus it seems likely that greenhouse gases—carbon dioxide and the remaining methane, possibly at concentrations that were orders of magnitude greater than in the atmosphere today—acted to maintain a relatively warm Earth.

Over Earth's history, the atmospheric content of N_2 has steadily increased through volcanic degassing. Today it represents over 3/4 of the Earth's atmosphere by volume. N_2 is very stable and as such does not react much with either the rocky surface of the Earth or other molecules in the atmosphere, which allows it to accumulate over time.

Today, by far, the 2nd most abundant gas is O_2, over ¼ of the atmosphere by volume, but it wasn't always this way. The Earth had very little free oxygen until

Precambrian

ionizing radiation • high-energy electromagnetic energy which can cause ionization in the material through which it passes, for example, x-rays and gamma rays.

magnetic field • a conceptualization of the strength and direction of the magnetic force at a distance from an object.

organic matter • decomposed remains of plants, animals, and their wastes.

			Present
Cenozoic		Quaternary	
			2.6
	Tertiary	Neogene	
			23
		Paleogene	
			66
Mesozoic		Cretaceous	
			145
		Jurassic	
			201
		Triassic	
			252
Paleozoic		Permian	
			299
	Carbon-iferous	Pennsylvanian	
			323
		Mississippian	
			359
		Devonian	
			419
		Silurian	
			443
		Ordovician	
			485
		Cambrian	
			541
		Precambrian	
			4600

Millions of Years Ago

Climate and Earth History

feldspar · *an extremely common group of rock-forming minerals found in igneous, metamorphic, and sedimentary rocks. There are two groups of feldspar: alkali feldspar (which ranges from potassium-rich to sodium-rich) and plagioclase feldspar (which ranges from sodium-rich to calcium-rich). Potassium feldspars of the alkali group are commonly seen as pink crystals in igneous and metamorphic rocks, or pink grains in sedimentary rocks. Plagioclase feldspars are more abundant than the alkali feldspars, ranging in color from light to dark. Feldspars are commercially used in ceramics and scouring powders.*

iron oxide minerals · *a range of minerals containing chemical compounds of iron and oxygen.*

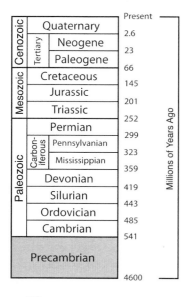

		Present
Cenozoic	Quaternary	
	Tertiary — Neogene	2.6
		23
	Paleogene	66
Mesozoic	Cretaceous	145
	Jurassic	201
	Triassic	252
Paleozoic	Permian	299
	Carboniferous — Pennsylvanian	323
	Mississippian	359
	Devonian	419
	Silurian	443
	Ordovician	485
	Cambrian	541
	Precambrian	
		4600

(Millions of Years Ago)

Figure 4.2: Banded iron formation (Fortescue Falls, Karijini National Park in Western Australia).

the evolution of photosynthesis in bacteria, perhaps beginning about 3.5 billion years ago. This would be one of the first of many instances of life changing the atmosphere. The abundant iron and organic matter in the environment quickly reacted with the oxygen they produced, but after hundreds of millions of years, these oxygen-absorbing sinks (such as extensive deposits of **iron oxide minerals** deposited in **"banded iron" formations**; *Figure 4.2 and Box 4.1*) were exhausted, and free oxygen built up in the atmosphere.

The increase in oxygen allowed the development of **ozone** in the **stratosphere**. The ozone layer blocks **ultraviolet light**, and its development may have decreased cell damage in microbial life near the surface. Stratospheric ozone also has a fundamental impact on the structure of the atmosphere. Ozone is responsible for the increase in temperature in the stratosphere with altitude because it absorbs the short wave radiation from the sun; this contributes the relative stability of the stratosphere, above the complex convection and weather of the **troposphere**.

The timing of extensive iron oxide deposition occurred about the same time as development of extensive glaciation 2.4 to 2.2 billion years ago, and it has been suggested that increased oxygen reacted with the greenhouse gas methane, converting it into carbon dioxide, a less effective greenhouse gas. This cooling is evidenced by globally distributed glacial deposits, some of which are thought to have occupied low (equatorial) latitudes. This glacial interval is known as the Huronian (named after deposits in Michigan). A significant fraction of the Earth's land may have been covered in ice for as long as 300 million years. At that time the continental plates made up less than half as much of the Earth's surface as they do today and were unified as a continent known as Arctica.

An ice-covered planet would remain that way because almost all of the sun's energy would be reflected by the ice back into space, but this did not happen on Earth, probably because of plate tectonics. The glaciation was eventually disrupted by ongoing volcanic activity, which added carbon dioxide and methane back into the atmosphere. These gases are usually removed from the atmosphere by organisms and the weathering of rocks, but these processes would have stopped while the continents and oceans were covered in glacial ice. After millions of years, the concentrations of methane and carbon dioxide increased to the point that greenhouse warming began to melt the ice

Climate and Earth History

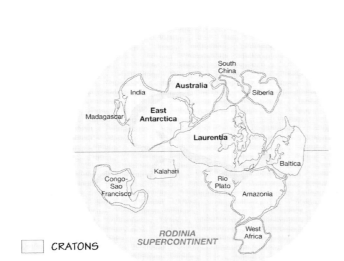

CRATONS

OROGENIC BELTS

Figure 4.3: The supercontinent Rodinia, circa 1.1 billion years ago. Laurentia represents proto-North America. (See Teacher-Friendly Guide website for a full color version.)

sheets. Once the melting started, more of the sun's energy was absorbed by the surface, and warming feedbacks began. Because the oceans had been covered, nutrients (like the mineral phosphorous) from chemical weathering of the rocks accumulated in the oceans. Population explosions of cyanobacteria used these nutrients to produce more and more oxygen capable of combining with freshly thawed carbon sources to make more carbon dioxide, further enhancing the warming. The oxygen release became part of a relatively rapid increase in atmospheric O_2.

Another very extensive glaciation occurred in the late Precambrian, about 717 million years ago, during the Cryogenian.[1] There is evidence suggesting that the entire surface of the planet became covered in ice, a hypothesis called "Snowball Earth," possibility involving cycles of decline and increase in greenhouse gases similar to those hypothesized for the Huronian glaciation. The North American portion of the supercontinent **Rodinia**, which had formed by 1.1 billion years ago, was near the equator and in the center of the supercontinent (Figure 4.3). Two extensive phases of glaciation occurred during this time, called the **Sturtian glaciation** (about 717 to 660 million years ago) and, as Rodinia began to break up, the **Marinoan glaciation** (about 640 to 635 million years ago) (*Figure 4.4*). The fact that North America was at such a low latitude, yet had glaciers (based, for example, on deposits in Idaho and Utah), is strong evidence that the Earth was cold enough to have experienced ice at a global scale.[2]

---

[1] There remains uncertainty about the degree to which the Earth was frozen over during the interval of "Snowball Earth," but it's clear that glaciation extended to the equator.

[2] The term "ice age" has different connotations depending on context. A common usage of the term refers to the whole time interval of large scale glacial-interglacial cycles in the Pleistocene (2.6 million years). The public usually thinks specifically of the most common glacial advance (the Last Glacial Maximum) about 20,000 years ago among a series of glacial-interglacial cycles. A broader definition is an interval over which there exists substantial glacial ice at the poles (or beyond).

Precambrian

"banded iron" formation
• geologic formations comprised of layers of PRECAMBRIAN, iron-rich, sedimentary rock.

ozone • a molecule (O_3) found in the STRATOSPHERE which absorbs ultraviolet light. When found near the surface of the Earth, ozone is considered a pollutant because it is a component of smog and can cause lung irritation.

stratosphere • the second layer above the Earth's surface in the ATMOSPHERE. The stratosphere reaches to about 50 kilometers (30 miles) above the Earth's surface.

ultraviolet light • electromagnetic radiation in the part of the spectrum with wavelengths from 10 to 400 nanometers.

			Present
Cenozoic		Quaternary	2.6
	Tertiary	Neogene	23
		Paleogene	66
Mesozoic		Cretaceous	145
		Jurassic	201
		Triassic	252
Paleozoic		Permian	299
	Carboniferous	Pennsylvanian	323
		Mississippian	359
		Devonian	419
		Silurian	443
		Ordovician	485
		Cambrian	541
	Precambrian		4600

Millions of Years Ago

59

4 Climate and Earth History

Precambrian

troposphere • *the layer of the ATMOSPHERE extending from the Earth's surface to about 7 to 20 kilometers (4 to 12 miles) above the surface. The height of the troposphere depends upon latitude and season.*

Rodinia • *a supercontinent that contained most or all of Earth's landmass, between 1.1 billion and 750 million years ago, during the PRECAMBRIAN. Geologists are not sure of the exact size and shape of Rodinia. It was analogous to but not the same supercontinent as PANGAEA, which formed several hundred million years later during the PERMIAN.*

Sturtian glaciation • *a time in Earth's history, around 717 to 660 million years ago, when the entire planet may have been covered in ice.*

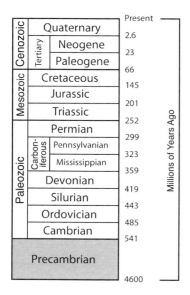

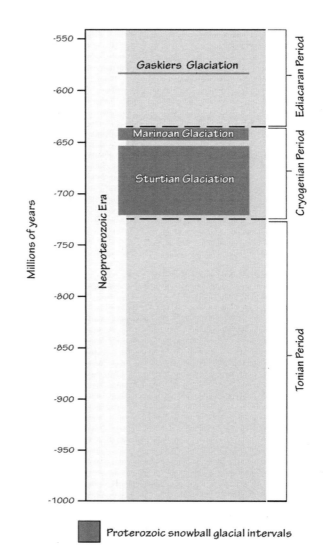

Figure 4.4: Snowball Earth periods during the late Precambrian.

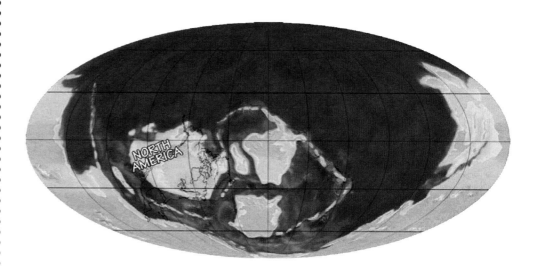

Figure 4.5: Earth during the early Cambrian, around 545 million years ago.

By 635 million years ago, the Earth had warmed again, and the North American continent had moved towards the equator (*Figure 4.5*). About this time we find some of the first animal fossils. It isn't clear what is the causal relationship between these major climate perturbations and major events in evolution.

3.2. The Early to Mid Paleozoic Era

The interval that covers, except for the the very beginning, most of the history of animal life, is known as the **Phanerozoic eon**; its history, particularly with respect to climate, is far better known scientifically than the Precambrian and far more commonly covered in science education and popular media. The Phanerozoic is split into the Paleozoic, Mesozoic, and Cenozoic eras.

From the **Cambrian** to **Silurian** animals primarily diversified in the seas; the Devonian period was an important transition, as the first sizable (but still coastal) forests and land vertebrate communities evolved. The early Paleozoic era is interesting from a climate perspective in part because there are numerous repeated patterns of changing climate and sea level associated with increased or decreased rates of evolution and extinction. Across the US there are opportunities to observe how communities of organisms responded (for example, in species composition, abundance, and size) from layer to layer, in fossil-rich marine sedimentary rocks. These patterns may give us clues to how marine organisms will respond long-term to current climate change.

3.2.1 Cambrian and Ordovician Periods

With the start of the Paleozoic era, global climates across the world were warm, and North America was located in the low, warm latitudes of the Southern Hemisphere. What would become the northern US was located just north of the equator. Broadly speaking, we find sedimentary deposits in North America throughout the Paleozoic Era that reflect tropical conditions (see *Box 4.1*). These deposits say more about the position of North America near the equator than they do about global climates, which varied widely through the Paleozoic. Evidence for warm climates in the Cambrian and **Ordovician** periods we see today in extensive limestone deposits and ancient reefs (see *Box 4.3*), for example, on the western (California and Nevada) and eastern (New York and Pennsylvania) side of the continent and in the Midwest. For some time in the Ordovician much of the Midwest was covered by very pure, quartz-rich sand, which suggests that the climate was intensely wet and warm and that the sand was washed or blown (or both) back and forth for a long time before being buried.

The Earth went through another ice age from 460 to 430 million years ago (*Figure 4.6*). The continent of **Gondwana** (modern South America, Africa, Australia, Antarctica, Arabia, and India) was located over the South Pole and became covered in glacial ice. This led to global cooling, which was associated with the first of five major **mass extinctions** that have occurred over the last half-billion years.

During the Phanerozoic not only has polar glaciation not extended to equatorial regions, but equatorial regions remained warm. For example, during this glacial interval, low latitude reefs grew around the shallow edges of a wide basin

---

Early to Mid Paleozoic

Marinoan glaciation • *a time in Earth's history, around 640 to 635 million years ago, when the entire planet may have been covered in ice.*

Phanerozoic eon • *a geological eon representing the entirety of geological history after the PRECAMBRIAN, from 541 million years ago to the present.*

Cambrian • *a geologic time period lasting from 541 to 485 million years ago. During the Cambrian, multicellular marine organisms became increasingly diverse, as did their mineralized fossils. The Cambrian is part of the PALEOZOIC Era.*

Silurian • *a geologic time period spanning from 443 to 419 million years ago. During the Silurian, jawed and bony fish diversified, and life first began to appear on land.*

			Present
Cenozoic	Quaternary		2.6
	Tertiary	Neogene	23
		Paleogene	66
Mesozoic	Cretaceous		145
	Jurassic		201
	Triassic		252
Paleozoic	Permian		299
	Carbon-iferous	Pennsylvanian	323
		Mississippian	359
	Devonian		419
	Silurian		443
	Ordovician		485
	Cambrian		541
	Precambrian		4600

Millions of Years Ago

4 Climate and Earth History

Early to Mid Paleozoic

Ordovician • *a geologic time period spanning from 485 to 443 million years ago. During the Ordovician, invertebrates dominated the oceans and fish began to diversify.*

Gondwana • *the supercontinent of the Southern Hemisphere, composed of Africa, Australia, India, and South America. It combined with the North American continent to form PANGAEA during the late PALEOZOIC.*

mass extinction • *the extinction (loss of the last living member of a species) of a large percentage of the Earth's species over a relatively short span of geologic time.*

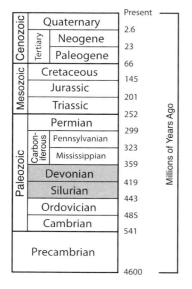

Box 4.1: Proxies from rocks

Sedimentary rocks are formed through breakdown of other rocks into sediment, which is then transported and deposited by wind or water. When the sediment is compressed or cemented and turned into rock, it retains clues about the environment in which it formed. By observing modern oceans, for example, scientists note that limy sediments and reefs (composed of calcium carbonate) usually accumulate in warm, shallow, clear seawater, and they then use this to conclude that ancient carbonates might have formed in similar environments.

Chemical elements in rocks, and even in some fossils, can also record information about the environment at the time that the rocks were formed. Particularly useful for recreating ancient climates are the different forms (or **isotopes**) of the element oxygen (see *Box 4.4* on isotope proxies).

Figure 4.6: Changing global climate throughout the last 542 million years. These data were compiled using the ratios of stable oxygen isotopes found in ice cores and the carbonate skeletons of fossil organisms. (See Teacher-Friendly Guide website for a full color version.)

centered in Michigan. These reefs were among the largest the world had ever seen and today the remains of the reefs (as limestone) can be found across much of the Midwest with the thickest deposits occurring in Indiana and Illinois.

3.2.2 Silurian and Devonian Periods

From 430 to 300 million years ago, North America moved north across the equator (*Figure 4.7*), and the cycle of warming and cooling was repeated again. Silurian deposits of salt in Michigan and New York indicate that the North American climate experienced dry climates and restricted circulation during a warm interval beginning 430 million years ago. Eventually, the salinity in the shallow seas of the ancient Midwest and Northeast returned to normal in the **Devonian**, when sea level rose. A diverse warm water reef fauna occupied the sea floor of shallow seas over broad swaths of the East and Midwest.

Climate and Earth History

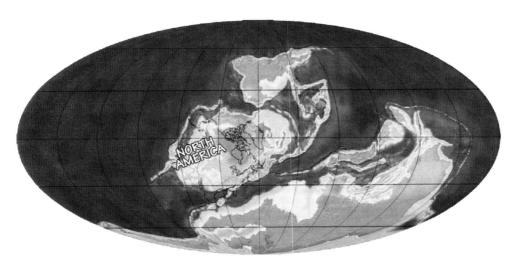

Figure 4.7: Earth during the late Devonian, about 370 million years ago.

In the Devonian a variety of tectonic changes occurred that led to the formation of continental basins with plankton productivity so high that their decay led to depletion of oxygen from the seafloor and sediments. The lack of oxygen allowed organic matter to accumulate instead of decaying, leading to the deposition of black, carbon-rich shale (see *Box 4.2*). Though all geologic periods have experienced such deposits, some Devonian-age marine rocks that are currently especially important sources for natural gas and petroleum include the Barnett shale (primarily northern Texas), Marcellus shale (especially Pennsylvania), and the Bakken Formation (especially North Dakota).

At the end of the Devonian the fauna suffered a mass extinction that eliminated many of the more important groups of reef-builders and other animals that occupied the shallow seas. The causes of this mass extinction, which actually occurred in a series of steps, are still uncertain. Dropping sea levels and cooling climates as the Earth entered another glacial interval have been implicated.

isotope • *a form of a chemical element that contains a specific number of neutrons. For example, the isotope of carbon with six neutrons is known as carbon-12 (^{12}C) and the isotope of carbon with eight neutrons is carbon-14 (^{14}C). All isotopes of an element contain the same number of protons.*

Devonian • *a geologic time period spanning from 419 to 359 million years ago. The Devonian is also called the "age of fishes" due to the diversity of fish that radiated during this time. On land, seed-bearing plants appeared and terrestrial arthropods became established. The Devonian is part of the Paleozoic.*

Box 4.2: Earth system links between ancient and modern climates

Throughout the Phanerozoic eon there have been circumstances during which large amounts of marine organic matter, particularly phytoplankton, were deposited in sediment before decaying. The decay rate of organic matter is controlled by the amount of oxygen in the bottom water and surface sediment, which itself is controlled by bottom circulation and quantity of organic matter decaying. When the amount is great, oxygen-loving bacteria use up the available O_2 faster than it's replenished. The process is affected by climate indirectly in the sense that temperature, nutrient availability and light are influenced by climate phenomena. In turn, the buried organic matter derived from photosynthesis removes carbon from the atmosphere and thus atmospheric CO_2. Such organic carbon, after being subjected to heat and pressure under additional sediments, became the source for petroleum and natural gas. Burning these fossil fuels releases the "fossil sunshine" and CO_2 that had been stored in rocks beneath the surface.

			Present
Cenozoic		Quaternary	
	Tertiary		2.6
		Neogene	23
		Paleogene	66
Mesozoic		Cretaceous	145
		Jurassic	201
		Triassic	252
Paleozoic		Permian	299
	Carbon-iferous	Pennsylvanian	323
		Mississippian	359
		Devonian	419
		Silurian	443
		Ordovician	485
		Cambrian	541
		Precambrian	4600

Millions of Years Ago

Late Paleozoic

arthropod • *an invertebrate animal, belonding to the Phylum Arthropoda, and possessing an external skeleton (exoskeleton), body segments, and jointed appendages. Arthropods include crustaceans, arachnids, and insects, and there are over a million described arthropod species living today. Trilobites are a major group of extinct arthropods.*

vertebrate • *an animal with a backbone, such as fishes, amphibians, reptiles, birds, and mammals.*

Carboniferous • *a geologic time period that extends from 359 to 299 million years ago. It is divided into two subperiods, the Mississippian and the Pennsylvanian. By the Carboniferous, terrestrial life had become well established.*

			Present
Cenozoic	Quaternary		
	Tertiary	Neogene	2.6
		Paleogene	23
			66
Mesozoic	Cretaceous		
	Jurassic		145
	Triassic		201
			252
Paleozoic	Permian		299
	Carboniferous	Pennsylvanian	
			323
		Mississippian	359
	Devonian		
	Silurian		419
			443
	Ordovician		485
	Cambrian		541
	Precambrian		
			4600

Millions of Years Ago

3.3 Late Paleozoic Era

The late Paleozoic is the interval during which widespread forests colonized the land and, with them, animal faunas, including particularly **arthropods**, but also **vertebrates**. The Paleozoic ended with the great mass extinction in geologic history. The interval is interesting from a climate systems perspective because of the clear influence of CO_2 in influencing the presence or absence of polar glaciation and, at sufficiently high levels of CO_2, in an extinction.

3.3.1 Carboniferous

The late Devonian and early **Carboniferous** periods were a time of transition for terrestrial ecosystems that had major implications for climate: for the first time, major assemblages of complex land plants, including large plants—trees—developed, first in wet, swampy coastal areas. A combination of the burial conditions and the early, and possibly limited, evolution of organisms that contribute to plant decay led to thick accumulation of organic "**peat**" deposits, trapping organic carbon in what would become coal in places such as southern Illinois, Indiana, Ohio, and western Pennsylvania. The drop in carbon dioxide led to the next glaciation: by the Early Carboniferous, ice capped the supercontinent Gondwana at the South Pole and began to expand northward. Although the Earth's temperature fell during this time and the frozen water trapped in southern hemisphere glaciers caused sea levels to drop, North America remained relatively warm because of its position near the equator. Deposits in the southern part of the Midwest, in particular, show a cyclicity of rising and falling sea level that was caused by advance and retreat of the large ice cap in the Southern Hemisphere.

By the late Carboniferous, North America had collided with Gondwana, eventually leading to the formation of **Pangaea**—a supercontinent composed of nearly all the landmass on Earth (*Figure 4.8*). Pangaea was so large that it created a strong monsoonal climate, much as Asia does today. Large swamps formed along broad floodplains that eventually became the rich coal beds of, for example, Pennsylvania, Tennessee, Kentucky, and West Virginia.

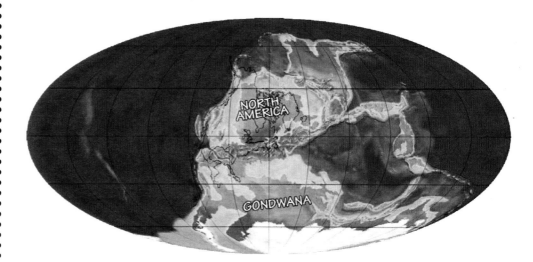

Figure 4.8: Initial formation of Pangaea during the late Carboniferous, around 300 million years ago.

In the late Carboniferous, since the continent was largely tropical, the climate remained warm, despite large southern ice sheets, but the continent had grown much drier. Thick salt deposits accumulated in Utah and Colorado as the seas evaporated. Where the land was exposed, deposits of dust (**loess**) accumulated and were blown across much of the Southwest. The ice age that began in the early Carboniferous lasted well into the **Permian** period, when warm temperatures again became the norm.

3.3.2 Permian

During the Permian, sea level gradually began to decrease, in this case not because of the development of glacial ice, but because of decreases in sea floor spreading associated with the formation of the supercontinent Pangea (*Figure 4.9*). Seafloor spreading (rifting) of hot, mantle-derived rock creates undersea mountain ranges (such as today's **mid-Atlantic Ridge**), which displace ocean water onto the continents. When the plates are connected, as in the supercontinent Pangea, seafloor spreading is reduced, ridges displace less water, and sea level drops.

The climate was drier than that in the Carboniferous, and mudflats with salt and **gypsum** formed across the Southwestern states. Sand dunes started to become widespread (*Figure 4.10*). A shift in plant type—from water-loving ferns and **horsetails** to those better adapted to drier conditions—further suggests a change in climate during the Permian (*Box 4.3*). A large, low-latitude desert formed along Pangaea's western margin, generating extensive dune deposits.

By the end of the Permian, the southern ice sheets had disappeared. As the **Triassic** period began, the Southwestern U.S. moved north from the equator. The world warmed, and would stay warm through the **Mesozoic**. Warm, arid desert conditions existed in the core of the supercontinent, as indicated, for example, by ancient sand dunes preserved in sedimentary rocks.

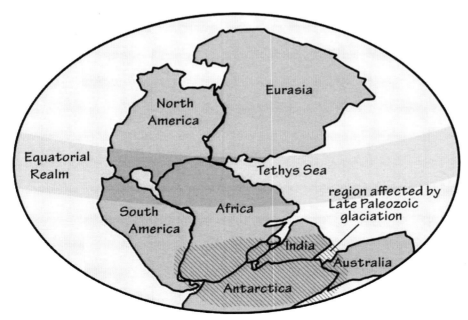

Figure 4.9: Pangaea during the late Paleozoic era.

Late Paleozoic

peat · *an accumulation of partially decayed plant matter. Under sufficient heat and pressure, it will turn into lignite COAL over geologic periods of time.*

Pangaea · *a supercontinent, meaning "all Earth," which formed over 300 million years ago and lasted for almost 150 million years, during which all of the Earth's continents were joined in a giant supercontinent. Pangaea eventually rifted apart and separated into the continents in their current configuration.*

loess · *very fine-grained, wind-blown sediment, usually rock flour left behind by the grinding action of flowing GLACIERS.*

			Present
Cenozoic		Quaternary	2.6
	Tertiary	Neogene	23
		Paleogene	66
Mesozoic		Cretaceous	145
		Jurassic	201
		Triassic	252
Paleozoic		Permian	299
	Carbon-iferous	Pennsylvanian	323
		Mississippian	359
		Devonian	419
		Silurian	443
		Ordovician	485
		Cambrian	541
		Precambrian	4600

(Millions of Years Ago)

Late Paleozoic

Permian • *the geologic time period lasting from 299 to 252 million years ago. During the Permian, the world's landmass was combined into the supercontinent PANGAEA. The Permian is the last period of the PALEOZOIC. It ended with the largest mass extinction in Earth's history, which wiped out 70% of terrestrial animal species and 90% of all marine animal species.*

mid-Atlantic Ridge • *a ridge on the floor of the Atlantic Ocean generally running North-South at the boundary of tectonic plates, where these plates are moving apart.*

gypsum • *a soft, sulfate mineral that is widely mined for its use as fertilizer and as a constituent of plaster. Alabaster, a fine-grained light colored variety of gypsum, has been used for sculpture making by many cultures since ancient times.*

horsetail • *a terrestrial plant belonging to the Family Equisetaceae in the plant division Pteridophyta, and characterized by hollow, jointed stems with reduced, unbranched leaves at the nodes.*

Triassic • *a geologic time period that spans from 252 to 201 million years ago. During this period, DINOSAURS, PTEROSAURS, and the first mammals appear and begin to diversify.*

Box 4.3: Proxies from fossils

Fossils—the remains or traces of once-living things preserved in the Earth's crust—can be compared to organisms in modern environments to infer the past environment in which they lived (*Figure A*). For example, fossil fish and seashells can reasonably be assumed to have lived in water, even though the place where the fossils were found is now dry land. Fossil reptiles or palm trees found in what are now much cooler, high-latitude locations testify to these areas once having a much warmer climate. Corals are mostly colonial, marine animals that make hard skeletons out of calcium carbonate ($CaCO_3$). Modern corals live mainly in warm, tropical seas. Fossil corals found today in very different environments, such as upstate New York, are therefore indicative of major changes in the climate of the area.

Figure A: Examples of fossil climate proxies. Top left and right are a fossil palm frond and alligator, respectively, both Eocene Epoch, Wyoming. Bottom left shows benthic foraminifera, found in marine sediments; the species are (clockwise from top left) Ammonia beccarii, Elphidium excavatum clavatum, Buccella frigida, and Eggerella advena. Bottom right image shows common pollen grains (greatly magnified), including sunflower and lily pollen.

Fossil leaves frequently have characteristic shapes that are, in part, the result of the habitat in which they live. Looking at their shape scientifically with a process called **leaf margin analysis** can help to reconstruct ancient environments and climates (*Figure B*). The edges of modern leaves are indicative of their climate and environment; smooth-edged leaves with narrow, pointed "drip tips" at the ends are common in rainforests where they function to rid the leaves of excess water, whereas toothed leaf edges are more common in temperate environments to preserve water. Scientists measure leaves in modern environments and correlate their size, shape,

Box 4.3: Continued

and edge appearances with the temperature and humidity of the region. That information can then be applied to fossil leaf measurements in ancient environments to calculate approximate temperature and humidity.

Figure B: Leaf margin shapes can be used as climate proxies. Plants with leaves with toothed or divided margins (above left) live today in cooler climates, whereas plants with leaves with smooth or entire margins (above right) live in warmer climates. This observation can be used to interpret the climates in which fossil leaves (lower left and right) grew.

Ancient plant pollen and spores (produced by plants such as ferns, lichens, and mosses) can also help us learn about ancient climates. **Palynology** (the study of pollen and spores) uses the fortunate circumstances of these objects being small, abundant, and easily preserved. Due to their tough organic coating, they are commonly preserved in the sand and sediment from places like lakes and rivers, even though trees and leaves are seldom preserved. If the pollen can be identified to a particular kind of plant, and if environmental constraints of that plant are known (by studying it or its descendants living today), the history of climate in the area can be inferred. Pollen and spores have, for example, been used to track how plant communities move north and south during fluctuations between glacial and warmer intervals.

Single-celled organisms, or **protists**, make up a large proportion of the plankton at the base of oceanic food webs. Some of these protists, especially shelled forms called foraminifera (see *Figure A* above), are particularly valuable as indicators of past climate conditions, either through analysis of the oxygen isotopes in their fossilized carbonate shells (see Box 4.4), or by comparing fossil forms to those alive today and inferring that they had similar environmental distributions.

Mesozoic • *a geologic time era that spans from 252 to 66 million years ago. This era is also called the "age of reptiles" since dinosaurs and other reptiles dominated both marine and terrestrial ecosystems. During this time, the last of the Earth's major supercontinents, PANGAEA, formed and later broke up, producing the Earth's current geography.*

leaf margin analysis • *a PROXY method for estimating past temperatures using known relationships between the shape of leaf margins (smooth or toothed) and temperature and humidity.*

palynology • *the study of modern and fossil pollen, spores, and other microscopic plant matter.*

Late Paleozoic

floodplain • *the land around a river that is prone to flooding. This area can be grassy, but the sediments under the surface are usually deposits from previous floods.*

basalt • *an extrusive igneous rock, and the most common rock type on the surface of the Earth. It forms the upper surface of all oceanic plates, and is the principal rock of ocean/seafloor ridges, oceanic islands, and high-volume continental eruptions. Basalt is fine-grained and mostly dark-colored, although it often weathers to reds and browns because of its high iron content.*

pyroclastic flow • *the rapid flow of lava, ash, and gases resulting from an explosive volcanic eruption.*

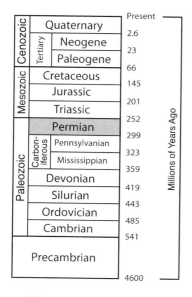

Figure 4.10: Dune cross-beds in the Coconino Sandstone at Sedona, Arizona.

The continued growth of Pangaea led to a gradual shift toward a humid climate in places such as the Northwest Central U.S., where abundant, seasonal rainfall fell as intense monsoons that impacted large swaths of the continent. The climate resembled that of modern India, where monsoons soak the land in the summer and completely dry out in the winter. As the monsoon's intensity increased, the vast dune deserts of the late Permian were replaced by rivers and **floodplains**. Soils associated with these floodplains testify to the extreme seasonality of rainfall during that time.

The Permian-Triassic boundary (252 million years ago) was marked by the eruption of million km³ of **basalt** and **pyroclastic flows**.[3] These deposits, called the Siberian Traps and found in present-day Siberia (Russia), burned through carbonate, evaporite, and organic rich sediments, which contributed to the load of greenhouse and other toxic gasses added to the atmosphere. Global shifts in carbon and oxygen isotopes preserved in the rock and fossil record indicate the widespread implications of these eruptions on the Earth's climate. Extreme warming of the ocean, possible acidification of the ocean by the dissolution of CO_2, and acid rain on the continents resulted in the largest mass extinction of the Phanerozoic, with the vast majority of marine and terrestrial faunas becoming extinct. This extinction interval is often referred to as the time when life nearly died, and the full recovery of biological diversity and the return of complex marine communities took many millions of years.

		Present
Cenozoic	Quaternary	
	Neogene	2.6
	Paleogene	23
		66
Mesozoic	Cretaceous	145
	Jurassic	201
	Triassic	252
Paleozoic	Permian	299
	Pennsylvanian	323
	Mississippian	359
	Devonian	419
	Silurian	443
	Ordovician	485
	Cambrian	541
	Precambrian	
		4600

Millions of Years Ago

---

[3] The amount of rock erupted in the Siberian Traps would be enough to cover the continental US (a little over 8 million km²) in a layer of rock half a kilometer thick!

3.4 The Mesozoic era

The Mesozoic era is known popularly as the Age of Reptiles—dominated by **dinosaurs** on land, **pterosaurs** in the air, and several groups of large marine reptiles in the ocean. Climate scientists are especially interested in the relationship between climate and mass extinctions on each end the Mesozoic, and the one at the end of the Triassic. The Cretaceous is of interest as an analog for a warm, high CO_2 world with no polar ice caps, were human-induced climate change to trigger a positive feedback loop that led, long-term, to complete melting of the Antarctic and Greenland ice sheets.

3.4.1 Triassic and Early Jurassic

By around 220 million years ago, in the mid-Triassic, what is now the U.S. moved north across the equator. Pangea began breaking up into continents that would drift toward their modern-day positions. The breakup of Pangea resulted in the development of continental **rift basins** along what is now the northeast coast of the U.S. These rift basins were filled by a string of big lakes from Virginia into Canada. One of these lakes, now called the Newark Basin, recorded in its sediments a very detailed record of climate. It shows that climate cycled annually between very wet and dry intervals, presumably connected to annual monsoons, but also over longer time periods. The record in the Newark Basin is so good and so long that we can also identify cycles occurring over tens and hundreds of thousands of years, cycles that correspond to the astronomical cycles ("**Milankovich Cycles**") that would become so influential on climate cycles of the late **Cenozoic** era.

See Chapter 3: What is Climate? for more about Milankovich Cycles.

This rifting also resulted in the eruption of extensive mantle-derived volcanic material known as the Central Atlantic Magmatic Province. These basalt deposits are preserved today in Northeastern US and Canada. This eruption, like the Siberian Traps, disrupted global climate and led to the 4th major mass extinction, of both marine and terrestrial life.

3.4.2 Jurassic

The **Jurassic** and **Cretaceous** climates remained warm, but in many areas gradually became wetter, but without the strong seasonality of the Triassic. Terrestrial environments became dominated by dinosaurs.

The intensity of the **monsoons** so prominent in the Triassic in the Southwestern US waned by the early Jurassic, and the rivers and floodplains of the Southwest were replaced by even larger deserts. The Southwest's Triassic-Jurassic dune deposits are some of the most extensive in the world, and the dune field that existed during the Jurassic may be the largest in Earth history. These deposits, including the Navajo Sandstone, are responsible for spectacular scenery in the national parks and recreation areas of northernmost Arizona and southern Utah (*Figure 4.11*).

Mesozoic

dinosaur • *a member of a group of terrestrial reptiles with a common ancestor and thus certain anatomical similarities, including long ankle bones and erect limbs. Most species of the large reptile groups, including the dinosaurs, disappeared at or before the MASS EXTINCTION at the end of the CRETACEOUS.*

pterosaur • *extinct flying reptiles with wingspans of up to 15 meters (49 feet). They lived during the same time as the dinosaurs.*

rift basin • *a topographic depression caused by subsidence within a rift (a break or crack in the Earth's crust); the basin, since it is at a relatively low elevation, usually contains freshwater bodies such as rivers and lakes.*

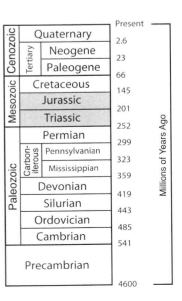

				Present
Cenozoic		Quaternary		
	Tertiary	Neogene		2.6
		Paleogene		23
				66
Mesozoic		Cretaceous		145
		Jurassic		201
		Triassic		252
Paleozoic		Permian		299
	Carboniferous	Pennsylvanian		323
		Mississippian		359
		Devonian		419
		Silurian		443
		Ordovician		485
		Cambrian		541
		Precambrian		
				4600

Millions of Years Ago

Mesozoic

Milankovich Cycle • *cyclical changes in the amount of heat received from the Sun, associated with how the Earth's orbit, tilt, and wobble alter its position with respect to the Sun. These changes affect the global climate, most notably alterations of glacial and interglacial intervals.*

Cenozoic • *the geologic time period spanning from 66 million years ago to the present. The Cenozoic is also known as the age of mammals, since extinction of the large reptiles at the end of the MESOZOIC allowed mammals to diversify. The Cenozoic includes the Paleogene, Neogene, and Quaternary periods.*

Jurassic • *the geologic time period lasting from 201 to 145 million years ago. During the Jurassic, dinosaurs dominated the landscape and the first birds appeared. The Jurassic is the middle period of the MESOZOIC.*

			Present
Cenozoic		Quaternary	
	Tertiary	Neogene	2.6
		Paleogene	23
			66
Mesozoic		Cretaceous	145
		Jurassic	201
		Triassic	252
Paleozoic		Permian	299
	Carbon-iferous	Pennsylvanian	323
		Mississippian	359
		Devonian	419
		Silurian	443
		Ordovician	485
		Cambrian	541
		Precambrian	
			4600

(Millions of Years Ago)

Figure 4.11: The Wave, a series of intersecting U-shaped troughs eroded into Jurassic Navajo Sandstone within the Paria Canyon-Vermilion Cliffs Wilderness, Arizona. The cycling layers in the sandstone represent changes in the direction of prevailing winds as large sand dunes migrated across the desert.

Meanwhile, the breakup of Pangea caused the Gulf of Mexico to rift open, flooding it with seawater. Because the climate was still relatively warm and dry, evaporation rates were high, and extremely thick deposits of salt accumulated there. These salt deposits have played a key role in trapping petroleum along the Gulf Coast.

Later in the Jurassic the climate of the Southwestern US became more moderate, and dune fields were replaced by rivers and floodplains populated by a rich dinosaur fauna (exemplified by the Morrison Formation). The terrestrial rocks of southeastern California contain **ginkgos** and **cycads** that indicate a warm, moderately wet climate.

3.4.3 Cretaceous

The Earth warmed near the beginning of the Cretaceous. Global temperatures were as much as 10°C (18°F) above those at present. Even though Alaska was closer to the North Pole than it is at present (*Figure 4.12*), fossil vegetation indicates that its climate was very similar to that of western Oregon today. Lush swamps and forests occupied lowland areas, and some swamps had become rich coal beds. Throughout the Cretaceous, sea level was an average of 100 meters (330 feet) higher than it is today; polar glaciers were already absent, so the increase must have been largely as a result of water displacement by rapid sea-floor spreading, such as along the mid-Atlantic Ridge as Pangea continued to split apart. Shallow seaways spread over many of the continents, and in the mid and late Cretaceous, an **inland sea**, called the **Western Interior Seaway**, divided North America in two (*Figure 4.13*). Cretaceous fossils from the Western Interior Seaway show that it supported large marine reptiles, while crocodiles and dinosaurs were abundant on land. Tropical marine fossils can be even be found as far north and inland as Minnesota. This seaway had substantial marine productivity, and its organic-rich rocks are now substantial sources of fossil fuels in the Northwest Central and Southwestern U.S.

Figure 4.12: Earth during the early Cretaceous, around 105 million years ago.

Figure 4.13: The Western Interior Seaway.

3.4.4 Late Cretaceous Climate Change and End-Cretaceous Extinction

In the late Cretaceous sea level dropped. As the continents moved closer to their modern positions, global climate—though still warmer than today—cooled.

At the very end of the Cretaceous, the Gulf Coast experienced an enormous disruption when a large asteroid or **bolide** collided with Earth in what is now the northern Yucatán Peninsula in Mexico. The impact vaporized both water and rock, blocking out sunlight for weeks to years, which led to a collapse

Mesozoic

monsoon • *a seasonal wind pattern in the Indian Ocean and South Asia which reverses direction between southwesterly and northeasterly, creating a wet season in summer and a dry season in winter.*

ginkgo • *a terrestrial tree belonging to the plant division Ginkgophyta, and characterized by broad fan-shaped leaves, large seeds without protective coatings, and no flowers. Ginkgos were very common and diverse in the Mesozoic, but today only one species exists,* Ginkgo biloba.

			Present
Cenozoic	Tertiary	Quaternary	
			2.6
		Neogene	
			23
		Paleogene	
			66
Mesozoic		Cretaceous	145
		Jurassic	
			201
		Triassic	
			252
Paleozoic		Permian	
			299
	Carbon-iferous	Pennsylvanian	
			323
		Mississippian	
			359
		Devonian	
			419
		Silurian	
			443
		Ordovician	
			485
		Cambrian	
			541
		Precambrian	
			4600

Millions of Years Ago

Climate and Earth History

cycad • *a palm-like, terrestrial seed plant (tree) belonging to the Class Cycadopsida, and characterized by a woody trunk, a crown of stiff evergreen leaves, seeds without protective coatings, and no flowers. Cycads were very common in the MESOZOIC, but are much reduced in diversity today, restricted to the tropical and subtropical regions of the planet.*

inland sea • *a shallow sea covering the central area of a continent during periods of high sea level. An inland sea is located on continental crust, while other seas are located on oceanic crust.*

Western Interior Seaway • *an INLAND SEA which divided North America in two along a North-South axis during the mid and late CRETACEOUS.*

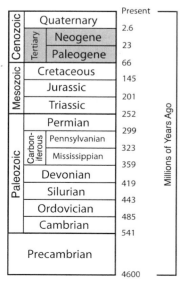

of photosynthesis and food webs on land and in the oceans. These factors resulted in the 5th and most mass extinction of the Phanerozoic (other than the one we may be in the middle of today.[4] This event famously led to the demise of non-avian dinosaurs,[5] marine reptiles, and many invertebrates such **ammonoids**. After this event, the climate may have cooled briefly, but it soon rebounded to a warmer state.

3.5 Cenozoic

The Cenozoic era started out warming, but ultimately was overall time of cooling, starting with developing of ice sheets in Antarctica and leading to Quaternary **glacial-interglacial cycles**. The interval is also the time over which modern ecosystems developed, dominated on land by mammals, birds, and flowering plants. The Cenozoic contains a diversity of climate analogs that climate scientists find useful because the position of continents and nature of the climate system is relatively similar to today.

3.5.1 Paleocene and Eocene

Climate warmed during the **Paleocene**, culminating at the boundary between the Paleocene and **Eocene** epochs (around 56 million years ago) with temperature spiking suddenly upward. Geologists call this the Paleocene-Eocene Thermal Maximum (PETM). During the warming event the atmosphere and ocean warmed by as much as 8°C (14°F) in as little as 4000 years, and deep oceans became acidic, resulting in the dissolution and extinction of shelly marine animals. The causes of this event remain unclear, but may have involved the sudden release of methane from sediments on the seafloor. The resulting greenhouse effect persisted for 100,000 years. The PETM is of great interest to climate scientists because it is in some respects the most similar analog to rapid increases in greenhouse gases that we are currently experiencing.

During the Eocene the climate remained relatively warm, with palm trees growing in southern Alaska. Records of plants and animals found in Oregon and Washington indicate that the northwestern US was home to a subtropical rainforest with (depending on the site) banana and citrus trees, palm trees, ferns, and dawn redwoods. The Southwest's climate was warm and wet, with strong volcanic activity. Large lakes covered parts of northern Utah, Colorado, and Wyoming (the Greater Green River Basin) (*Figure 4.14*). Climates were warm enough for crocodiles to live as far north as 50°N in the interior of North America and on Ellsemere Island of Northern Canada around 78°N. Warm climate are also reflected in the land plants and diversity of marine life, for example, in the rich fossil record of clams, snails, and echinoderms found in the Gulf and Southeast Coastal Plain.

During the Eocene, India began to collide with Asia to form the Himalayas. The formation of the Himalayas over the span of tens of millions of years had a

---

[4] There is an extensive literature estimating modern rates of extinction, comparing them to mass extinctions of the geologic past, and estimating the role climate change may have in future extinctions. Elizabeth Kolbert's book The Sixth Extinction: An Unnatural History (Henry Holt and Co.: NY, 336 pp.) is a very readable introduction to the topic.

[5] Because birds evolved from dinosaurs, they are technically considered to be dinosaurs. Thus, for clarity, paleontologists use the term "non-avian" dinosaurs to refer to all dinosaurs that are not birds.

bolide • *an extraterrestrial object of any composition that forms a large crater upon impact with the Earth. In astronomy, bolides are bright meteors (also known as fireballs) that explode as they pass through the Earth's atmosphere.*

ammonoid • *a group of extinct cephalopods belonging to the Phylum Mollusca, and possessing a spiraling, tightly-coiled shell characterized by ridges, or septa.*

glacial-interglacial cycle • *an alternation between times in Earth's history when continental ICE SHEETS grow and advance toward lower latitudes (GLACIALS), and times when the climate is warmer and ice sheets melt back (INTERGLACIALS).*

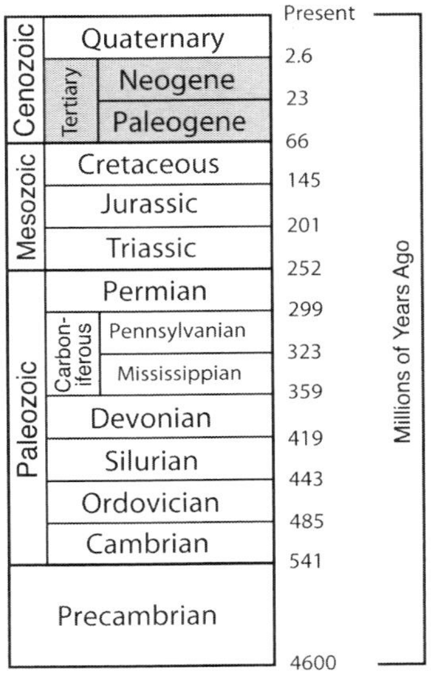

Figure 4.14: Well-preserved fossils from the Green River Formation, southwestern Wyoming. A) Palm frond, Sabalites powelli, *about 1.2 meters (4 feet) long, with fossil fish* Knightia. *B) An undetermined bird species with preserved feathers, about 25 centimeters (10 inches) long. C)* Heliobatis radians, *a stingray, about 40 centimeters (16 inches) long, with fossil fish. D)* Borealosuchus wilsoni, *a crocodilian, reached lengths of 4.5 meters (15 feet).*

Eon/Era	Period	Epoch	Millions of Years Ago
			Present
Cenozoic	Quaternary		2.6
	Tertiary	Neogene	23
		Paleogene	66
Mesozoic	Cretaceous		145
	Jurassic		201
	Triassic		252
Paleozoic	Permian		299
	Carboniferous	Pennsylvanian	323
		Mississippian	359
	Devonian		419
	Silurian		443
	Ordovician		485
	Cambrian		541
	Precambrian		4600

significant impact on global climate, with the chemical weathering of the newly exposed rock serving as a sink for atmospheric CO_2. With the reduction of this greenhouse gas, global temperatures began cooling, the start of a long downward trend through much of the remainder of the Cenozoic.

4 Climate and Earth History

Cenozoic

Paleocene · *first geologic time interval of the Cenozoic era, spanning from about 66 to 56 million years ago.*

Eocene · *a geologic time interval extending from 56 to 33 million years ago. The Eocene is the second epoch of the Cenozoic era.*

Oligocene · *third geologic time epoch of the Cenozoic era, spanning from about 34 to 23 million years ago.*

Miocene · *fourth geologic epoch of the Cenozoic era, extending from 23 to 5 million years ago.*

		Present	
Cenozoic	Quaternary		
	Neogene	2.6	
		23	
	Paleogene		
		66	
Mesozoic	Cretaceous	145	
	Jurassic	201	
	Triassic	252	
Paleozoic	Permian	299	
	Pennsylvanian	323	
	Mississippian	359	
	Devonian	419	
	Silurian	443	
	Ordovician	485	
	Cambrian	541	
	Precambrian		
		4600	

(Tertiary spans Neogene and Paleogene; Carboniferous spans Pennsylvanian and Mississippian; vertical axis labeled "Millions of Years Ago")

3.5.2 Oligocene, Miocene, and Pliocene

Global temperatures fell sharply at the boundary between the Eocene and **Oligocene** epochs (around 35 million years ago), due in part to the separation of South America's southern tip from Antarctica. This allowed for the formation of the Antarctic Circumpolar Current, which insulated Antarctica from warm ocean water coming from lower latitudes. Antarctica moved south, and by 30 million years ago, temperatures were low enough that glaciers began to grow on its mountains. An "ice age" can be described as the presence of long-term high-latitude glaciers, and by this broad definition, the current (today's) ice age began over 30 million years ago with the appearance of ice sheets on Antarctica.

Between 35 and 20 million years ago the climate in the Western U.S. became cooler and drier, and prairies and deciduous trees such as oak, maple, and alder flourished. On the Great Plains, grasses, and mammals specialized to feed on them, increased in prominence as the **Miocene** became drier. This coincided with the initial uplift of the Cascade Range (37–7 million years ago), which began to create a rain shadow to the east. The final uplift of the Cascades and Sierra Nevada created the intense rain shadow that is responsible for the aridity of eastern Washington, eastern Oregon, and Nevada today.

Global temperatures fell further in the Miocene as the Himalayas continued to grow and weather, serving as a sink removing CO_2 from the atmosphere. With the reduction of this greenhouse gas, temperatures cooled worldwide, and this cooling continued more-or-less into the **Pleistocene**. By about 15 million years ago ice covered much of Antarctica and had begun to form on Greenland. As high latitude glaciers grew, sea levels dropped.

In the mid-Miocene, especially around 17 to 14 million years ago, eruptions in eastern Oregon produced enormous amounts of basalt that flowed north and west, filling the Columbia River basin. These are some of the largest such eruptions in the history of the Earth, and they continued over a span of about 11 million year, finally ceasing about 6 million years ago. While evidence that these eruptions influenced global climate is ambiguous, climatic changes are recorded in soils that formed atop some of the lava flows. These soils indicate a decrease in temperature after a period known as the Middle Miocene Climatic Optimum, a brief warming episode that occurred around 16 million years ago. Miocene warming is reflected in the diverse marine and terrestrial fossils of the Atlantic Coastal Plain, which extends from Maryland to Florida.

Around 3.5 million years ago, glacial ice began to form over the Arctic Ocean and on the northern parts of North America and Eurasia (*Figure 4.15*). Surprisingly, a major contributing factor to this event was a geological change that occurred half a world away. The Central American Isthmus, which today makes up most of Panama and Costa Rica, rose out of the ocean at around this time, formed by undersea volcanoes. The new dry-land isthmus blocked the warm ocean currents that had been flowing east-to-west from the Atlantic to the Pacific for more than 100 million years, diverting them into the Gulf of Mexico and ultimately into the western Atlantic Gulf Stream. The strengthened Gulf Stream carried more warm, moist air with it into the northern Atlantic, which caused increased snowfall in high latitudes, leading to enhanced glacier development and accelerating cooling. Such changes contributed to the high

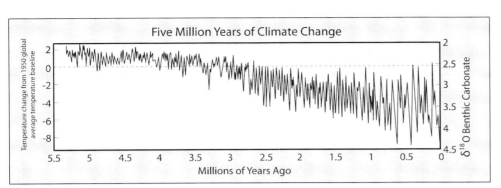

Figure 4.15: Five million years of climate change. In the graph, oxygen isotopes from fossil shells of deep-sea marine organisms (foraminifera) have been used to show relative global temperatures for the last 5.5 million years. The curve is influenced both by the amount of water stored in ice sheets and by temperature at the bottom of the ocean; both cooler temperatures and larger ice sheets cause higher $\delta^{18}O$ values. On the left vertical axis are proxy temperature data from an ice core. See Box 4.4 for more about using oxygen isotopes.

Box 4.4: Using oxygen isotopes to determine past climates

The different chemical elements, like oxygen, carbon, and hydrogen that we encounter in the Periodic Table in chemistry class are distinguished by their differing numbers of subatomic particles: each element has a distinct number of protons, and an equal number of electrons. Isotopes are variants of elements that have the same numbers of protons and electrons, but differ in the number of neutrons. This means that different isotopes of an element have a slightly different mass.

The most common isotope of oxygen has 16 neutrons and is therefore called oxygen 16, abbreviated ^{16}O. A small proportion of the oxygen in the universe has 18 neutrons; oxygen 18 (^{18}O). Because ^{16}O has fewer neutrons than ^{18}O, it behaves differently. For example, it is more easily integrated into water vapor, and so clouds and their associated precipitation contains relatively more ^{16}O than the lake or ocean from which the water evaporated. When this precipitation is stored for a long time in the form of compacted snow in glaciers, as a result of colder climate, the oceans of the world have relatively less ^{16}O in their water than they do in warmer times. We call oceans that are enriched in ^{18}O, during these glacial intervals, isotopically "heavy" because they contain more of the neutron rich oxygen 18.

^{16}O is also more easily incorporated into chemical compounds. Many marine organisms make their shells out of calcium carbonate ($CaCO_3$), and need to take dissolved carbonate ions out of the seawater to do this. Therefore, when they build their shells, marine organisms record the proportion of ^{16}O that exists in seawater at the time. Because of the different behavior of the two isotopes of oxygen, shells have a higher proportion of ^{16}O in a warmer climate when the lighter isotope of oxygen is more prevalent in ocean water and not stored in glaciers. When the shells are preserved as fossils on the sea floor, and then extracted in a sediment core, they can be analyzed for their amount of ^{16}O relative to their amount of ^{18}O to estimate ancient temperatures. Scientists commonly use the quantity $\delta^{18}O$ (pronounced "delta-18-oh"), which reflects the ratio of ^{18}O to ^{16}O compared to a standard; smaller values of $\delta^{18}O$ indicate higher temperatures (e.g., in Figures 4.6 and 4.15).

Cenozoic

Pleistocene • an epoch of the QUATERNARY period, lasting from 2.5 million to about 11,700 years ago. During the Pleistocene, continental ice sheets advanced south and retreated north several dozen times.

			Present
Cenozoic	Quaternary		2.6
	Tertiary	Neogene	23
		Paleogene	66
Mesozoic	Cretaceous		145
	Jurassic		201
	Triassic		252
Paleozoic	Permian		299
	Carboniferous	Pennsylvanian	323
		Mississippian	359
	Devonian		419
	Silurian		443
	Ordovician		485
	Cambrian		541
	Precambrian		4600

Millions of Years Ago

Climate and Earth History

Cenozoic

Pliocene • *fifth geologic epoch of the Cenozoic era, extending from roughly 5 to 2.5 million years ago.*

Quaternary • *a geologic time period that extends from 2.6 million years ago to the present. This period is largely defined by the periodic advance and retreat of continental glaciers. The Quaternary is part of the CENOZOIC.*

glacial • *a time in Earth's history when a cold climate leads to the advance of GLACIERS and ICE SHEETS. See also INTERGLACIAL.*

interglacial • *a time in Earth's history between GLACIAL advances; there have been about 50 glacial advances and interglacials in the past 2.5 million years.*

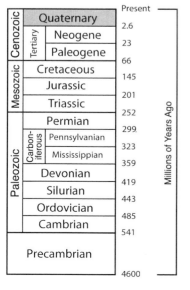

amplitude glacial-interglacial cycles of the Pleistocene. These changes in ocean circulation throughout the Caribbean and Gulf of Mexico also affected nutrient supplies in the coastal ocean, which may have contributed to an increase in the extinction of marine animals (including everything from mollusks and corals to whales and dugongs) during the late **Pliocene**.

3.5.3 Pleistocene

The start of the **Quaternary** Period, and the Pleistocene Epoch, are defined by a global drop in Earth's temperatures as recorded by ice and ocean sediment records (see *Box 4.7*). A sheet of sea-ice formed over the Arctic, and ice sheets spread over northern Asia, Europe, and North America, as the most recent "Ice Age" took hold. Ice sheets have advanced and retreated dozens of times over the past 2.6 million years (see *Box 4.5*), controlled by variations in the Earth's orbit, rotational tilt, and relative amount of wobble around its rotational axis (See *Box 4.6* on Milankovitch cycles). Since each glacial advance scrapes away rock and reworks the geologic evidence of previous glacial events, it can be difficult to reconstruct the precise course of events. Therefore, to investigate the details of any associated climate change we must seek environments that record climate change and are preserved in the geologic record. Since the 1970s, the international Deep Sea Drilling Project has provided a treasure trove of data on coincident changes in the ocean, preserved in sediments at the ocean bottom (*Figure 4.16*). In the 1980s, coring of ice sheets in Greenland and Antarctica provided similar high resolution data on atmospheric composition and temperature back nearly one million years (*Figure 4.17*). The data from these programs have revealed that the Earth experienced dozens of warming and cooling cycles over the course of the Quaternary period (the past 2.6 million years). Traces of the earlier and less extensive Pleistocene glacial advances that must have occurred have been completely erased on land, so these advances were unknown before records from deep-sea cores and ice cores revealed them.

Chemical, sedimentological, and marine organism data has enabled researchers to compile an extensive and precise record of changes in global ice volume and thus glacial advances, and to make sense of the glacial cycles in terms of orbital variations of the Earth around the sun. These orbital variations, called Milankovitch cycles (see *Box 4.6*), result in changes in incoming solar radiation (insolation). While they occurred throughout Earth's history, no matter the average global temperature, they have an especially large impact during cooler intervals of Earth's history where ice forms at the poles. When Earth was relatively warm, these orbital variations most notably caused changes in precipitation. When the Earth became cooler, however, as happened approximately 2.6 million years ago, the orbital variations resulted in changes in global temperature. Thus, roughly every 40,000 years from 2.6 million to 0.7 million years ago, and every 100,000 years since 0.7 million years ago, ice sheets have expanded into lower latitudes, at their greatest extent reaching the northern parts of what is now the United States. Scientists call these expansions **glacials**, the last one peaking approximately 20,000 years ago in what is called the Last Glacial Maximum. The warmer intervals between glacials, when the ice retreated northward, are called **interglacials**. Earth is currently in an interglacial interval. Prior to the present, the most recent interglacial period occurred approximately 125,000 years ago when temperatures at the poles were 3-5 degrees C warmer than at present, and global sea level was 4-6 meters (13-20 feet) higher than it is today.

Climate and Earth History

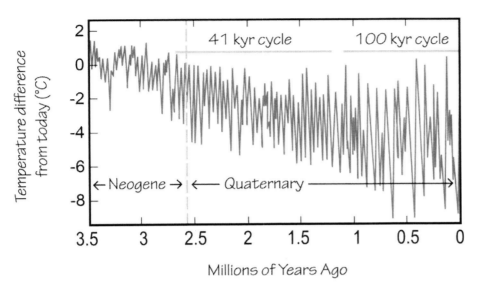

Figure 4.16: Ocean bottom temperatures from 3.6 million years ago to present, based on chemical analyses of foraminifera shells. Notice how the amplitude of glacial-interglacial variations increases through time, and how the length of cycles changes.

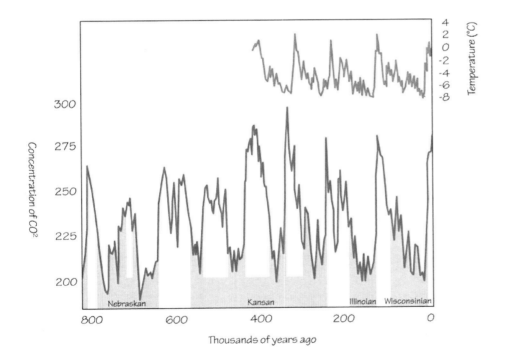

Figure 4.17: Ice core atmospheric temperature and carbon dioxide concentrations from an ice core taken in Vostok in Antarctica along with CO_2 data from several cores in Greenland give a record of glacial advances over the past 800,000 years. Note that Kansan and Nebraskan deposits represent more than one glacial advance.

			Present
Cenozoic	**Quaternary**		
			2.6
	Tertiary	Neogene	23
		Paleogene	66
Mesozoic	Cretaceous		145
	Jurassic		201
	Triassic		252
Paleozoic	Permian		299
	Carbon-iferous	Pennsylvanian	323
		Mississippian	359
	Devonian		419
	Silurian		443
	Ordovician		485
	Cambrian		541
	Precambrian		
			4600

Millions of Years Ago

Climate and Earth History

Box 4.5: Age of the Quaternary

In 2009, scientists at the International Commission on Stratigraphy voted to move the beginning of the Quaternary period to 2.6 million years ago, shifting it 0.8 million years earlier than the previous date of 1.8 million years ago—a date set in 1985. They argued that the previous start date was based on data that reflected climatic cooling that was only local to the region in Italy where it was first observed. In contrast, the 2.6-million-year mark shows a global drop in temperature, and it includes the entirety of North American and Eurasian glaciation, rather than having it divided between the Quaternary and the earlier Neogene period.

Box 4.6: Astronomic cycles and ice sheets

The cyclical movements of ice sheets seem primarily to be caused by specific astronomic cycles called Milankovitch cycles, which change the amount of light the Earth receives, particularly when comparing the summer to the winter. The cycles, predicted through principles of physics a century ago, are related to the Earth's eccentricity, or the shape of Earth's orbit around the sun which varies on 100,000 year time scales, the degree of tilt of the Earth, which varies on 41,000 year cycles, and the precession, or wobble of Earth as it rotates over periods of 23,000 years. When the cycles interact such that there is milder seasonality (cooler summers and warmer winters) at high latitudes in the Northern Hemisphere, less snow melts in summer, which allows glaciers to grow. The cyclicity of glacial-interglacial advances was about 40,000 years from before the start of the Quaternary until about a million years ago, likely controlled by Earth's rotational angle. For reasons that aren't clear, however, the cycles changed to about 100,000 years, controlled more by the eccentricity of Earth's orbit. If not for human-induced climate change, we might expect glaciers to approach Kansas and Missouri again in about 80,000 years.

For graphics and more detailed information about the mechanisms of Milankovich Cycles, see Chapter 3: What is Climate?

The continental glaciers that repeatedly covered parts of North America during the Quaternary had their origin in northern Canada. As the climate cooled, more snow fell in the winter than melted in the summer, causing the snow to pack into dense glacial ice. As more snow and ice accumulated on the glacier (and less melted), the ice began to move under its own weight and pressure. The older ice on the bottom was pushed out horizontally by the weight of the overlying younger ice and snow. Glacial ice then radiated out from a central point, flowing laterally in every direction away from the origin (*Figure 4.18*). And thus, a continental glacier originating in far northern Canada began to move south towards the Northeastern U.S. (*Figure 4.19*). The ice sheet crept slowly forward, scraping off the loose rock material and gouging the bedrock beneath as it advanced. Glaciers stop growing when the rate of flow of the glacier from the north is offset by the rate of melting along the southern edge of the glacier.

Using bubbles and water trapped in ice cores (see *Box 4.7*), scientists can measure the past atmospheric concentration of CO_2. Atmospheric CO_2 co-

			Present
Cenozoic	Cenozoic	Quaternary	
			2.6
	Tertiary	Neogene	
			23
		Paleogene	
			66
Mesozoic	Cretaceous		
			145
	Jurassic		
			201
	Triassic		
			252
Paleozoic	Permian		
			299
	Carbon-iferous	Pennsylvanian	
			323
		Mississippian	
			359
	Devonian		
			419
	Silurian		
			443
	Ordovician		
			485
	Cambrian		
			541
	Precambrian		
			4600

Millions of Years Ago

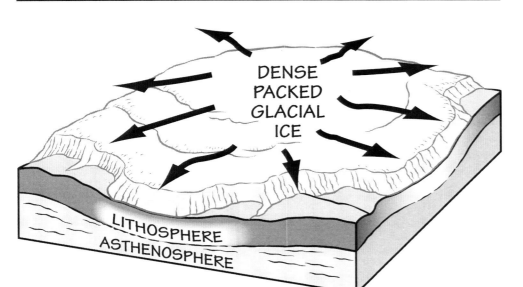

Figure 4.18: As ice piles up, a glacier forms, then begins to flow outward under its own weight and pressure.

Figure 4.19: A simplified version of the advancement of the most recent ice sheet over North America.

Cenozoic

Milankovitch cycles • *cyclical changes in the amount of heat received from the Sun, associated with how the Earth's orbit, tilt, and wobble alter its position with respect to the Sun. These changes affect the global climate, most notably alterations of glacial and interglacial intervals.*

varies with temperature in a way that reflects a positive feedback (*Figure 4.20*). For example, transitions from a cooling (glaciation) interval to a warming (deglaciation) interval occur due to changes in solar insolation associated with **Milankovitch cycles**; the warming in turn leads to release of CO_2 from warming ocean water and uncovered soils, increasing atmospheric CO_2 concentrations and further contributing to warming. The reverse occurs in transitions from warm intervals to cool intervals.

The most extensive glacial advances were recognized by their moraines long before we could date them precisely or knew the total number of glacial advances from isotopes in cores. In North America, these glacial-interglacial cycles are known as the pre-Illinoian (1.8 million to 302,000 years ago), Illinoian (191,000–131,000 years ago), Sangamonian (131,000–85,000 years ago), and

			Present
Cenozoic	Quaternary		2.6
	Tertiary	Neogene	23
		Paleogene	66
Mesozoic	Cretaceous		145
	Jurassic		201
	Triassic		252
Paleozoic	Permian		299
	Carboniferous	Pennsylvanian	323
		Mississippian	359
	Devonian		419
	Silurian		443
	Ordovician		485
	Cambrian		541
Precambrian			4600

Millions of Years Ago

Climate and Earth History

Cenozoic

Holocene • *the most recent portion of the QUATERNARY, beginning about 11,700 years ago and continuing to the present. It is the most recent (and current) interglacial, an interval of glacial retreat. The Holocene also encompasses the global growth and impact of the human species.*

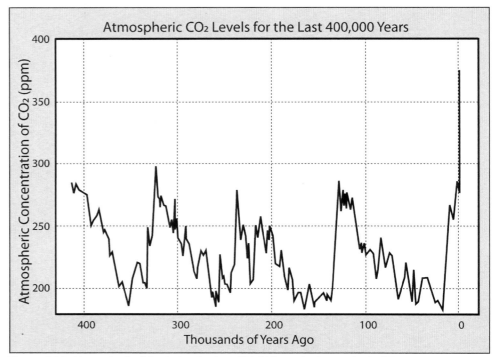

Figure 4.20: *Atmospheric CO$_2$ during the last 400,000 years. Atmospheric CO$_2$ concentration has been recorded for almost 800,000 years from ice-core air-bubble samples. During that interval, including the last 450,000 years depicted on this graph, the atmospheric concentration of CO$_2$ has never gone above 350 parts per million until the 1980s, about 100 years after the start of the Industrial Revolution.*

Wisconsinan (85,000–11,000 years ago). The Illinoian and Wisconsinian were cooler periods that saw glaciers advance, while the Sangamonian was a warm interglacial period.

The pre-Illinoian glaciation included many glacial and interglacial periods that were once subdivided into the Nebraskan, Aftonian, Kansan, and Yarmouthian ages. New data and numerical age dates suggest that the deposits are considerably more complicated; they are now lumped together into a single interval. The problem is that it can be very difficult to date glacial deposits precisely, and glacial advances wipe out much of the evidence of the previous advance. Today study of glacial cycles focuses on deep sea and ice cores, where oxygen isotopes can be measured and correlated with numbered isotope stages.

Ice sheets have come as far south as northern Missouri and northeastern Kansas, but the ice sheets did not extend into southern U.S. states, even at their largest. However, there were influences even on areas without ice sheets. For example, mountain glaciers were at high elevations in the Southwestern US, and large lakes formed in low areas. Much of the Mississippi River's great delta and alluvial fan was deposited when the glacial ice melted, creating rivers that eroded older rocks as well as carrying sediments previously scoured by the glaciers.

There are countless examples of distributions of organisms that show that temperatures in southern parts of the U.S. were cool by comparison with **Holocene** temperatures. For example, in southern New Mexico, Pleistocene fossil mammals are found that now live at higher elevations in the mountains

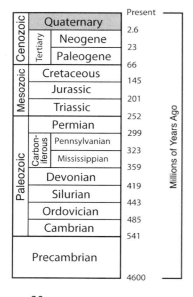

Climate and Earth History

Box 4.7: Proxies from ice cores

In a few cases, scientists can sample ancient atmospheres directly. Ice sheets and glaciers, which can be hundreds or thousands of feet thick, are formed from snow that has collected each year on the surface, has been compressed by overlying snow and ice for many years, and ultimately re-crystallizes into thick glacial ice. Bubbles in this ice can contain air that was trapped when the ice formed. The chemical composition of the air in these bubbles, as well as the frozen water surrounding them, can reveal, for example, the amount of CO_2 in the ancient atmosphere.

An **ice core** (*Figure*) is a large cylinder of ice extracted from an ice sheet or glacier, such as is found in Antarctica, Greenland, or on very high mountains worldwide. To collect ice cores, scientists use a hollow drill a few inches wide that cuts around a central cylinder of ice. Drillers carry out many cycles of lowering the drill, cutting a limited section (usually 4–6 m long), then raising all the equipment to the surface, removing the core section and beginning the process again. Much care is taken to ensure that the core is uncontaminated by modern air and water. The core is stored in an airtight plastic bag as soon as it reaches the surface, and analyzed only in a "clean room" designed to prevent contamination. To keep the ice core from degrading, it is kept well below freezing, usually below -15°C (5°F).

Ice cores record history. They can tell scientists about temperature, ocean volume, rainfall amount, levels of CO_2 and other gases in the atmosphere, solar variability, and sea-surface productivity at the time that the ice formed. Scientists can conduct chemical and isotopic studies on the ice itself, but they can also physically look at inclusions in the ice, like wind-blown dust, ash, or radioactive substances that can tell us about the extent of deserts, volcanic eruptions, forest fires, and even meteor impacts. The length of the record is extremely variable. Some cores only record the last few hundred years, whereas the longest core ever taken (from Vostok Research Station, Antarctica) allows study of climate change for over 400,000 years. Compiling information from multiple cores, scientists have now assembled a climate history of almost 800,000 years.

An ice core from Vostok Research Station, Antarctica, at the National Ice Core Laboratory in Denver, Colorado.

Climate and Earth History

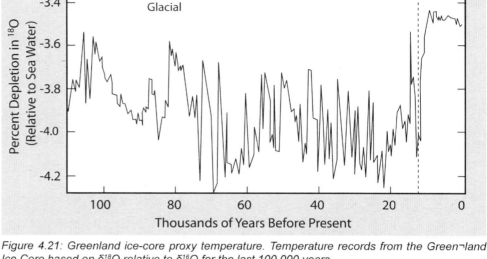

Figure 4.21: Greenland ice-core proxy temperature. Temperature records from the Green¬land Ice Core based on δ18O relative to δ16O for the last 100,000 years.

of northern New Mexico, indicating cooler temperatures and more available moisture in the area during the late Pleistocene. California's coastal climate was cooler: for example, microfossil evidence from the Rancho La Brea Tar Pits in Los Angeles tells us that southern California's climate around 40,000 years ago was similar to San Francisco's today.

3.5.4 Most Recent Glacial-Interglacial Cycle (110,000–10,000 Years Ago)

Using oxygen isotopes from ice cores (see *Box 4.7*), scientists can reconstruct Earth's global temperature during the last 100,000-year cycle (*Figure 4.21*). Tracing the midpoint of all of the high and low values in the line shows that temperature slowly dropped over this time. Geologically, scientists equate this cooling with the most recent glacial interval, when mastodons and mammoths roamed North America and a thick sheet of ice covered places like New York, Michigan, and northern Europe. The most significant recent advance of glacial ice over North America—the Laurentide Ice Sheet—peaked about 20,000 years ago, known as the "Last Glacial Maximum."

The ice sheet's maximum extent reached into Washington, Montana, the Dakotas, and Nebraska (*Figure 4.22*); it extended to where Chicago is now located, covering the northern half of the Midwestern US; and to the east as far as northern Pennsylvania and across to Long Island. The temperatures in areas not then covered in ice were moderated by its presence: the portions of the Northern US that were not covered by ice experienced a variety of cold climates and abundant lakes. The ice sheet did not, however, extend northwest into central or northern Alaska since the local climate was very dry, though an ice cap covered the Brooks Range.

After the Last Glacial Maximum ice then began melting back as global temperatures relatively abruptly increased. The Laurentide Ice Sheet and alpine ice caps throughout the Rockies melted back, leaving behind rugged

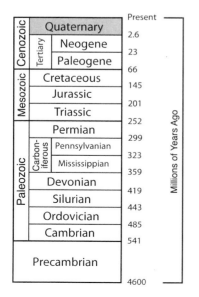

Cenozoic

esker • *a sinuous, elongated ridge of sand and gravel. Most eskers formed within ice-walled tunnels carved by streams flowing beneath a glacier. After the ice melted away, the stream deposits remained as long winding ridges. Eskers are sometimes mined for their well-sorted sand and gravel.*

kettle • *a depression formed where a large, isolated block of ice became separated from the retreating ICE SHEET. The ice becomes buried by sediment; when it melts, it leaves a shallow depression in the landscape that often persists as a small lake.*

Figure 4.22: Extent of glaciation over North America during the last glacial maximum.

mountain ranges, deep glacial valleys, and plains covered with thick deposits of glacial sediment. Glaciers left behind many geologic features that define the landscape of northern parts of the U.S., including **eskers**, **kettles**, and thick deposits of sand and gravel. They scraped the surface and left behind sediment that filled uneven surfaces, having the overall effect of smoothing the landscape. But they also left behind basins carved by glaciers such as the Great Lakes, and the Finger Lakes in New York State. The northern U.S. owes a large share of its present topography and drainage patterns to the last glacial advance and meltback.

Post-glacial lakes in the Northwest Central U.S. were a part of two famously large flooding events, among the largest floods on Earth. The first was the Bonneville megaflood: melting glaciers fed the waters of ancient Lake Bonneville (the remains of which is today the Great Salt Lake), which broke through a dam of loose sediment and rapidly drained northward through southern Idaho, along what is now the Snake River, all the way to northern Idaho.

The second was a series of floods that occurred when the ice sheet alternately blocked and retreated from what is now the Clark Fork River in northwestern Montana and northern Idaho. When the river was blocked, an enormous lake built behind the ice dam, and when the ice dam failed, the water was released catastrophically. Although the floods mostly affected central Washington, large ripples from the intense flow are preserved both near Missoula, Montana, and just downstream from where the ice dammed the river in northern Idaho. These floods cut through the dust deposits and basalt that covered much of the region, leaving islands, escarpments, and channels so large that ground-based geologists did not at first recognize their origins.

			Present
Cenozoic	Quaternary		2.6
	Tertiary	Neogene	23
		Paleogene	66
Mesozoic	Cretaceous		145
	Jurassic		201
	Triassic		252
Paleozoic	Permian		299
	Carboniferous	Pennsylvanian	323
		Mississippian	359
	Devonian		419
	Silurian		443
	Ordovician		485
	Cambrian		541
Precambrian			4600

Millions of Years Ago

Climate and Earth History

Medieval Warm Period • *a period of warm climate in the North Atlantic region during approximately the years 950 to 1100.*

With glacial retreats, vegetation gradually changed from cold-adapted taxa along the margins of the ice sheet to the flora we see today. For example, around 12,000 years ago, New England's climate was much like that of modern-day northern Canada. Temperatures increased with time (though interrupted by a cooling period from 10,800 to 10,000 years ago called the Younger Dryas). Pollen records from New York, Connecticut, and Maine indicate a landscape dominated by boreal forests during this time, with trees such as spruce, fir, and birch. Between 13,000 and 8500 years ago, fossil evidence shows that spruce and aspen forests grew in areas of North Dakota that are now warmer, drier, and covered with prairie. Idaho became more humid and warmer than it was during the last glacial maximum.

If the past is predictor of the future, then without human intervention, global average temperature and atmospheric levels of CO_2 should slowly decrease for the next 60,000 to 80,000 years.

3.5.5 The Holocene: The Last 10,000 Years

The last 10,000 years or so look dramatically different from the variation in temperature of the previous glacial interval; there has been much less variation. Presently, the continental ice sheets and ice caps of the Pleistocene are gone, but some 150,000 alpine glaciers remain worldwide, and this time from the end of the Pleistocene is regarded as an interglacial period (a warm spell with diminished glaciers) rather than the "end" of the Ice Age.

Figure 4.23 shows that after the global average temperature increased approximately 10,000 years ago, temperatures in the Northern Hemisphere began a slow, steady decline, which lasted for most of the last 7,500 years. These data (from ice cores from Greenland) support the hypothesis that, at least in the Northern Hemisphere, if natural climate variation were unhindered by humans, temperature would remain nearly constant, or would very slowly decline over the next few thousand years.

3.5.6 The Last 1000 Years

As scientists look closer to the present, climate resolution continues to improve. As indicated by ice-core temperature proxies, the last 1,000 years show very little significant global average temperature change prior to the 20th century (see *Figure 4.24*). A careful eye might notice, however, that the period from year 1000 to 1300 CE is slightly warmer and more "noisy" than from 1300 to present. This represents a time called the **Medieval Warm Period**, during which the Viking people inhabited Greenland. In the centuries following (from 1400 to 1800 CE), in contrast, fisherman living in nearby Iceland, where the weather is more temperate, were unable to leave their fishing ports for up to three months out of each year. Although the Medieval Warm Period resulted in only a small increase in global average temperature, it was substantial enough in that region to impact the lives of the people living there.

In the last 100 to 150 years, global average temperature has dramatically increased (*Figure 4.24*). This increase is a significant departure from the trend of the last

Find more on recent climate change in Chapter 5: Evidence for Recent Climate Change.

		Present
Cenozoic	Quaternary	
		2.6
	Neogene	
		23
	Paleogene	
		66
Mesozoic	Cretaceous	
		145
	Jurassic	
		201
	Triassic	
		252
Paleozoic	Permian	
		299
	Pennsylvanian	
		323
	Mississippian	
		359
	Devonian	
		419
	Silurian	
		443
	Ordovician	
		485
	Cambrian	
		541
	Precambrian	
		4600

Millions of Years Ago

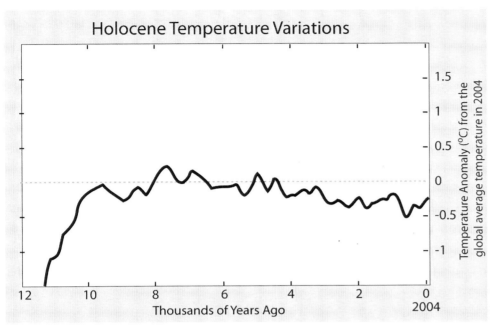

Figure 4.23: Holocene temperatures. Proxy temperature reconstruction from ice-core data after the end of the last glacial period, measured in °C difference from the global temperature average in 2004.

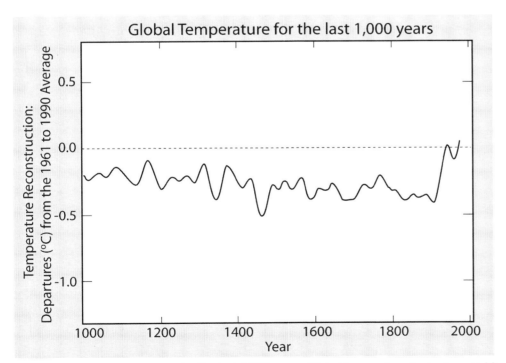

Figure 4.24: Global temperature for the last 1,000 years. Global temperature fluctuations in °C for the last 1,000 years relative to the global average temperature from 1961 to 1990, based on oxygen isotopes from ice cores.

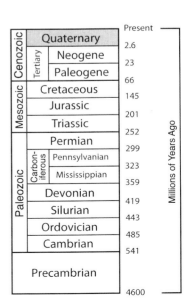

Climate and Earth History

Box 4.8: Using living organisms to determine past temperatures

Scientists can also use proxy records stored in living things and their ancient ancestors to recreate climates of the recent past with an amaz¬ing degree of precision.

Dendrochronology—the study of climate change as recorded by tree ring growth—is an excellent example of how climate researchers get information about climates of the relatively recent past. Trees can live for hundreds of years and in some extraordinary cases, like giant se-quoias and bristlecone pines, thousands of years. Each year, a tree adds a layer of growth between the older wood and its bark. This layer, or "ring" as seen in cross section, varies in thickness. A wide tree ring records a good growing season, usually moister and/or warmer, where-as a narrow ring records a poor growing season, usually drier and/or cooler. Especially in environments near the edge of a tree's comfort¬able living range, such as near the treeline on a mountain, where differences in weather make a large difference in growth rates, these data can provide highly reliable records of climate patterns.

To know more about climate over an even longer period of time, scientists look at dead trees that are still well preserved. They correlate the dead tree rings with the rings of a living tree whose age is known, looking for overlapping patterns, and can thereby get a longer record of climate through time. An amazing example is seen in the tree-ring chronologies established by looking at bristlecone pines from the southwestern U.S. (*Figure A*). Not only are these trees the longest-lived trees on Earth, they also live in a place where, even when they do die, they remain well preserved for hundreds or thousands of years. By comparing rings of living to dead bristlecone pines, scientists have established a tree ring record of climate in the Western U.S. for the past 9,000 years.

Figure A: Bristlecone pines, like this Pinus longaeva, *in Ancient Bristlecone Pine Forest, White Mountains, California, are among the longest-lived organisms on Earth. Their tree rings have provided scientists with climate data for the past 9,000 years.*

Box 4.8: Continued

There are, however, limitations to dendrochronology. Trees in the temperate zone only record the growing season, so the winter season is not usually visible in their wood. Trees in tropical regions grow year-round and therefore show no obvious annual growth rings, so climate data from equatorial areas is more difficult to obtain. And the variable most responsible for variable tree growth rate (temperature, moisture, or another factor) is not always unambiguous, thus research requires large data sets to overcome the uncertainty of individual data points.

Living Coral as a Climate Proxy

Because they build their own calcium carbonate ($CaCO_3$) skeletons, corals (*Figure B*) keep a record of climate in a way very similar to trees – by periodic rings of growth in the skeleton. Thicker rings represent better conditions for the coral, whereas thinner rings represent poor conditions. The coral colony grows both in winter and in summer, but the density of the skeleton is quite different due to seasonal changes in ocean temperature, the availability of nutrients, and differences in light. Additionally, the coral rings contain carbon and oxygen isotopes that indicate environmental conditions at the time that that part of the skeleton was secreted.

Figure B: A living colony of pillar coral at Discovery Bay, Jamaica. Such colonies can be hundreds of years old and the characteristics of older layers can provide proxy evidence of past environmental conditions.

Climate and Earth History

800 to 900 years, an interval without major anthropogenic influence. In fact, *the warming seen in the last 50 years may be more pronounced than at any time in at least the last 65 million years.*

4. Climate Analogs and Models

We cannot do global experiments on climate processes, but we can observe what sort of processes have occurred during a wide range of Earth system changes in the past. More recent analogs are strong because the starting conditions (such as continental positions and ecosystems) are more similar to today, and also because recent analogs often provide more and better preserved data. On the other hand, some scenarios that are less perfect analogs provide scenarios that may not be present in more recent records, such as rapid increases in methane (Paleocene-Eocene) and climate-related mass extinctions (e.g., end-Permian). Because each analog has different pros and cons, paleoclimatologists collectively study a variety of past scenarios toward better understanding of current climate change.

We can also use paleoclimate data to test computer climate models by observing how well the models reproduce actual past climate changes, at either ecological or geological time scales, in order to better gauge how accurately they may estimate future changes. Some models are focused not specifically on predicting future climates, but on reproducing past climates well enough for us to understand how the evolving climate system works. These models are important because they could enable us to consider what may happen to future climates, even if past climates are not good analogs in some respects.

Climate and Earth History

Resources

Books

A technical yet relatively readable book put together by a committee for the National Research Council on the potential of the deep-time geological record to inform us about the dynamics of the global climate system: Understanding Earth's Deep Past Lessons for our Climate Future, 2011, National Academies Press, Washington, DC. Available as a free download from the National Academies Press: http://www.nap.edu/download.php?record_id=13111.

The standard college textbook on the history of climate is by William F. Ruddiman Ruddiman, 2014, Earth's Climate: Past and Future, 3rd edition, W. H. Freeman, New York, 445 pp. A comprehensive review of the research literature can be found in Paleoclimates: Understanding Climate Change Past and Present, by Thomas Cronin, 2009, Columbia University Press, New York, 448 pp.

Online Resources

The Howard Hughes Medical Institute (HHMI) devotes one module of its program Changing Planet Past, Present, and Future to "Paleoclimate: A History of Change": http://www.hhmi.org/biointeractive/paleoclimate-history-change.

Paleomap Project: a set of detailed maps of the world showing the past positions of the continents and describing Earth's past climates, going back to the Cambrian period: http://www.scotese.com/climate.htm.

The Paleontology Portal: North American fossil record and geologic and climate histories. Use the Exploring Time & Space section to investigate geological history state by state and period by period: http://paleoportal.org/.

Paleo Perspectives: a series of informational websites on paleontological perspective on modern issues, including "A Paleo Perspective on Global Warming": https://www.ncdc.noaa.gov/data-access/paleoclimatology-data/perspectives.

Geologic Time

There are numerous resources on teaching geologic time, many of them focused on putting Earth history events along a timeline of a convenient scale. The Texas Memorial Museum at the University of Texas at Austin website has a pdf "Understanding Geologic Time" with timeline activities for middle school students: http://www.jsg.utexas.edu/glow/files/Understanding-Geologic-Time-6-8.pdf.

Climate and Earth History

Graphing Paleoclimate

This series of lesson plans is designed for 9th grade students to better understand the factors that drive climate change over geologic time: https://scied.ucar.edu/graphing-paleoclimate.

Paleoclimates and Pollen

In this activity directed at 7th to 9th grade students, students learn about how fossil pollen could be used to understand ancient climates: https://scied.ucar.edu/activity/paleoclimates-and-pollen.

Anthropocene

The Anthropocene is the interval since humans became a major geologic force and the term is under study for formal recognition by the International Stratigraphic Commission. Educational resources for discussing with students the nature of human impacts, including climate change, can be found at the HHMI website: http://www.hhmi.org/biointeractive/anthropocene-human-impact-environment.

Critical Zone Science

The critical zone extends from the bottom of the water table to the tops of vegetation, and critical zone science the interactions among air, water, life and rock, over time scales of seconds to geologic time. The CZ and how it is studied is well-suited to addressing The Next Generation Science Standards (NGSS). The Critical Zone Observatory website contains K-16 resources for integrating the critical zone into science education. http://criticalzone.org/national/education-outreach/k-12-education-1national/.

Chapter 5:
Evidence for and Causes of Recent Climate Change

Earth's climate has changed dramatically in the past, between extremes of hot and cold and over time scales ranging from millions of years to only decades (see Chapter 4). The rock record shows that at one time almost the whole planet was likely covered in ice, and at another time warm-loving palm trees grew in the present-day location of Alaska. These climate shifts were brought on by natural **forcings** such as changes in Earth's orbit around the sun, release of carbon dioxide (CO_2) from volcanic activity, removal of atmospheric CO_2 through **rock weathering**, biomass of photosynthetically-active life, and changes in **ocean circulation**. One common feature of the shifts in Earth's climate is that warm and cool periods generally correspond to high and low atmospheric concentrations of CO_2, respectively. CO_2 can be thought of as the "biggest control knob" for Earth's temperature.[1]

In Earth's very recent history—the last 100 to 200 years—CO_2 emissions have increased rapidly as industrial societies have grown. People discovered **fossil fuels** such as coal, oil, and natural gas, and invented clever ways to use them to heat and cool buildings, generate electricity, and power transportation. Industrialization also led to increased emission of other gases such as methane (CH_4) and **chlorofluorocarbons**. In 1895 a Swedish physical chemist, Svante Arrhenius, calculated the effect of CO_2 on Earth's temperature and predicted that increased CO_2 in the atmosphere would lead to a warmer global climate (see Chapter 3 on the **greenhouse effect**). Today, datasets collected over many decades show evidence of recent rapid change in our atmosphere and climate. These are discussed here.

Changing Temperatures and Carbon Dioxide

In the last 100 years both the ocean and land have warmed, and atmospheric CO_2 has risen sharply. *Figure 5.1* shows the global surface **temperature anomaly** over time from 1880 to 2015 (temperature anomaly is the difference in temperature relative to a reference time period, in this case 1951-1980).

As of the time this guide was written (2017), the ten warmest years on record have occurred since the year 1998. As of 2017, 2016 was the warmest year on record (a useful source for finding current climate summaries and reports is the

---

[1] Richard Alley, the Evan Pugh Professor of Geosciences at Pennsylvania State University, uses this metaphor of a control knob in his excellent lecture, The Biggest Control Knob: Carbon Dioxide in Earth's Climate History. December 2009. 30 June 2016. http://www.agu.org/meetings/fm09/lectures/lecture_videos/A23A.shtml.

forcing • *a change that has a directional impact on what is being changed (e.g., a solar forcing on the Earth directly impacts the Earth's heat absorption).*

rock weathering • *the breaking down of solid rock into small particles. See CHEMICAL WEATHERING and PHYSICAL WEATHERING.*

ocean circulation • *global-scale patterns of water movement throughout the world's oceans.*

fossil fuel • *a non-renewable, carbon-based fuel source like OIL, NATURAL GAS, or COAL, developed from the preserved organic remains of fossil organisms.*

CHAPTER AUTHORS

Ingrid H. H. Zabel

and authors of

A Very Short Guide to Climate Change

Recent Climate Change

Temperature and CO₂

chlorofluorocarbons • compounds of carbon, hydrogen, chlorine, and fluorine, usually ANTHROPOGENIC gases used as refrigerants or in aerosol cans. Released into the ATMOSPHERE, these compounds are GREENHOUSE GASES and are responsible for the OZONE HOLE.

greenhouse effect • the influence of GREENHOUSE GAS molecules in the Earth's atmosphere to retain heat (infrared radiation) radiating from the Earth's surface that would otherwise escape into space.

remote sensing • a method of scientific investigation that instruments on satellites or aircraft to make measurements of the Earth's surface. It is particularly useful for studying areas that are large in extent, difficult to access on the ground or ocean, and in some cases for areas that are dark for much of the winter.

infrared light • electromagnetic radiation in the part of the spectrum with wavelengths from 750 nanometers to 1 millimeter. People sense infrared radiation as heat.

microwave radiation • electromagnetic radiation in the part of the spectrum with wavelengths from about 0.1 to 100 centimeters.

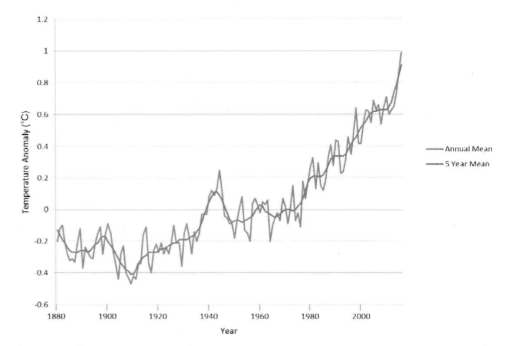

Figure 5.1: Global land-ocean surface temperature anomaly over time. Base period: 1951-1980. (See Teacher-Friendly Guide website for a full color version.)

National Centers for Environmental Information's *State of the Climate* website: http://www.ncdc.noaa.gov/sotc/). As Earth's temperature has increased, the ocean has been storing most of this heat energy. Scientists estimate that from 1971 to 2010 the oceans absorbed over 90% of the heat that has been added to our planet.

Global CO_2 also follows an upward trend in the recent past. The Mauna Loa, or Keeling, curve is a graph of atmospheric CO_2 measurements started by Charles David Keeling in 1958 at an observatory atop Mauna Loa, a mountain on the island of Hawai'i. Keeling's successors continue to make these measurements today, and the graph shows a steady upward trend and an annual oscillation which results from plants in the northern hemisphere taking in more CO_2 during the spring and summer than in the winter (*Figure 5.2*).

This recent increase in atmospheric CO_2 can be compared with CO_2 concentrations farther back in Earth's past. *Figure 5.3*, which plots the Mauna Loa data together with historic CO_2 data from an Antarctic ice core, shows how large the 20th century rise in CO_2 really is relative to pre-industrial levels.

See Chapter 4: Past Climates for information on how we can learn about past climates by analyzing ice cores.

Scientists measure land and sea surface temperatures through **remote sensing** from satellites, and using thermometers on land and on ships, coasts, and ocean buoys. The satellite sensors give a much broader coverage than point measurements, and they give access to areas that are difficult to access on the surface or are dark for much of the winter. Point measurements are used to check ("ground truth") the satellite data. The surface of the Earth emits **infrared light** and **microwave radiation** (see Box 5.1), and the intensity of that

Recent Climate Change

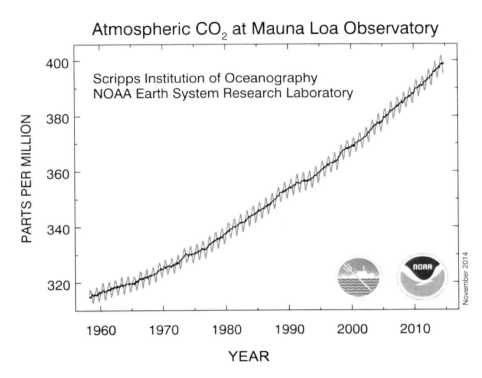

Figure 5.2: Atmospheric CO2 concentration at Mauna Loa Observatory from 1958 to 2014.

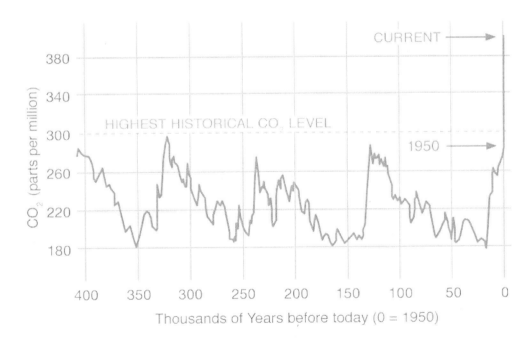

Figure 5.3: Atmospheric CO$_2$ measurements from Antarctic ice cores and Mauna Loa observatory.

ice sheet • *a mass of glacial ice that covers part of a continent and has an area greater than 50,000 square kilometers (19,000 square miles).*

Recent Climate Change

> ### Box 5.1: The electromagnetic spectrum and remote sensing
>
> Electromagnetic radiation can be thought of as traveling waves of energy, being emitted, absorbed, scattered, and reflected all around us. There is a spectrum—a broad range—of these waves in the universe with different frequencies and wavelengths. In our everyday experience we are most familiar with visible light because we sense it with our eyes and it contains the colors that we see. But we have everyday experience with other parts of the spectrum as well, such as radiowaves (which carry radio broadcasts), infrared radiation (which we experience as heat), ultraviolet radiation (which can give us sunburn), x-rays (in medical tests), and microwaves (in microwave cooking and police radar).
>
> Scientists measuring characteristics of the Earth's surface and atmosphere design sensors of electromagnetic radiation that fit the phenomena and conditions they want to observe. For example, scientists studying melting and freezing of the Greenland ice sheet have used microwave sensors on satellites because microwaves can penetrate clouds, they can be detected during the dark Arctic winter when visible light would not be useful, and they are sensitive to changes that occur on the ice sheet when the surface melts or freezes.
>
>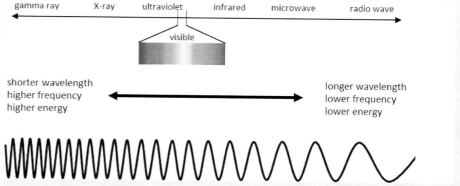
>
> *The electromagnetic spectrum. Adapted from NASA's Imagine the Universe. (See Teacher-Friendly Guide website for a full color version.)*

radiation depends on the surface temperature in a known way. Instruments on satellites can detect this emitted radiation, from which scientists can calculate the surface temperature.

Shrinking Ice Sheets and Glaciers

Although it may not feel like we are living in an ice age, when the Earth's current climate is viewed through the perspective of geological time scales it is evident that the Earth is in an interglacial period of an ice age (see Chapter 4), with the poles containing huge masses of ice. The Greenland and Antarctic **ice sheets** together store over 99% of the Earth's fresh water. The Earth's warming is having an effect on these ice sheets, however. *Figure 5.4* shows measurements of the mass of ice, in gigatonnes, lost from these two ice sheets since 2002. Diminished ice sheets can have a profound effect on regional and

Recent Climate Change

Box 5.2: Climate and weather records from your backyard

You can find temperature and precipitation data, graphs, and maps for your region from your NOAA Regional Climate Center (https://www.ncdc.noaa.gov/customer-support/partnerships/regional-climate-centers). The lengths of the data records available to you vary by location, but you may be able to find data going back to the late 19th century.

Another source of historical climate data for the US is NOAA's Climate at a Glance website: http://www.ncdc.noaa.gov/cag/. Here you can generate maps and time-series plots of temperature, precipitation, and drought data for a broad choice of regions and time periods. Data are also available for cities, from two reliable sources: either the Global Historical Climatology Network or the US Historical Climatology Network.

albedo • *the fraction of solar energy that a surface reflects back into space.*

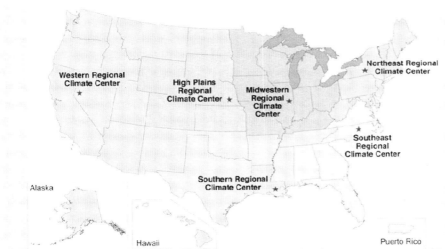

Map showing geographic coverage of NOAA's Regional Climate Centers. (See Teacher-Friendly Guide website for a full color version.)

global climate. For example, freshwater added to the ocean changes ocean surface salinity and thereby currents. Large amounts of water melted from land ice also raises sea level. Less ice cover decreases **albedo**: highly reflective sea ice is replaced by much less reflective open water, and loss of reflective land ice exposes darker soil and rocks beneath.

Scientists can measure the change in an ice sheet's mass in several ways: by using satellite and ground measurements to compare the amount of snow accumulating on the ice sheet to the amount of melted water flowing out, by using satellite and airborne instrument measurements to calculate the change in ice sheet elevation and volume, and by measuring changes in gravity over the ice sheet using very sensitive instruments on satellites.[2]

---

[2] This information and much more on ice sheets, sea ice, and glaciers can be found at the National Snow and Ice Data Center's website, https://nsidc.org/.

Recent Climate Change

ablation • *the loss of snow and ice from a GLACIER or ICE SHEET by melting, evaporation, sublimation (a phase transition from solid directly to gas), iceberg calving, and other processes.*

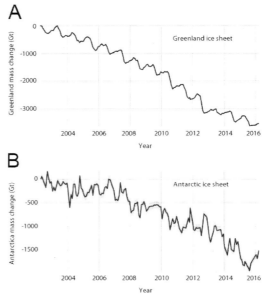

Figure 5.4: Measured mass change of A) the Greenland and B) Antarctic ice sheets, showing mass loss between 2002 and 2016.

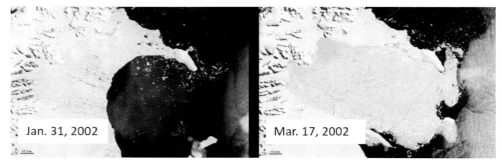

Jan. 31, 2002

Mar. 17, 2002

Figure 5.5: Satellite images showing the breakup of the Larsen B ice shelf in West Antarctica. Note the scale marker (10 km) in the lower left corner of the images.

Ice sheets lose mass in several ways: melting at the surface followed by runoff of meltwater to the ocean, melting when ice on the edge is in contact with seawater, **ablation**, and loss of solid ice when pieces of ice break off from the edge of the ice sheet and float in the sea. This breaking at the edge is called calving, and it is how icebergs form. Additionally, very large pieces of ice sheets sometimes break off, such as in 2002 when the Larsen B Ice Shelf disintegrated in Antarctica (*Figure 5.5*). The portion of the ice sheet that collapsed initially was about the size of Rhode Island.

Warmer air and water temperatures accelerate these processes, which lead to mass loss. The Greenland ice sheet has been breaking records in the last few years for the earliest onset of spring melting. In Antarctica, a recent study suggested that the ice sheet is actually gaining mass in some regions to the point where total mass losses are offset, but that increasing rates of mass loss will overtake this gain in a few decades.[3]

---

[3] See Vinas, Maria-Jose, "NASA Study: Mass Gains of Antarctic Ice Sheet Greater than Losses." 30 October 2015, http://www.nasa.gov/feature/goddard/nasa-study-mass-gains-of-antarctic-ice-sheet-greater-than-losses.

Recent Climate Change

Changing Sea Ice

sea ice • *frozen seawater at the surface of the ocean.*

Mountain glaciers have also been shrinking around the globe, although a few glaciers are holding steady or growing in mass. Generally, however, the trend is overwhelmingly towards glacial retreat and loss. Communities who depend on glacial meltwater for agriculture and drinking water are at risk as this trend continues. Water from melting glaciers also contributes to sea level rise, and is contributing at an accelerated pace in the last few decades. According to the latest Intergovernmental Panel on Climate Change (IPCC, see Box 5.3) report, most of the glacier mass loss around the world has taken place in the Arctic, the Southern Andes, and in Asian mountains.

Box 5.3: The Intergovernmental Panel on Climate Change (IPCC)

The IPCC, founded in 1988 by the World Meteorological Organization and the United Nations Environment Programme, is a group of scientists from 195 countries who assess the state of the world's climate, climate science, impacts and risks of climate change, and options to respond to it. Over three thousand scientists are involved in writing and reviewing the IPCC's climate assessments approximately every six years, and these assessments are considered by many to be the authoritative source of information on climate change science. The assessments do not include policy suggestions, but they are intended to provide information to help government officials develop sound, research-based climate change policies.

Changing Sea Ice Extent

The Arctic Ocean over the North Pole is covered by frozen seawater or **sea ice**, a feature of the Arctic that has long limited shipping and underwater exploration, and that is part of the natural environment of Arctic marine life, from plankton to polar bears. The area covered by sea ice grows in the winter when temperatures drop and seawater freezes, and shrinks in the summer as some of the new, thin ice melts during the warmest part of the year. Scientists can measure the extent of Arctic sea ice using remote sensing instruments on satellites, with records going back to the late 1970s. Measurements include total area, distribution, and thickness.

Arctic sea ice extent has decreased over the past few decades as the region has warmed, and decreased more rapidly since the turn of the 21st century. *Figure 5.6* shows images based on satellite data of Arctic sea ice extent, for the annual September minimum and March maximum, for 2000-01 compared with 2015-16. The decline in sea ice cover over fifteen years is evident, especially at the end of summer.

Around Antarctica, though some portions of the ice shelves have broken, total sea ice extent has shown the opposite trend to that seen in the Arctic, increasing on average since the late 1970s. The rate at which the Arctic has lost sea ice extent, in square miles per year, is about three times as big as the rate at which the Antarctic has gained sea ice extent. Scientists think the increase in sea ice extent is driven by cold continental winds and a strong, cold current that circles around Antarctica, isolating Antarctica from transport of heat from lower latitudes in ways that the Arctic is not.

Recent Climate Change

permafrost • *a layer of soil below the surface that remains frozen all year round. Its thickness can range from tens of centimeters (inches) to a few meters (yards). Permafrost is typically defined as any soil that has remained at a temperature below the freezing point of water for at least two years.*

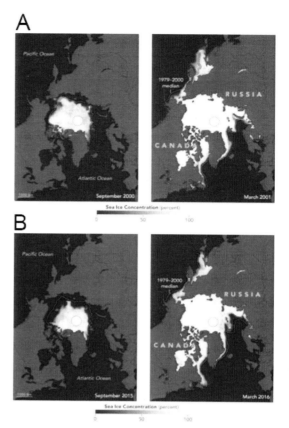

Figure 5.6: Arctic sea ice extent for the months of September (annual minimum extent) and March (annual maximum extent) for the years A) 2000-2001 and B) 2015-2016. (See Teacher-Friendly Guide website for a full color version.)

Thawing Permafrost

About a quarter of the land surface in the Arctic is covered by **permafrost**: ground where a thick layer of soil is permanently frozen due to year-round cold temperatures. The Arctic is warming more rapidly than any other part of the world, and this means that permafrost is thawing. The IPCC's (see Box 5.3) latest report on global climate change concluded that it is "virtually certain" that permafrost extent in the Arctic will continue to decline, by 37% to 81% by the end of the 21st century, depending on the rate of carbon emissions from human activities.

As permafrost thaws the mechanical properties of the ground change, and structures such as roads and oil pipelines that have been built on frozen ground are at risk of damage. Another hazard from thawing permafrost is the release of CO_2 and CH_4 that have been frozen in the ground. These are powerful greenhouse gases, and CH_4 in particular can have a large, short-term warming effect.

Rising Sea level

Global sea level is rising, mainly as a result of a warming ocean. When water warms it expands, whether at the scale of a kettle of water on the stove or the

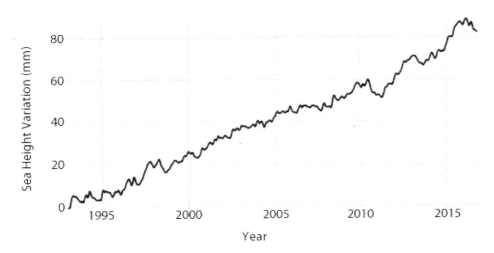

Figure 5.7: Global average sea level change as a function of time, with a base year of 1993.

Causes of Change

mantle • *the layer of the Earth between the crust and core. It consists of solid silicate rocks that, over long intervals of time, flow like a highly viscous liquid. Convection currents within the mantle drive the motion of plate tectonics.*

vast volume of water that fills the world's ocean basins. Sea level is also rising as water is added to the ocean from melting glaciers and ice sheets. Melting glaciers (other than ice sheets) contributed to sea level rise at the rate of 0.76 mm per year (0.03 inches per year) from 1993 to 2009. Global average sea level has risen about 17.8 centimeters (7 inches) in the past 100 years (*Figure 5.7*). (Note that melting sea ice does not contribute to sea level rise because it's already displacing sea water as it floats.)

Sea level rise is close to, but not exactly, uniform everywhere. Ocean currents can pull water toward or away from coasts, effectively raising or lowering sea level. In some places the land is sinking (subsiding) or rising (being uplifted) because of geologic forces. In many places land uplift and subsidence occurs due to tectonic changes, which may occur over many millions of years. In high latitudes where glaciers covered the landscape, the ice sheet depressed the continental crust downward into the **mantle**; since melting back the land has been "rebounding" upward. This is happening wherever ice sheets covered the land, for example, across the northern part of North America. Land subsidence may occur over extended periods due to deposition of sediment from rivers, and over shorter time scales due to human activities such as groundwater and petroleum extraction. Where land is subsiding, such as along the US's East and Gulf coasts, the relative rate of sea level rise is higher than the global average. Where land is rebounding, sea level can be decreasing. *Figure 5.8* shows a map of sea level trends along coasts worldwide. The highest sea level rise rates in North America are along the coast of Louisiana, where rates are in the range of 9-12 millimeters per year (3 to 4 feet per century).

Causes of Recent Climate Change

How can we be sure that changes going on now are not just part of natural climate variation? It is worthwhile to consider the potential causes of recent climate change, both natural and anthropogenic (human-caused), and to evaluate the effects of each one.

Recent Climate Change

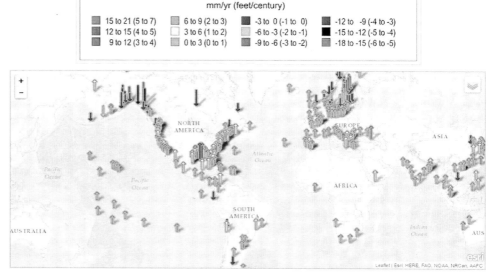

Figure 5.8: Regional sea level trends worldwide. The arrows represent the direction and magnitude of the change. (See Teacher-Friendly Guide website for a full color version.)

Changes in Earth's orbit around the sun. The Earth's tilt, wobble, and orbit around the sun go through predictable cyclical changes (Milankovitch cycles; see Chapter 3). These changes can have dramatic effects on the climate, and are thought to have brought on and ended glacial advances and retreats during the Ice Age (the ultimate long term cause of the Earth's transition to the Pleistocene Ice Age had separate causes). The changes in these cycles over last 200 years have been too small to have any significant effect on Earth's temperature, and over the next fifty to eighty thousand years would be expected to take the Earth toward another glacial advance.

Changes in incoming solar radiation. Changes in the energy output from the sun do not successfully account for the current warming trend. Eleven-year sunspot cycles have been consistently recorded, but these have risen and fallen as expected, never increasing their net output of energy. No other solar outputs correlate with the warming trend, either. So for the period for which we have direct, observable records, the Earth has warmed dramatically even though there has been no corresponding rise in any kind of solar activity.

Volcanic eruptions. Volcanos emit greenhouse gases when they erupt, which can lead to climate warming if the input of CO_2 to the atmosphere is sufficiently large. Volcanic eruptions can also have a short-term cooling effect because the sulfate particles they emit block incoming sunlight. The eruption of Mt. Pinatubo in 1991 led to an almost 0.6°C (1°F) decrease in average global temperatures over 15 months. The net long-term effect of volcanism over the last 200 years has not been significant enough to warm the climate. According to the IPCC (Box 5.3) "the emissions of CO_2 from volcanic eruptions are at least 100 times smaller than anthropogenic emissions, and inconsequential for climate on century time scales."[4]

---

[4] Stocker, T.F., et al., 2013, Summary for Policymakers. In: Climate Change 2013: The Physical Science Basis. Contribution of Working Group I to the Fifth Assessment Report of the Intergovernmental Panel on Climate Change. Cambridge University Press: NY. http://www.ipcc.ch/report/ar5/wg1/

Recent Climate Change

Box 5.4: How do we measure sea level change?

Scientists measure sea level in two main ways: with tide gauges along the coasts, and with altimeters on satellites. Modern tide gauges use a radar fixed on a structure such as a pier or bridge, pointing down at the water to measure the distance from the surface of the sea to a fixed point. A detector measures the round-trip travel time t of the radar (microwave) beam between the instrument and the sea surface, and then distance is calculated in the following way:

$$d = ct/2$$

where t = round trip travel time and c = speed of light (i.e., the speed of the electromagnetic wave transmitted by the radar). Changing sea surface levels from waves and tides are averaged over time. GPS readings can be used to correct for any upward or downward motion of the land.

Since 1992, scientists have been able to measure sea level very accurately using data from altimeters on satellites. Altimeters work according to very similar principles to the radar tide gauge described above. Because they are on satellites they can gather data over large areas and in the middle of the ocean instead of just along the coast.

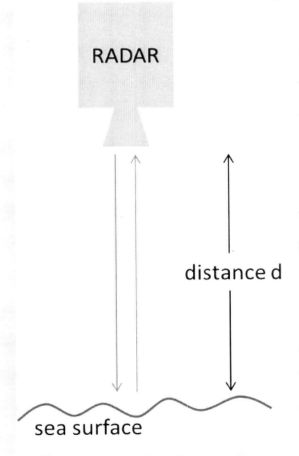

Schematic of a radar-based tide gauge.

Recent Climate Change

Land use changes. When people cut down forests to plant crops, the physical properties of the land's surface change. Crops tend to be lighter colored than forests so they reflect away more incoming sunlight (i.e., they have a higher albedo), leading to cooling. Changes in the land surface roughness and water runoff from land use changes can also change the surface temperature. According to the 2013 IPCC report (Box 5.3) these changes tend to offset the albedo effect, but all these changes are hard to quantify and the scientific community does not have a good understanding on if these effects of land use change lead to a small net cooling or small net warming. It is clear that deforestation leads to increased CO_2 in the atmosphere because intact forests are carbon sinks. The loss of these carbon sinks, especially tropical rain forests, accelerated in the late 20th century.

Aerosols. Aerosols are tiny particles in the air, from both natural and human-made sources such as dust, volcanic eruptions, biomass burning, sea salt, and vehicle and factory emissions. Their presence in the stratosphere tends to have a net cooling effect on Earth's climate because they reflect incoming sunlight back into space. Aerosols can also serve as cloud nucleation sites and can alter the reflectivity of clouds. The impact of clouds on Earth's climate is not as well understood as other parts of the climate system, but according to the 2013 IPCC report (Box 5.3,) aerosols are thought to cool the climate.

Greenhouse gases. As discussed above and as seen in *Figure 5.9*, carbon emissions from human activity and concentrations of CO_2 and other greenhouse gases in the atmosphere have risen dramatically since the industrial revolution began in the early 1800s. Earth's average temperature has been rising in a way that cannot be accounted for by natural variation alone. Climate models that incorporate increasing CO_2 explain this warming trend better than any models based on natural variation alone. The pattern of the observed warming fits the pattern that we would expect from warming caused by the buildup of greenhouse gases, that is, almost all areas of the planet are warming; the Earth's surface and lower atmosphere are warming; and the temperature changes are greatest in the Arctic during winter.

We have seen natural variations in climate over the past several thousand years, some of which are not well explained. Is it possible that current changes are just one of those fluctuations? The reason most scientists do not think so is that (a) the magnitude of the current trend is larger than any that we have seen in the past several thousand years, and (b) the current trend shows strong directionality in not just warming, but *rate* of warming, through time. Such variation does not look like any of the temperature changes seen in the past 10,000 years or so. And there are no known sources of natural variation that would give rise to changes as rapid as those observed in global temperature over the past 150 years.

Could current changes just be unusually extreme variation that we do not yet understand? Yes. In science (by definition), all phenomena are open to new explanations, so scientists must always be ready to consider other options. Scientists do not, however, favor or give equal weight to random or unknown variation if another known explanation fits the available data. Some explanations are better than others, and it would be ineffective to act as if every explanation, no matter how unlikely, should receive equal treatment. The explanation of

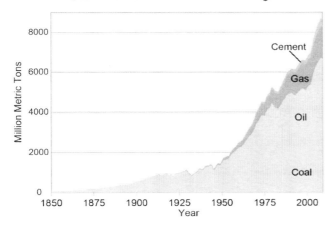

Carbon Emissions in the Industrial Age

Figure 5.9: Global carbon emissions from burning coal, oil, and gas and producing cement (1850-2009). These emissions account for about 80% of the total emissions of carbon from human activities, with land-use changes (like cutting down forests) accounting for the other 20% in recent decades. (See Teacher-Friendly Guide website for a full color version.)

Box 5.5: Carbon emissions from cement production

About 5% of global CO_2 emissions come from cement production. Making cement involves heating limestone to very high temperatures in kilns. The CO_2 escapes directly from limestone during heating, and it is also released in burning the fossil fuels used to run the kilns.

---

increased greenhouse gases in our atmosphere causing current warming fits the data extremely well.

What are the Likely Effects of Climate Change Going to Be?

Over the past billion years, the Earth has experienced climates that were much warmer than those of today, as well as much colder periods. This fact, however, does not mean that future warming is nothing to worry about. The geological record tells us that these changes in Earth's past were usually much more gradual—occurring over thousands or millions of years—than many of the changes likely to occur in the very near future. And natural climate changes that have occurred rapidly have been linked to very rapid environmental change. Some periods of rapid climate change are associated with very large extinction events to organisms that had previously been thriving. The geological record, furthermore, tells us that our species—*Homo sapiens*—has not experienced since civilization developed about 10,000 years ago anything like what we are about to experience if current trends continue. Billions of people are and will be affected by the impacts of climate change, including coastal flooding, strained water supply, heat waves, and disease occurrence. It will change where and how we live and access food. We will need to learn how to adapt, and to act to limit further future warming.

Recent Climate Change

Online Resources

Climate Data

Information, maps, plots, visualizations, and other multimedia on global climate change from NASA: http://climate.nasa.gov/

Time-series map animation showing the five-year average variation of global surface temperatures from 1884 to 2015: http://climate.nasa.gov/vital-signs/global-temperature/

State of the Climate (monthly summaries and reports, including news about when new records are set): http://www.ncdc.noaa.gov/sotc/

Climate Indicators

Time-series plots of atmospheric CO_2 measurements, from Mauna Loa and ice core data, on time scales varying from the current week to 800,000 years ago to present: https://scripps.ucsd.edu/programs/keelingcurve/

Time series of maps of Arctic sea ice in September, from 1979-2014: https://nsidc.org/cryosphere/sotc/sea_ice_animation.html. The visualization shows the decline of Arctic sea ice over the last few decades.

A section of a U.N. report on changes in mountain glaciers: http://www.grid.unep.ch/glaciers/pdfs/5.pdf

Interactive map of global sea level trends, showing variation in regional sea level changes: http://tidesandcurrents.noaa.gov/sltrends/sltrends.html

The Third National Climate Assessment: http://nca2014.globalchange.gov/

Ways of Measuring Climate Indicators

Information about remote sensing of surface temperature from satellites: https://podaac.jpl.nasa.gov/SeaSurfaceTemperature

Information about satellite altimeters and how they are used to measure sea level: http://www.star.nesdis.noaa.gov/sod/lsa/SeaLevelRise/

An article about the history of measuring sea level and the evolution of tide gauges: https://www.climate.gov/news-features/climate-tech/reading-between-tides-200-years-measuring-global-sea-level

Recent Climate Change

Causes of Climate Change

An infographic on potential causes of climate change from 1880-2005 and their effects, based on datasets from NASA: http://www.bloomberg.com/graphics/2015-whats-warming-the-world/.

Other Visualizations and Teaching Resources

Interactive, maps, graphics, videos, publications, and more on climate change: http://www.climatecentral.org/

Innovative visualizations of greenhouse gas emissions and other topics: http://www.carbonvisuals.com/

Reviewed collection of teaching resources: Climate Literacy and Energy Awareness Network (CLEAN) http://cleanet.org/index.html

Chapter 6:
US Regional Climates, Current and Future

Describing Climates

The United States—which extends south to the tropics and north to the Arctic Circle, and which has over 12,000 miles of coastline as well as vast inland regions—has within its borders a wide variety of regional climates. Each of these regional climates—from the equatorial **wetlands** of Florida to the arid deserts of Arizona—is impacted by the changing global climate, but these impacts are and will not be uniform. Coastal communities are being affected by rising sea levels and increased **storm surges**, while desert communities may be facing longer and more frequent **droughts** and heat waves. Ski resorts in the Rocky Mountains may have to adapt to less snowfall and smaller **snowpacks**, while communities in the Northeast are experiencing more heavy rainfalls. In this section, we present an overview of the existing regional climates and the impact that climate change will have on these regional climates in the future.

A commonly used way to categorize climate is with the Köppen-Geiger map, developed by Wladimir Köppen in the late 19th century and early 20th century and refined by Rudolf Geiger (see *Box 6.1*). The US contains all five main climate groups of the Köppen-Geiger map (Equatorial, Arid, Warm Temperate, Continental, and Polar). For the purposes of discussion, in this chapter we divide the contiguous US into seven regions (Northeast, Southeast, Midwest, South Central, Northwest Central, Southwest, and West), and we consider Hawaii and Alaska separately. We will follow the sun as it rises in the east and moves westward, starting at the easternmost point in the US—West Quoddy Head, Maine—and ending at the westernmost point—Cape Wrangell, Alaska.

Another way of describing climate is through **climate normals**: averages of climate variables over 30-year periods. These can be useful for comparison purposes, as an indicator (though not the only one) of how climate has changed from one 30-year period to another. *Figure 6.1* shows averages over the period of 1981-2010 of annual minimum temperature, maximum temperature, and precipitation for the contiguous US.

This chapter presents projections of future climate that come from **climate models**: numerical simulations performed on a computer that incorporate scientists' best understanding of the interactions, **forcings**, and **feedbacks** within the Earth's climate system. A useful analogy for building and working with a climate model is that of trying to understand a complex sports car without looking under the hood (*Box 6.2*).

wetland • *land region where the soil is covered or saturated with water, either for part or all of the year.*

storm surge • *a large volume of ocean water pushed onto land by offshore winds during a storm.*

drought • *a long period of unusually low rainfall, resulting in lack of water for plants, animals, and people.*

snowpacks • *snow accumulated over time, often in mountainous areas that have a long cold season. When snowpack melts it feeds streams and rivers.*

climate normal • *thirty-year averages of variables such as daily temperature, rainfall, snowfall, and frost and freeze dates that can be compared with thirty-year averages of these variables from other time periods.*

CHAPTER AUTHORS

Ingrid H. H. Zabel

Benjamin Brown-Steiner

climate model • *a computer-generated simulation of the Earth's climate system, projected through time.*

forcings • *a change that has a directional impact on what is being changed (e.g., a solar forcing on the Earth directly impacts the Earth's heat absorption).*

feedback • *the response of a system to some change that either balances/opposes or reinforces/enhances the change that is applied to a system. Balancing feedback (sometimes called negative feedback) tends to push a system toward stability; reinforcing feedback (sometimes called positive feedback) tends to push a system towards extremes.*

Köppen system • *a commonly used system of climate categorization developed by Russian climatologist Wladimir Köppen. It is based on the kinds of vegetation that areas sustain, and defines 12 climate types: rainforest, monsoon, tropical savanna, humid subtropical, humid continental, oceanic, Mediterranean, steppe, subarctic, tundra, polar ice cap, and desert. Updated by Rudolf Geiger, it has been refined to five groups each with two to four subgroups.*

US Regional Climates

Box 6.1: Köppen-Geiger maps

The Köppen-Geiger map is based on the kinds of vegetation areas can sustain. As originally conceived by Köppen, it defined 12 climate types, many of which are familiar: rainforest, **monsoon**, tropical **savanna**, humid subtropical, humid continental, oceanic, Mediterranean, **steppe**, subarctic, **tundra**, polar ice cap, and desert. The updated version has five main climate groups, each with two to four subgroups. In the following sections we refer to this map and the lettered climate categories (A, B, C, D, E) described in the figure legend.

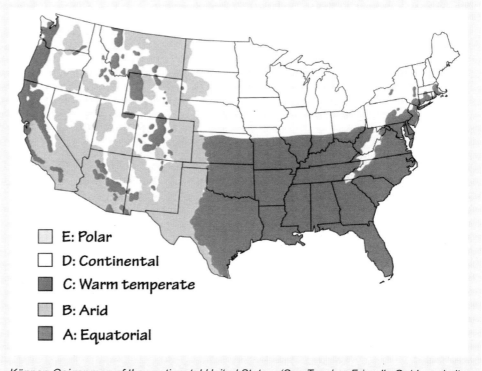

- ☐ E: Polar
- ☐ D: Continental
- ■ C: Warm temperate
- ☐ B: Arid
- ■ A: Equatorial

Köppen-Geiger map of the continental United States. (See Teacher-Friendly Guide website for a full color version.)

1. Northeast

1.1 Description

The sun first rises in the United States in West Quoddy Head, Maine. Maine is one of the states in the Northeastern US, which also includes New Hampshire, Vermont, Massachusetts, Rhode Island, Connecticut, New York, Pennsylvania, New Jersey, Delaware, and Maryland. The Northeast shares a border with Canada, the Atlantic Ocean, and two of the Great Lakes: Lake Ontario and Lake Erie. Climate, of course, does not follow state boundaries, so as with all the regions in this chapter the climate characteristics of this region can overlap with those of neighboring regions.

monsoon • *a seasonal wind pattern in the Indian Ocean and South Asia which reverses direction between southwesterly and northeasterly, creating a wet season in summer and a dry season in winter.*

savanna • *a grassland in tropical or subtropical regions.*

steppe • *a large, flat, dry grassland area.*

tundra • *a region and climate zone with frozen ground (PERMAFROST) and no trees.*

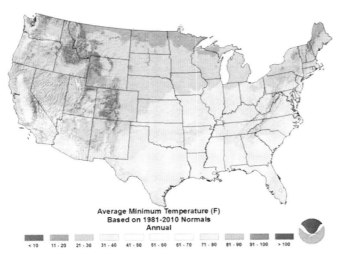

Average Minimum Temperature (F)
Based on 1981-2010 Normals
Annual

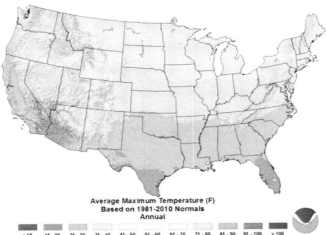

Average Maximum Temperature (F)
Based on 1981-2010 Normals
Annual

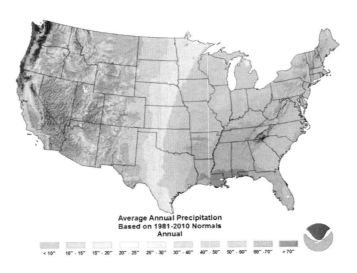

Average Annual Precipitation
Based on 1981-2010 Normals
Annual

Figure 6.1: Maps of 1981-2010 climate normals (30-year averages for this time period) for the contiguous United States: A) annual minimum temperature (°F); B) annual maximum temperature (°F); and C) annual precipitation (inches). (See Teacher-Friendly Guide website for a full color version.)

Northeast

relative humidity • the ratio of the water vapor density in the air to the maximum water vapor density possible in the air at a given temperature and pressure (the saturation water vapor density).

solar radiation • electromagnetic energy emitted by the Sun.

Box 6.2: The climate system as a fancy sports car[1]

Imagine the Earth's climate system as a fancy sports car owned by a playful friend. Your friend is happy to let you look and listen to the car and will on occasion give you a ride in it. But he's unwilling to let you look under the hood or study the user's manual. If you want to try and understand how the car works, and maybe even build your own, you are going to need to be clever and use all the tools at your disposal to figure out how this car works.

This is very much like how Earth scientists try to understand the real world. The real world, even more so than the fancy sports car, is very complex and intricate. We are unable to look under reality's hood or read reality's user's manual. What we are able to do is to make careful observations, come up with hypotheses as to how the real world works, test our hypotheses with experiments, and create models to test and explore our understanding.

When you start to build your own car, the first thing you are going to gather are the major parts: a frame, an engine, wheels, rods, doors, spark plugs, fuel and so on. For the Earth's climate, instead of parts we have variables: ocean temperature, **relative humidity**, **solar radiation**, carbon dioxide (CO_2) concentrations, and many others.

However, you need a plan to put your parts together. You need an understanding of some of the interactions between the parts you have and the function of your car. You know that fuel needs to be injected into the engine in a particular way. You know that the wheels need to be connected both to the engine and to the brakes if you ever want to actually drive your car. Earth scientists know that sunlight heats the surface of the Earth, which in turn heats the atmosphere. They know that warm air holds more water than cold air. Any successful climate model needs to have these elementary parts.

To put these parts together you need a design framework. For our car, this is a engineering schematic of the parts and their functionality. We know when brakes are applied, the velocity of the car decreases. For Earth scientists, this is typically in the form of code and equations. We know that precipitation falls as rain if the temperature is above freezing and falls as snow if the temperature is below freezing.

During our first attempt, there are many things we don't know. We know that there is an interaction between the stick shift and the engine. We know that there is some interaction between the oceans and the atmosphere. But we don't know the exact details. To begin to understand these unknowns we must make careful observations of the thing we're trying to model and come up with tentative hypothesis and theories. We can listen to the revving of the engine or make observations of ocean and atmospheric temperatures.

---

[1] This analogy is adapted from a blog post by Ben Brown-Steiner, "The Climate System as a Foreign Sports Car," originally published in the Climate Change 101 Blog, October 27, 2014. http://climatechange101.blogspot.com/

Box 6.2: Continued

You then put together a scheme that you think might work like the real thing. You design some system (or write some code) that combines what you know with the things you have hypothesized. Because you know that you are uncertain about particular interactions, you make those parts easy to observe and easy to modify or swap out with another part. This is what often is described as a parameterization or a scheme in a climate model. It's a variable or equation that you know you'll have to tweak or change out later on.

For instance, after you run the car you notice that your car moves backwards when you think it should be moving forwards or your climate snows when it should be raining. You look carefully at your variables and design and equations and parameters and try to find the error. You may have had your wires mismatched our you may have had inaccurately represented the relationship between moisture and temperature.

The next step takes this newfound understanding and incorporates it into your next model. You fix your mistakes and you tune your parameterizations. Then you test it again and repeat the whole process over and over until your understanding grows. Fundamentally, this is the way that science functions. It is an interactive process. It's never ending. You test and tune and observe and reformulate and repeat. Eventually, if you are clever and lucky, your model gets better and you gain a deeper understanding.

Unfortunately, since we are not able to look at the actual fancy sports car (because our friend is too secretive) and since we will never see the inner workings of the real world, we are never going to have a perfect model. Models by definition are simplifications of the real thing. You strive to have a really good simplification that provides insight and understanding. And you keep trying. This is science.

1.2 Present Climate

The Northeast has two broad climate regions, described in the **Köppen system** (see Box 6.1) with prefixes D (moist, continental, mid-latitude) in the north and C (moist, subtropical, mid-latitude) in the south. "D" climates tend to have cold winters, while "C" climates experience hot, humid summers. Average temperatures can vary from summer to winter by as much as 22°C (72°F) in Maine and 16°C (61°F) in Maryland. The Northeast can get hot—Pennsylvania experienced a record high of 44°C (111°F) in 1936—but in general, the Northeast's climate is cool enough that even the states in its southern portion have average low temperatures below freezing during the winter.

Average annual precipitation typically ranges from about 90 to 125 centimeters (35 to 50 inches) in the Northeast, though a few spots receive over 150 centimeters (60 inches) of rain annually due to their location on the windward side of a mountain range. Coastal areas tend to get more rain than do inland areas, and flooding is common in the Northeast due to extreme rainfall events, as well as from snowmelt and ice jams.

6

Northeast

hurricane · *a rapidly rotating storm system with heavy winds, a low-pressure center, and a spiral arrangement of thunderstorms. These storm systems tend to form over the tropical ocean, and are classified as hurricanes, typhoons, or cyclones (depending on their location in the world) once winds have reached 199 kilometers per hours (74 miles per hour). See also TROPICAL CYCLONE.*

Nor'easter · *a storm, often severe, along the U.S. East coast which forms when warm air from the Atlantic Ocean meets cold air from the north and west.*

lake-effect snow · *snowfall caused by the movement of cold weather systems over a lake, in which an air mass picks up water from the lake and deposits it in the form of snow across an adjacent land mass.*

heat waves · *a prolonged period of extremely high air temperatures.*

The Atlantic Ocean and the Great Lakes influence the Northeast's climate heavily. The Atlantic Ocean has a moderating effect on the temperatures of coastal regions because of air masses that pass from the ocean over the coast, warming in winter and cooling in summer. It is also the source of **hurricanes** that originate close to the equator over the Atlantic. In addition, a **Nor'easter**—a severe winter storm that regularly batters the Northeast—can form when cold polar air mixes with warm moist air from the Atlantic Ocean. The Great Lakes and Lake Champlain produce **lake-effect snow**, a wintertime phenomenon that occurs when cold, Arctic air moves south and east across the lakes, warms and picks up moisture, and deposits it as snow over land to the east. The town of Montague, New York lies east of Lake Ontario and once received 195 centimeters (77 inches) of snow during a 24-hour period in 1997, an astonishing amount for a non-mountainous area. Parts of the Buffalo, NY area received as much as 224 centimeters (88 inches) of snow during a late November storm in 2014.

In addition to adjoining large bodies of water, the Northeast contains the northern part of the Appalachian Mountain chain, which influences the climates in its subregions. In the southern part of the Northeast, the Appalachians partially protect the east coast from the prevailing winds coming from the west and the interior of North America. They also limit moist, Atlantic air from traveling to the western subregions. Several times a year the mountainous topography, coupled with a high-pressure air mass, produces a phenomenon called cold air damming. Cold air from the Northeast that would normally flow around the high-pressure region is blocked by the mountains; so instead, it flows south along the eastern side of the mountain chain, rapidly channeling cold air to the Southeast.

The Northeast is the most densely populated region of the United States, with almost all the counties along the east coast from New Hampshire to Maryland having 300 or more people per square mile. New York City—the largest city in the US, with over 8 million people living within the city limits—and other coastal cities are vulnerable to extreme weather hazards, such as public health risks brought on by **heat waves** (see Box 6.3,) water supply contamination during flooding, and transportation disruptions and power outages from ice and snow storms. The Northeast experiences its share of these weather hazards, as well as drought and fog. In 2012, Hurricane Sandy devastated communities on the mid-Atlantic coast, and rainfall from Hurricane Irene in 2011 led to severe flooding inland as well as major damage along the coast. An ice storm in 1998 caused hundreds of thousands of Northeast residents to lose power for weeks.

1.3 Future Climate

Studies show that the Northeast's climate is changing right now, and that change has accelerated in the latter part of the 20th century. These changes include the following:

- Temperatures have increased almost 1°C (2°F) between 1895 and 2011.
- Average winter temperatures are 2°C (4°F) higher than in 1970.
- In New York State, average annual rainfall is up more than eight centimeters (three inches) since 1950, and precipitation across the Northeast has both increased and become more variable year to year.
- As of 2005, flowering bushes and fruit trees were blooming four to nine days earlier than they did in the 1960s.
- Sea level on the coast rose three centimeters (1.2 inches) per decade on average in the 20th century.
- Sea level is rising three to four times faster on the East Coast than it is worldwide.

US Regional Climates

Box 6.3: Urban heat islands

During the summer, cities and metropolitan areas can be as much as 9°C (16°F) hotter than nearby rural areas as a result of absorption and re-radiation of heat by pavement and buildings. This phenomenon is called the urban heat island effect. In addition, the density of cars, air conditioning systems, and other machinery found in cities adds additional heat to their environments. Heat waves, already a public health threat, can be more deadly in cities because of this effect. The heat island effect can be reduced somewhat by planting trees and other vegetation, painting roofs white to reflect away sunlight, building green roofs (roofs with a layer of plants growing on them), or using pavement that reflects sunlight and increases water evaporation.

climate model • a computer-generated simulation of the Earth's climate system, projected through time.

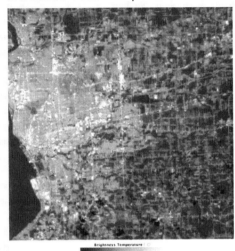 

Satellite images of surface heat (A) and developed land (B) in the Buffalo, NY metropolitan area. (See Teacher-Friendly Guide website for a full color version.)

See Chapter 7: Climate Change Mitigation for more on the cooling effect of trees.

Climate models (see Box 6.2) predict that the Northeast's average annual temperature will rise 2.5°C to 5.5°C (4.5°F to 10°F) by the 2080s if carbon emissions remain high, and 1.7°C to 3.3°C (3°F to 6°F) by the 2080s if carbon emissions are reduced dramatically.[2] By the latter part of 21st century, rising temperatures and increased humidity mean that summers in New Hampshire are likely to feel more like summers today in Virginia, North Carolina, or Georgia. More intense heat waves are a concern for the populations of large cities, dairy farmers, and anglers. In the last few decades, winters have been warming more rapidly than summers have, but models suggest that whether this trend continues will depend on future greenhouse gas emissions.

Winter precipitation is projected to increase by about 5% to 20% across the Northeast by the end of the 21st century. Because of warming temperatures,

---

[2] These projections for the Northeast and for other parts of the country can be found in the Third National Climate Assessment (US Global Change Research Program, 2014, http://nca2014.global-change.gov/). National Climate Assessments have been published in 2000, 2009, and 2014, with interim assessments in between. Additional assessments are expected approximately every four years.

US Regional Climates

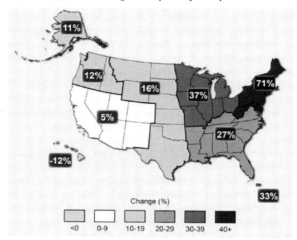

Observed Change in Very Heavy Precipitation

Figure 6.2: The map shows percent increases in the amount of precipitation falling in very heavy events (defined as the heaviest 1% of all daily events) from 1958 to 2012 for each region of the continental United States. These trends are larger than natural variations for the Northeast, Midwest, Puerto Rico, Southeast, Great Plains, and Alaska. The trends are not larger than natural variations for the Southwest, Hawai'i, and the Northwest. The changes shown in this figure are calculated from the beginning and end points of the trends for 1958 to 2012. (See Teacher-Friendly Guide website for a full color version.)

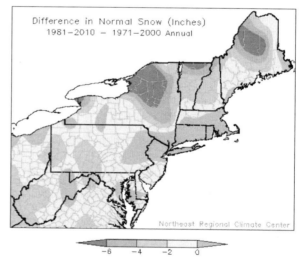

Figure 6.3: Difference between 30-year averages of snow depth for the Northeast. The comparison shows a decline in snow depth over much of the Northeast when comparing the years 1981-2010 and 1971-2000. (See Teacher-Friendly Guide website for a full color version.)

a bigger fraction of winter precipitation will fall as rain rather than snow. Heavy downpours have been increasing in frequency, a trend that is expected to continue. Increases in extreme rain have been greater in the Northeast than in any other region of the US (*Figure 6.2*).

Snow cover, a common winter feature across much of the Northeast, has been decreasing and will likely continue to do so. Changes in snowmelt and rainfall will change the flow of water in streams, affecting fish and other wildlife as well as human communities subject to flooding. Short-term droughts—lasting one to three months—brought on by warmer temperatures and less and earlier snow melt are likely to become more common, especially in the Adirondack and Catskill Mountains and in New England (*Figure 6.3*).

US Regional Climates

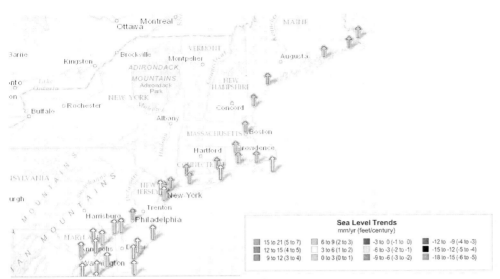

Figure 6.4: Sea level trends along the Northeast US coast. Arrows represent the direction and magnitude of the change. (See Teacher-Friendly Guide website for a full color version.)

Sea level rise is a great concern in the Northeast, with its extensive coastline and many vulnerable low-lying areas, especially in big cities. A rising sea leads to loss of wetlands, coastal erosion and property damage, larger and more damaging storm surges, inundation of populated areas, and stresses on municipal water and sewer systems. Sea level has risen steadily in the 20th century (*Figure 6.4*) and is projected to continue rising as the world's glaciers and ice sheets melt and a warmer ocean undergoes thermal expansion. By the year 2100, sea level may rise by 46 to 191 centimeters (18 to 75 inches) along New York's coast.[3]

2. Southeast

2.1 Description

The sun rises in Virginia Beach, Virginia—part of the Southeastern US—approximately twenty minutes after it rises in West Quoddy Head, Maine. The Southeast consists of West Virginia, Virginia, Kentucky, Tennessee, North Carolina, South Carolina, Georgia, Florida, Alabama, and Mississippi. The Southeast has a longer coast on the Atlantic Ocean than any other region, but also borders the Northeast, the Midwest, and the South Central US.

2.2 Present Climate

The location of the Southeast and its direct relationship to the Gulf of Mexico and Atlantic Ocean strongly influence the area's weather. Since it encompasses locations along the coast as well as areas farther inland, the Southeast experiences nearly every variety of extreme weather. Heat and cold waves, droughts, floods, blizzards, tornados, and hurricanes are all considerations for residents of the Southeast.

---

[3] Sea level rise projections vary locally based on factors such as vertical land motion and ocean currents that move water toward or away from the coast. These projections for New York's coast can be found on the NY State Department of Environmental Conservation's website at http://www.dec. ny.gov/energy/45202.html.

US Regional Climates

Köppen system • a commonly used system of climate categorization developed by Russian climatologist Wladimir Köppen. It is based on the kinds of vegetation that areas sustain, and defines 12 climate types: rainforest, monsoon, tropical savanna, humid subtropical, humid continental, oceanic, Mediterranean, steppe, subarctic, tundra, polar ice cap, and desert. Updated by Rudolf Geiger, it has been refined to five groups each with two to four subgroups.

tropical cyclone (hurricane) • a rapidly rotating storm system with heavy winds, a low-pressure center, and a spiral arrangement of thunderstorms. These storm systems tend to form over the tropical ocean, and are classified as HURRICANES, typhoons, or cyclones (depending on their location in the world) once winds have reached 199 kilometers per hours (74 miles per hour).

tornado • a vertical funnel-shaped storm with a visible horizontal rotation.

Although much of the Southeast falls within the category of a "warm temperate zone" (represented by "C" in the **Köppen system**; see Box 6.1), using a single label to describe the Southeast's climate doesn't really represent the range of the region's climate. In the wintertime, southern Florida is frequently warm and humid while the rest of the Southeast (and the rest of the United States) is cold and dry. The main features that influence the Southeast's climate are latitude, the presence of the Atlantic Ocean and the Gulf of Mexico, and regional topography. For example, the Florida peninsula has a distinct summer rainy season, while other inland areas receive uniform precipitation all year round, and the highest elevations in North Carolina and Tennessee can receive as much snow as parts of New England. The warmest temperatures are found in Florida, Georgia, and Mississippi, while the coolest are found in West Virginia and Virginia. The Southeast's overall average high temperature of 22°C (72°F) and average low of 9°C (48°F) are indicative, on the whole, of a warmer and more uniform climate than that found in most other parts of the United States.

Another factor besides latitude that influences temperature in the Southeast is proximity to the ocean, which has a moderating influence. Air masses that have passed over the Gulf of Mexico rarely get either extremely hot or extremely cold, and the Gulf Stream current that travels northward past the Atlantic seaboard carries warm tropical water with it, influencing temperatures on land. Thus the most extreme temperatures in the Southeast are found toward the center of the continent: The region's record high and low temperatures are both held by Kentucky, which has experienced a high of 46°C (114°F) and a low of -38°C (-37°F). Of course, major temperature fluctuations can occur in every state. In July, average daily maximum temperatures range from 35°C (95°F) in southern Georgia and Florida to 24°C (75°F) in mountainous parts of West Virginia. Wintertime has a broader range of temperatures, with average daily minimums in January varying from around −7°C (20°F) in northern Kentucky to 16°C (60°F) in South Florida. Although the Southeast's climate is subtropical, it can get cold, and sub-freezing temperatures are sometimes a concern for Florida orange growers.

The Southeast gets higher levels of annual precipitation than the rest of the US: the Southeast generally receives 100-125 centimeters (40-50 inches), and sometimes over 150 centimeters (60 inches), while the rest of the United States averages only 85 centimeters (34 inches). Some pockets of high precipitation also occur in the Appalachian Mountains (along the Eastern Continental Divide, a topographical high point where air is forced upward from both sides of the mountain range), and along the Atlantic coast. . In the summer and fall **tropical cyclones (hurricanes)** often bring heavy rains to the Gulf and Atlantic coasts. Some of these cyclones, such as Hurricane Andrew in 1992, are extremely powerful and have devastated communities in the Southeast. Thousand-year weather events, referring to the 1-in-1000 chance of intense events happening in a given year, have increased in frequency in recent years, and climate models (see Box 6.2) predict a continuation of that increase. One such event occurred in the fall of 2015 when heavy rains associated with Hurricane Joaquin (but not actually part of the hurricane) brought over 50 centimeters (20 inches) of rain to parts of South Carolina, causing over one billion dollars in damage.

Snow is not unusual during winter in the northern and higher elevation parts of the Southeast, but in some of the southern regions snowfall and ice is rare enough that the communities do not invest in snow removal equipment like communities farther north do. As a result, when snow and ice do form in parts of the Southeast, the impact and damage tends to be more severe.

Severe thunderstorms and **tornados** are an additional threat—the geography and climate of the Southeast are nearly ideal for their formation, especially in the summer. Only Kansas has more tornados per square mile than Florida, and several other Southeastern states rank in the top ten for tornado frequency.

2.3 Future Climate

The Southeast's average annual temperature fluctuated between warming and cooling periods during the 20th century, and has most recently risen since 1970 by about 1°C (2°F) on average. **Climate models** (see Box 6.2) predict that the Southeast's climate will continue to warm, and that the average annual temperature in most of the area will rise about 2° to 4.4°C (4° to 8°F) by the end of the 21st century.[4] Winter temperatures have risen the most—today, most of the Southeast experiences four to seven fewer freezing days than it did in the 1970s. By the middle of the 21st century one can expect 20 to 30 more days of freeze-free weather each year (*Figure 6.5*). Currently, the northern part of the Southeast typically has ten days a year with temperatures below −12°C (10°F). By the middle of the 21st century we can expect zero days with temperatures that low. These increased temperatures lead to a whole host of other effects, including drier soils from more evaporation, and the increased likelihood of drought and fires.

Precipitation has become more variable from year to year, and heavy downpours have increased since the late fifties (*see Figure 6.2*). Models for future precipitation do not predict large changes, but they predict generally less

climate model • *a computer-generated simulation of the Earth's climate system, projected through time.*

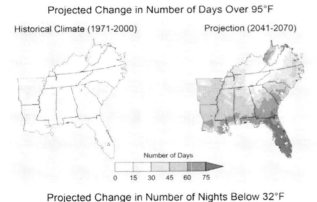

Figure 6.5: Projected changes in number of days over 35°C (95°F) and number of nights below 0°C (32°F) for the Southeast over the next several decades. (See Teacher-Friendly Guide website for a full color version.)

---

[4] These projections for the Southeast and for other parts of the country can be found in the Third National Climate Assessment (US Global Change Research Program, 2014, http://nca2014.global-change.gov/). National Climate Assessments have been published in 2000, 2009, and 2014, with interim assessments in between. Additional assessments are expected approximately every four years.

US Regional Climates

thermal expansion • *the increase in size or extent of a material as it warms.*

rain in the far southwest part of the Southeast, and generally more rain in the far northeast part of the region. Water supply is an important issue in the Southeast, and communities will need to adapt to changes in precipitation, snowmelt, and runoff as the climate changes. Drier days and higher temperatures will amplify evaporation, increasing the desertification of already arid areas and affecting natural ecosystems as well as increasing pressure on the water supply for agriculture and cities. In low-lying areas, especially Florida, important aquifers are at extreme risk of being contaminated by saltwater thanks to rising sea levels.

Sea level rise from **thermal expansion** of a warmer ocean and from melting ice sheets is a major concern in the Southeast, with its extensive coastline and many low-lying areas, including coastal cities such as Miami, Tampa, Charleston, and Norfolk. A rising sea leads to retreating tidal forests, coastal erosion, larger and more damaging storm surges, inundation of populated areas, and stresses on municipal water and sewer systems. Increased inland flooding will impair stormwater drainage systems that empty into the ocean and destroy tidal wetlands, reducing environmental protection against storm surge and damaging important fishery habitat. Oil and gas production infrastructure located in areas protected by barrier islands will be at greater risk to storm surge. Regional studies project that by 2030, climate change could cause $4.6 billion in damages to coastal property and assets on the Gulf Coast alone. By the end of the 21st century, the projected sea level rise around the Southeast is as much as a meter (3 feet), and could be higher with continued high carbon emissions.

Florida is especially susceptible to the risks of sea level rise. Nearly 10% of the state is within 1.5 meters (5 feet) of the mean sea level, and 40% of Florida's beaches are at risk of erosion and coastal flooding. *Figure 6.6* shows flood exposure for south Florida under different levels of rising seas. A one foot rise in sea level could threaten large portions of relatively flat coastal land up to 30 to 60 meters (approximately 100 to 200 feet) inland from the coasts.[5]

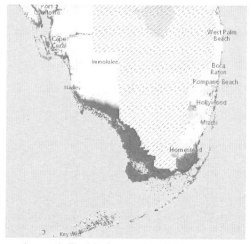

Figure 6.6: Flood exposure in south Florida for sea level rise scenarios of 0 to 6 feet, which represent a rise in water above the average of the highest high tides (called mean higher high water, or MHHW) for hydrologically connected areas. Areas that are lower in elevation will be exposed to flooding from sea level rise first and are represented by the darkest red. Areas in yellow will be exposed to flooding at the highest sea level rise (6 feet). (See Teacher-Friendly Guide website for a full color version.)

[5] "Saving Florida's Vanishing Shores" (US Environmental Protection Agency, 2002, www3.epa.gov/climatechange/Downloads/impacts-adaptation/saving_FL.pdf) provides an overview of threats to Florida's beaches and what communities and individuals can do to help protect Florida's coasts.

3. Midwest

3.1 Description

The sun rises in Columbus, Ohio—on the eastern side of the Midwestern US—approximately one hour after it rises in West Quoddy Head, Maine and about forty minutes after it rises in Virginia Beach, Virginia. The Midwestern US consists of Ohio, Michigan, Indiana, Illinois, Wisconsin, Iowa, and Minnesota and shares a border with all of the Great Lakes except for Lake Ontario. The Midwest also shares a border with Canada, the Northeast, the Southeast, as well as the South Central and Northwest Central regions. The Midwest, therefore, shares many of the regional climate features of a number of surrounding regions.

3.2 Present Climate

Nearly all of the Midwest has a humid continental climate, with temperatures that vary greatly from summer to winter, and appreciable precipitation year-round. This is represented in the **Köppen system** with the prefix "D" (see Box 6.1). At an average temperature of 10°C (50°F), it seems similar to that of England, which has an average of 8°C (47°F). The Midwest, however, has a much more extreme range than England.

England—which is located only a few degrees latitude farther north than the Midwest—has a substantially smaller range of temperatures due to the buffering effect of the Atlantic Ocean. Average daily temperatures in England range from a low of 2°C (35°F) up to a high of 21°C (70°F). The Midwest, which has no nearby ocean to buffer its temperatures, has nearly twice as large of a temperature range, with average daily temperatures as low as -9°C (15°F) and as high as 29°C (85°F). The difference is even more apparent when we look at record temperature extremes. England has record low temperatures of -26.1°C (-14.9°F) and record high temperatures of 38.5°C (101.3°F)—a range of nearly 65°C (116°F)—while the Midwest has record low temperatures of -34°C (-30°F) and record highs of 43°C (110°F)—a range of 77°C (140°F)!

The Midwest is one of the most productive agricultural areas in the world, and the economies of its states depend on farmland. Its excellent soil, relatively flat geography, and bodies of water make it uniquely suited to cropland. Yet without a humid climate with warm summers, agriculture here would be completely different. It is one of the few places on earth where huge amounts of corn and soybeans can be grown with little or no irrigation.

In part because of its climate's extreme temperature variation and humidity, the Midwest experiences nearly every variety of **severe weather**. Because the states are so far from the coasts, they rarely experience hurricanes, but heat and cold waves, droughts, floods, blizzards, and tornados are all fairly regular events.

The nearly flat geography and variable climate of the Midwest create ideal conditions for the formation of **thunderstorms**. Storms occur when there is strong convection in the atmosphere. Warm and moist air flowing north from the tropics clashes with cold and dry air flowing south from the Arctic. When these air masses collide, the strong **gradients** in both temperature and pressure create **turbulence**, strong **convection**, and large amounts of condensation and precipitation. Usually a thunderstorm loses energy once the warm air

Köppen system • a commonly used system of climate categorization developed by Russian climatologist Wladimir Köppen. It is based on the kinds of vegetation that areas sustain, and defines 12 climate types: rainforest, monsoon, tropical savanna, humid subtropical, humid continental, oceanic, Mediterranean, steppe, subarctic, tundra, polar ice cap, and desert. Updated by Rudolf Geiger, it has been refined to five groups each with two to four subgroups.

severe weather • dangerous weather events that can cause harm to life and property.

thunderstorm • a storm characterized by thunder and lightning, and also typically with heavy rain and high winds.

gradient • a change, either increasing or decreasing, in the magnitude of a quantity over space or time.

turbulence • irregular or chaotic movement of a fluid such as air or water.

convection • movement of a fluid, such as air or water, resulting from gravitational force on the fluid. Warmer, less dense matter rises and cooler, more dense matter sinks, producing heat transfer.

Midwest

tornado • *a vertical funnel-shaped storm with a visible horizontal rotation.*

lake-effect snow • *snowfall caused by the movement of cold weather systems over a lake, in which an air mass picks up water from the lake and deposits it in the form of snow across an adjacent land mass.*

and the cool air mix. In the Midwest, however, currents of air from the south can continue to mix with currents of air flowing from the north and west. This tends to add additional energy to the storm and can create storms of unusual magnitude that can persist for long periods of time. These conditions are also the reason for the Midwest's unusually high incidence of powerful **tornados.**

Tornado Alley is a nickname for an area extending from Texas to Minnesota (including the western Midwest) that experiences a high number of exceptionally strong tornados. During the period from 1991 to 2010, Illinois and Iowa had 54 and 51 tornados annually on average, respectively. The United States has more tornados per year (over 1,000) than any other country, followed by Canada with around 100 per year. Tornados tend to form in mid-latitude regions where cold air from the north meets warm, moist air from the subtropics, generating thunderstorms. The reasons why some rotating storms spawn tornados and some don't are not entirely understood, but scientists think that tornados develop when there are temperature changes across specific air boundaries within a type of rotating storm called a mesocyclone.

Large bodies of water can retain heat better than land surfaces, and during the wintertime this can create **lake-effect snow** in many regions in the Midwest—especially those regions on the eastern shores of the Great Lakes. Lake-effect snow occurs when the warmer and moister air over the Great Lakes mixes with colder and drier air that blows across the lakes from the north and west. The moisture picked up and dropped as snow creates strong bands of snow that can form quickly and which can quickly overwhelm communities. The Upper Peninsula of Michigan usually receives over five meters (200 inches) of snow per year, second only in the US to Tug Hill Plateau in New York, east of Lake Ontario, which also gets lake-effect snow.

3.3 Future Climate

The Midwest's climate has changed in the last century, with average annual temperature rising 1.5°F from 1895 to 2012 (*Figure 6.7*).[6]

The average temperature in the Midwest is predicted to continue to increase for the foreseeable future, likely by 3.1°C to 4.7°C (5.6°F to 8.5°F) at the end of the century (2081-2100), depending on the rate at which carbon emissions from burning fossil fuels continues. These average changes are not evenly distributed and can vary from location to location and from year to year. For example, since 1980, the average annual temperature for northern Illinois has increased from around 7°C (45°F) to 9°C (49°F), a change of 2°C (4°F), yet the average *winter* temperature has increased by 4°C (8°F). Higher temperatures and higher carbon dioxide levels are, up to a point, expected to extend the growing season and increase crop yields. In the longer term, however, higher temperatures are expected to reduce crop yields, and crops may face increased freeze damage when the early springs brought on by climate change are followed by damaging frosts. The US Government's Global Change Research Program expects the plant hardiness zones (see Box 6.4) for the Midwest to become warmer by up to one zone every 30 years, rapidly changing what kinds of plants and crops can survive. Translating this change to the Köppen climate classification, much of the Midwest will be redesignated as humid subtropical and feel more like states within the Southeast. Coupled with less precipitation

---

[6] These projections for the Midwest and for other parts of the country can be found in the Third National Climate Assessment (US Global Change Research Program, 2014, http://nca2014.global-change.gov/). National Climate Assessments have been published in 2000, 2009, and 2014, with interim assessments in between. Additional assessments are expected approximately every four years.

US Regional Climates

Temperatures are Rising in the Midwest

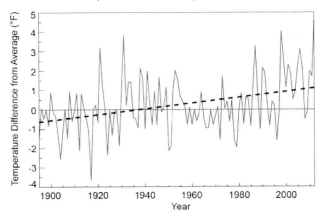

Figure 6.7: Annual average temperatures (red line) across the Midwest show a trend towards increasing temperature. The trend (heavy black line) calculated over the period 1895-2012 is equal to an increase of 1.5°F. (See Teacher-Friendly Guide website for a full color version.)

Box 6.4: Plant hardiness zones

The US Department of Agriculture defines plant hardiness zones for gardeners and growers, to help them choose plants that will grow well in their regions. Plant hardiness zones are determined by the average annual minimum winter temperature. As of 2016, the USDA last updated its Plant Hardiness Zone Map in 2012. An interactive version of this map can be found online at http://planthardiness.ars.usda.gov/phzmweb/interactivemap.aspx.

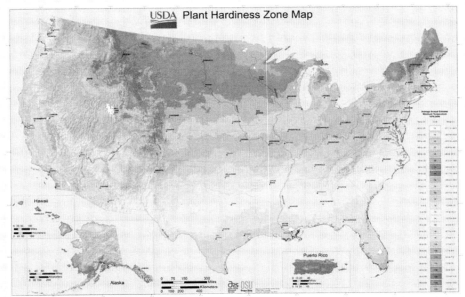

2012 USDA Plant Hardiness Zone map. (See Teacher-Friendly Guide website for a full color version.)

US Regional Climates

overall, a garden you planted in Michigan as a child will look like one from Arkansas by the time you are an adult, and then like one from Texas after 30 more years.

The Midwest can also expect more incidences of extreme weather, including heat waves and heavy rainfall. While individual weather events depend on a combination of large-scale and small-scale factors—which are difficult for global-scale climate models (Box 6.2) to predict—the large-scale climate changes that will impact the Midwest are very likely to increase extreme weather events in the region (see Box 6.5). For instance, since higher temperatures mean greater evaporation and the ability of the air to hold more water, precipitation will occur in greater amounts at a time, but less frequently. During the cooler spring this will lead to flooding, while in hot summers, droughts will become more frequent. Finally, higher atmospheric moisture content has also been correlated with an increased incidence of tornados, which is of particular concern for communities in the Midwest.

> ## Box 6.5: Climate change and extreme weather
>
> What is the relationship between a warming Earth and the frequency and intensity of extreme weather events? This is nicely described in an article by Richard Alley, the Evan Pugh Professor of Geosciences at Pennsylvania State University:[7]
>
> *There's very high scientific confidence that our fossil-fuel burning and other activities, which add carbon dioxide to the air, are turning up the planet's thermostat. In a warmer world, we expect more record highs and heat waves but fewer record lows, just as we're observing. Warmer air can carry more water vapor, so a warmer rainstorm can deliver more inches per hour. Hair dryers have a "hot" setting for good reasons, and warmer air between rainstorms can dry out the ground faster.*
>
> *Thus, we expect rising CO_2 to bring more floods in some places and more droughts in others, with some places getting more of both. That might seem contradictory, but it's not. And with more energy to drive hurricanes, the peak winds may increase, even if the number of storms drops.*
>
> *But couldn't nature have caused the ongoing changes without our help? Imagine playing dice with a shady character. Suppose, after you lose, you discover that some of the corners are filed off and there are carefully positioned weights inside. In court, your lawyer could say, 'The dice were loaded, double-sixes came up three times in a row, so the defendant owes restitution.'*
>
> *His lawyer, however, might counter, 'My client doesn't recall where he got the dice, the modifications are really quite small, dice games are inherently variable, anomalous events do happen, so my client is innocent and should get to keep all the money plus the plaintiff's wallet.'*
>
> *Out in the climate, the dice are being loaded to favor some unusual events. We can't prove that global warming caused any single new record, just as we can't prove that the weighted dice caused a run of double-sixes. But for many extreme weather events such as record heat, it is much harder to prove that our CO_2 is innocent, just as it is very hard to prove that loaded dice didn't affect the game.*

---

[7] For Alley's full article, see "Why the extreme weather?" USA Today 19 April 2012. http://usatoday30. usatoday.com/news/opinion/forum/story/2012-04-18/global-warming-climate-change-tornadoes-heat/54394742/1.

South Central

4.1 Description

The sun rises in New Orleans, Louisiana—part of the South Central US—approximately one hour after it rises in West Quoddy Head, Maine and only a few minutes after it rises in Columbus, Ohio. The South Central US consists of Louisiana, Arkansas, Missouri, Nebraska, Oklahoma, and Texas, and shares a border with Mexico, the Gulf of Mexico, as well as the Southeast, Midwest, Northwest Central, and Southwest regions of the US. The South Central US contains both coastal and desert regional climates.

4.2 Present Climate

The location of the South Central and its direct relationship to the Gulf of Mexico strongly influences the region's weather. And with locations along the coast, as well as the presence of areas farther inland, the South Central experiences nearly every variety of extreme weather—heat and cold waves, droughts, floods, blizzards, tornadoes, and hurricanes are all considerations for the residents of the South Central region.

Today, the South Central lies at the intersection of several distinct climate zones, with much of the region characterized as warm temperate (represented by "C" in the **Köppen system**; see Box 6.1). Northern Missouri and northern Kansas are characterized as continental (represented by "D"), and the eastern parts of Kansas and Texas are arid (represented by "B").

Average temperatures in the South Central are highest over land away from the coasts in the southernmost states and coolest in the northernmost states. The average high temperature of the whole region is 20°C (68°F) and the average low is 9°C (49°F). This is indicative, on the whole, of a more uniform climate than that found in most other regions of the United States (see Section 3: Midwest). The record high daily temperature in the South Central region is 49°C (121°F) and the record low is -40°C (-40°F).

States in the South Central region are generally wetter than the average US state; while the average US state gets only 85.6 centimeters (33.7 inches) of rain each year, states in the South Central receive rainfall amounts ranging from a minimum in Kansas of 74.4 centimeters (29.3 inches) to a maximum in Louisiana of 146.3 centimeters (57.6 inches). This is due to the additional moisture that comes from the adjacent Gulf of Mexico. Louisiana is south of the path of many winter storm centers, but the northern parts of the state are susceptible. For this reason, the precipitation pattern of the winter is the reverse of that of the summer, with the heaviest precipitation found in the north (43 centimeters [17 inches]) and the lightest in the south (33 centimeters [13 inches]).

Like those of Louisiana, the winters of Arkansas are short. With its long growing season, coupled with the heaviest precipitation coming in the summer months, agriculture is the state's largest industry. In the winters, snow does fall, but it is primarily restricted to the northwest section of the state.

Farther inland, Oklahoma, Missouri, and Kansas enjoy a continental type of climate. In Oklahoma, summers are long and warm, and winters are shorter than

Köppen system • *a commonly used system of climate categorization developed by Russian climatologist Wladimir Köppen. It is based on the kinds of vegetation that areas sustain, and defines 12 climate types: rainforest, monsoon, tropical savanna, humid subtropical, humid continental, oceanic, Mediterranean, steppe, subarctic, tundra, polar ice cap, and desert. Updated by Rudolf Geiger, it has been refined to five groups each with two to four subgroups.*

US Regional Climates

tornado • *a vertical funnel-shaped storm with a visible horizontal rotation.*

climate model • *a computer-generated simulation of the Earth's climate system, projected through time.*

in other states of the Great Plains. Because of the moist warm air moving northward from the Gulf, rainfall decreases dramatically from east to west, with an average of 43 centimeters (17 inches) in the west and 142 centimeters (56 inches) in the far southeast. In the winter, the snowfall follows the reverse pattern, with more snow in the west than in the east. A similar pattern is found in Kansas, which, due to its flat topography, is home to a large number of **tornados** and dust storms. The warm moist air of the Gulf similarly influences the precipitation of Missouri in the summers, while the dry cold air from the north affects the winters.

Covering nearly 700,000 square kilometers (270,000 square miles), Texas is the second largest state. In the far west, annual precipitation is driven more by elevation than location. The remaining part of the state possesses significantly less complicated topography, with the terrain descending from northwest to southeast. Precipitation ranges from near-desert conditions in the west to annual accumulations close to 152 centimeters (60 inches) along the coast, where monthly average precipitation ranges from less than 1.3 centimeters (half an inch) to over 10 centimeters (4 inches). In the winter, significant snowfall is typically confined to the mountainous areas of the far west.

Tornado Alley is a nickname for an area extending from Texas to Minnesota that experiences a high number of exceptionally strong tornadoes. Most of the South Central resides within Tornado Alley, leading to more tornadoes in this region of the United States than in any other. From 1991 to 2010, for example, an annual average of 115, 62, and 96 tornadoes occurred in Texas, Oklahoma, and Kansas, respectively. To the east of Tornado Alley, far fewer tornado strikes occur, with an annual average of 37, 39, and 45 striking Louisiana, Arkansas, and Missouri, respectively.

4.3 Future Climate

Studies show that the South Central's climate has already experienced notable changes and that these changes have accelerated in the latter part of the 20th century. These changes include the following:

- The number of days with temperatures above 35°C (95°F) has been steadily increasing for the last 25 years
- The city of St. Louis experiences about four heat waves each summer—a number which has doubled over the last 60 years.
- Locations along the Gulf of Mexico have experienced over 8 inches of sea level rise in the last 50 years.
- Altered flowering patterns due to more frost-free days have increased the South Central's pollen season for ragweed, a potent allergen, by 16 days since 1995.

Climate models (see *Box 6.2*) predict that the South Central will continue to warm, and that the average annual temperature will continue to increase for the foreseeable future—likely a 3°C (5°F) increase by 2100. Summer temperatures in Oklahoma, for example, are expected to increase by 3 to 6°C (6 to 10°F) by 2100. These increased temperatures lead to a whole host of other effects, including drier soils from more evaporation, and the increased likelihood of drought and fires. Texas, which contains the largest acreage of crop-, pasture-,

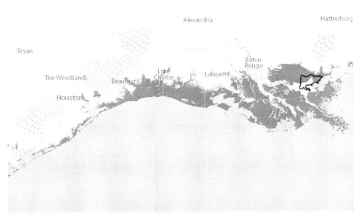

Figure 6.8: Map of areas flooded from sea level rise scenarios of 0 to 6 feet, which represent a rise in water above the average of the highest high tides (called mean higher high water, or MHHW) for hydrologically connected areas. Areas that are lower in elevation will be exposed to flooding from sea level rise first and are represented by the darkest red. Areas in yellow will be exposed to flooding at the highest sea level rise (6 feet). (See Teacher-Friendly Guide website for a full color version.)

and rangeland in the United States, could be severely impacted by these changes.

Sea level rise from thermal expansion of a warmer ocean and melting ice sheets will be a concern for populated coastal areas, including major cities such as New Orleans and Houston. The coastal zones of the South Central region are one of the US's areas most vulnerable to sea level rise. *Figure 6.8* shows areas subject to flooding along the Texas and Louisiana coasts under different sea level rise scenarios. Regional studies project that by 2030, climate change could cause $4.6 billion in damages to coastal property and assets on the Gulf Coast alone.

Northwest Central

5.1 Description

The sun rises in Omaha, Nebraska—part of the Northwest Central US— approximately two hours after it rises in West Quoddy Head, Maine and about one hour after it rises in New Orleans, Louisiana. The Northwest Central consists of Nebraska, North and South Dakota, Montana, Idaho, and Wyoming. It shares a border with Canada, as well as the Midwest, South Central, Southwest, and Western US_regions. The Northwest Central region is inland, and does not border any ocean or any of the Great Lakes.

5.2 Present Climate

Due to their diverse topographical features, the Northwest Central states encompass a broad range of climates, including subarid steppe in the Great Plains, warm temperate highlands in the Cordilleran, and humid continental plains in the eastern Central Lowland. Even individual states can have tremendous diversity—all of the Northwest Central states (*see Box 6.1*) have two or three climate types, including everything but polar and equatorial. The

US Regional Climates

Northwest Central

rain shadow · *an area on one side of a mountain that experiences little rainfall.*

Continental Divide · *a ridge of high land on a continent, which separates regions where water flows to oceans or seas on different sides of the continent.*

main drivers of climate in the Northwest Central US are exposure to Arctic air from Canada in the winter, the lack of large bodies of water nearby (except for Idaho, whose climate is influenced by the Pacific Ocean), and the presence of the Rocky Mountain chain in the west. These mountains block moist Pacific Ocean air from the interior of the continent and create a cold, high altitude zone.

Temperatures in the Northwest Central are cool on average relative to the average temperature of the contiguous US, and characterized by seasonal extremes. South Dakota's temperature, for example, varies between an average low of -14° C (6° F) in January and an average high of 86° F (30°C) in July. Record lows and highs are astonishing: -57° C (-70° F) in Montana in 1954 and 49° C (121° F) in North Dakota in 1936. Average temperatures in the Northwest Central tend to decrease northward, which is in part the influence of latitude: lower latitudes receive more heat from the sun over the course of a year. The overall warmest temperatures are found in Nebraska, and the coolest found in North Dakota and parts of Wyoming.

The Northwest Central US is dry compared with many other parts of the United States, so dry that all the states within it except Nebraska rank within the top 10 driest states based on annual precipitation. Precipitation generally tends to decrease to the west across the Rocky Mountains, with an average annual precipitation of 65–90 centimeters (25–35 inches) in the Central Lowland region of the eastern Dakotas and Nebraska, about 25–50 centimeters (10–20 inches) in the Great Plains, and less than 25 centimeters (10 inches) in parts of Wyoming and Idaho (*Figure 6.9*). By comparison, the average annual amount of precipitation for the United States is 85.6 centimeters (33.7 inches). The decrease in precipitation is due in large part to **rain shadow** effects from mountain ranges located west of as well as within the Northwest Central. Rain shadows occur when moist air moves eastward with the prevailing winds, and is pushed upward and cools when it encounters a mountain chain. Water vapor condenses from this cool air and falls as rain or snow on the western side of the mountain. The air that continues to move east over the mountains is now much drier, and as it moves down the eastern side of the mountain range it warms, promoting evaporation (*Figure 6.10*). The mountainous **Continental Divide**, which runs through western Montana, creates a rain shadow effect that contributes to the aridity of the plains and badlands in the eastern part of the state. Nebraska's semi-arid west and fairly uniform average temperatures are moderated by dry, warm rain shadow winds blowing eastward from the Rocky Mountains.

Exceptions to the westward drying trend are found in the mountainous parts of northwestern Wyoming and Montana, and in northern Idaho, where average annual precipitation is typically 40 to 50 inches, demonstrating the impact of moisture carried inland from the Pacific Ocean. Idaho's climate is strongly moderated by the Pacific Ocean, even though the state lies nearly 560 kilometers (350 miles) from the coast. In the winter, humidity from the ocean creates heavy cloud cover and precipitation that helps to moderate temperature.

Harsh winter storms are a fact of life in the Northwest Central US, carried in by the polar jet stream which typically falls near or over the area, especially in the winter. Blizzards with high winds, large amounts of snowfall, and low visibility are common and are brought on by cold air masses known as the Alberta Low from the north and the Colorado Low from the south. Since the Rocky Mountain region is dry, some residents use fences to capture snow for later use as a water source. Spring storms are also common, and heavy downpours can lead to flash flooding. Rain coupled with rapid snowmelt in the spring is another common source of flooding in the Rocky Mountain region's river basins.

US Regional Climates

ANNUAL PRECIPITATION

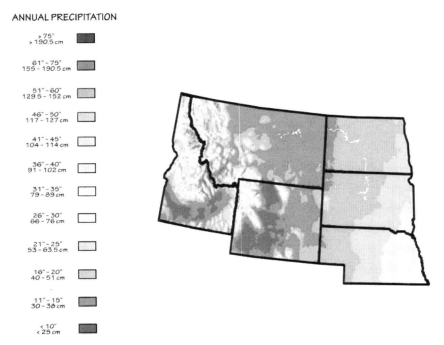

Figure 6.9: Mean annual precipitation for the Northwest Central States. (See Teacher-Friendly Guide website for a full color version.)

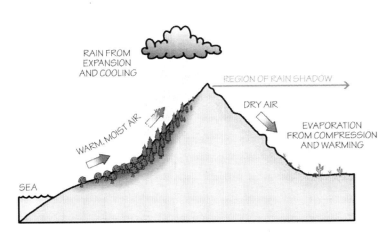

Figure 6.10: The key characteristics of a rain shadow. (See Teacher-Friendly Guide website for a full color version.)

The Northwest Central US is sparsely populated, with less than seven million people. Weather hazards are a concern for communities and for agriculture. When the area experiences severe drought as Wyoming did from 1999 to 2004, residents experience costly losses in food and water supply, grazing land for livestock, soil erosion, wildfire damage, and air quality. The Red River in North Dakota is highly susceptible to flooding, and since it runs through Fargo and Grand Forks, the populations and infrastructure of those cities are put at risk during floods. In the winter, cold waves brought on by Arctic air masses entering the area can damage livestock and crops. Nebraska, located in a corridor known as Tornado Alley, commonly experiences violent thunderstorms and tornados in spring and summer.

climate model • *a computer-generated simulation of the Earth's climate system, projected through time.*

US Regional Climates

5.3 Future Climate

Studies show that the Northwest Central region's climate is changing right now, and that change has accelerated in the latter part of the 20th century. North Dakota's average temperature increased 3.4° F (1.9° C) during the last 130 years, the fastest increase in the US. Soils in Nebraska are becoming warm enough to plant corn one to three weeks earlier in the 2000s compared with the 1990s. Springtime snowmelts in Wyoming in 1990 were flowing 4 days earlier than in 1950. In 1850, Montana's Glacier National Park contained an estimated 150 glaciers (*Figure 6.11*). Today, only 25 glaciers remain. Models predict that all of them will have disappeared by 2030.

Climate models (see *Box 6.2*) predict that the Northwest Central region's climate will continue to warm, and that the average annual temperature in most of the region will rise by 6° to over 10° F (3° to 6° C) by the end of the 21st century. Models also predict that much of the region's climate will become wetter, with more precipitation especially in winter and spring. In Idaho, it is likely that increasingly a higher proportion of precipitation will fall as rain rather than snow, and snow in the mountains will melt earlier in the spring. This could strain the water supply in the warm season. Whether climate change will change the frequency of extreme storms in the Northwest Central region is not clear.

Agriculture is a huge industry in the Northwest Central region, especially in the Great Plains and Central Lowland. To the advantage of soybean and corn growers in Nebraska, warmer temperatures and more soil moisture have brought on longer growing seasons. Warmer temperatures, however, also make it easier for insect pests to overwinter and produce more generations. The European corn borer, a devastating pest found in the central and eastern US, produces more generations in warmer parts of the country. As the Great Plains and Central Lowland warm, one can expect three or four generations of these pests annually in regions that previously had one or two (*Figure 6.12*).

Figure 6.11: Sperry Glacier in 1981, in Glacier National Park, Montana. This glacier still exists today, but its mass is decreasing.

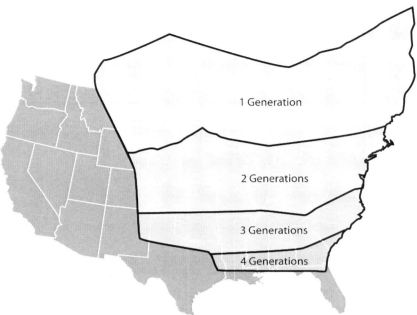

Figure 6.12: The European Corn Borer, an agricultural insect pest, currently produces one to four generations a year depending on its location in the US. As the climate warms further north, they are expected to produce more generations in the Great Plains and Central Lowland, causing more crop damage. (See Teacher-Friendly Guide website for a full color version.)

Köppen system • *a commonly used system of climate categorization developed by Russian climatologist Wladimir Köppen. It is based on the kinds of vegetation that areas sustain, and defines 12 climate types: rainforest, monsoon, tropical savanna, humid subtropical, humid continental, oceanic, Mediterranean, steppe, subarctic, tundra, polar ice cap, and desert. Updated by Rudolf Geiger, it has been refined to five groups each with two to four subgroups.*

6. Southwest

6.1 Description

The sun rises in Denver, Colorado—part of the Southwest—approximately two and a half hours after it rises in West Quoddy Head, Maine and about thirty minutes after it rises in Omaha, Nebraska. The Southwestern US consists of Colorado, Arizona, New Mexico, and Utah. It shares a border with Mexico, as well as the South Central US, the Northwest Central US, and the Western US.

6.2 Present Climate

The Southwest regional climate is strongly influenced by the topographical extremes across this area. Generally, the Southwest's climate is mostly dry and hot, with much of the region characterized as arid (represented by "B" in the **Köppen system**; see Box 6.1). Cold continental conditions (represented by "D") dominate the higher altitudes, especially within the Rocky Mountains. Scattered pockets of drier, Mediterranean temperatures (represented by "C") can also be found.

The Southwest is known for its topography, but also its dryness. The driest desert regions, such as southwestern Arizona, receive the least annual precipitation of any other region—as low as 8 centimeters (3 inches)—and some of the highest day-night temperature swings. A day that has a daytime maximum of 32°C (90°F) can fall below freezing during the night! At higher altitudes in the Southwest such as the Rocky Mountains of Colorado, annual snowfall can exceed 8 meters (25 feet). This snowpack melts in the warmer

US Regional Climates

months and flows into rivers that provide a welcome relief to the otherwise dry desert conditions.

Average temperatures found in the Southwest tend to decrease northward, following the increasing latitude and increasing elevations. Lower latitudes receive more heat from the sun over the course of a year: for each degree increase in latitude, there is about a 1°C (2°F) decrease in temperature. Higher elevations (such as those found in the Rockies and on the Colorado Plateau) are also cooler, with about a 1.5°C (3°F) decrease in mean annual temperature for each 300-meter (1000-foot) increase in elevation.

An additional factor that influences temperatures in the Southwest is the region's aridity. The lack of moisture in the air allows heat trapped during daylight hours to rapidly radiate away, leading to cool evenings. Thus, each Southwestern state experiences both extreme highs and lows. In New Mexico, for example, the average difference between the daily high and low temperatures ranges from 14 to 19°C (25 to 35°F). Record high temperatures for the Southwest range from 53°C (128°F) in Arizona to 47°C (117°F) in Utah, while record low temperatures range from −56°C (−69°F) in Utah to −40°C (−40°F) in Arizona. The average amount of precipitation for the United States is 85.6 centimeters (33.7 inches). In the Southwest, average precipitation ranges from only 34 centimeters (13.4 inches) in Utah to 39.9 centimeters (15.7 inches) in Colorado, which is indicative of the area's general aridity. Elevation does, however, play a key role in precipitation received throughout the Southwest. In New Mexico, for example, average annual precipitation ranges from less than 25 centimeters (10 inches) within the Great Plains and Basin and Range regions to more than 50 centimeters (20 inches) at the higher elevations to the northwest. Arizona's highest elevations receive an average of 65 to 76 centimeters (25 to 30 inches), with lower areas in the state's southwestern portion averaging less than 8 centimeters (3 inches). In Utah, areas below 1200 meters (4000 feet) receive less than 25 centimeters (10 inches) per year, while higher elevations in the Wasatch Mountains receive more than 100 centimeters (40 inches).

Across New Mexico, Arizona, and Utah, summer rains originate from moisture brought into the area from the Gulf of Mexico. Warm, moist air from the south occasionally but infrequently moves into Colorado during the summer. During the winter, moisture travels from the west, as storms from the Pacific Ocean move east. Pacific storms lose most of their moisture as they pass over the Rocky Mountains, so much of the Southwest's winter precipitation falls as snow within the area's mountainous regions.

6.3 Future Climate

The Southwest's climate is already changing, and these changes are expected to accelerate in the latter part of the 20th century. These changes include the following:

- The number of days with temperatures above 35°C (95°F) and nights above 24°C (75°F) has been steadily increasing since 1970, and the warming is projected to continue (*Figure 6.13*).
- The onset of stream flows from melting snow in Colorado has shifted two weeks earlier due to warming spring temperatures. Flows in late summer are correspondingly reduced, leading to extra pressure on the state's water supplies.

Southwest

Projected Temperature Increases

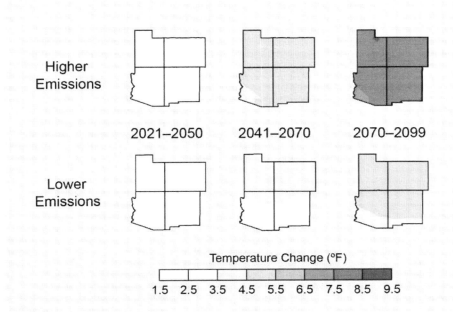

Figure 6.13: Projected temperature increases for the Southwestern states over the next century, as compared to the average for 1971–1999. The "higher emissions" scenario assumes emissions continue to rise, while the "lower emissions" scenario assumes a substantial reduction in emissions. In both cases, temperatures will continue to rise. (See Teacher-Friendly Guide website for a full color version.)

- Streamflow totals for the last decade in the Great Basin, Rio Grande, and Colorado River were between 5 and 37% lower than their 20th century averages.
- Increased heat in the Pacific Ocean has altered the weather patterns of Pacific storms, decreasing snowfall in the mountains of western Utah and Arizona.
- In the last decade, the Southwest's frost-free season has increased by around 7% compared to the average season length for the 20th century.

Recent warming within the Southwest has been among the most rapid in the United States, and models predict that the area's climate will continue to warm. The average annual temperature in most of the Southwest is predicted to rise 2.2 to 5.5°C (4 to 10°F) by 2100. Summer **heat waves** will become hotter and longer, while winter cold snaps will occur less often. These increased temperatures lead to a whole host of other effects, including a decrease in **snowpack,** declines in river flow, drier soils from more evaporation, and the increased likelihood of drought and fires. In winter, rising temperatures have increased the number of frost-free days—today, most of the Southwest experiences about 17 fewer freezing days than it did over the last century. By 2070, one can expect up to 38 more days of freeze-free weather each year (*Figure 6.14*). These warmer temperatures and increased precipitation have helped bring on longer growing seasons. While changes in the growing season can have a positive effect on some crops (such as melons and sweet potatoes), altered flowering patterns due to more frost-free days can lead to early bud bursts, damaging perennial crops such as nuts and stone fruits.

US Regional Climates

Projected Changes in Frost-Free Season Length

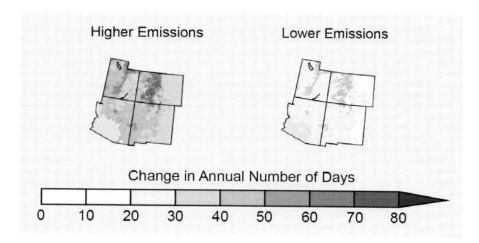

Figure 6.14: Projected changes in the number of frost-free days for the Southwestern states over the next century, as compared to the average for 1971–2000. The "higher emissions" scenario assumes emissions continue to rise, while the "lower emissions" scenario assumes a substantial reduction in emissions. Gray areas are projected to experience more than 10 frost-free years. (See Teacher-Friendly Guide website for a full color version.)

Water supply is an important issue in the Southwest, and communities will need to adapt to changes in precipitation, snowmelt, and runoff as the climate changes. Agriculture accounts for more than half of the Southwest's water use, so any major reduction in the availability of water resources will create a serious strain on ecosystems and populations. Drier days and higher temperatures will amplify evaporation, increasing the desertification of already arid areas and affecting natural ecosystems as well as increasing pressure on the water supply for agriculture and cities (*Figure 6.15*). An increased frost-free season length also leads to increased water demands for agriculture and heat stress on plants. Cattle ranches throughout the Southwestern states rely on rain-fed grazing forage, making them extremely susceptible to climate change and drought. In addition, temperature increases and recent drought lead to earlier spring snowmelt and decreased snow cover on the lower slopes of high mountains, bringing about more rapid runoff and increased flooding. These changes to rain and snowpack are already stressing water sources and affecting agriculture.

Precipitation has become more variable from year to year, and heavy downpours across the US have increased in the last 20 years. Because higher temperatures mean greater evaporation and warmer air can hold more water, precipitation will occur in greater amounts at a time, but less frequently. Although there has so far been little regional change in the Southwest's annual precipitation, the area's average precipitation is expected to decrease in the south and remain stable or increase in the north. Most models predict a decrease in winter and spring precipitation by the middle of the century, and more frequent precipitation extremes during the last half of the century.

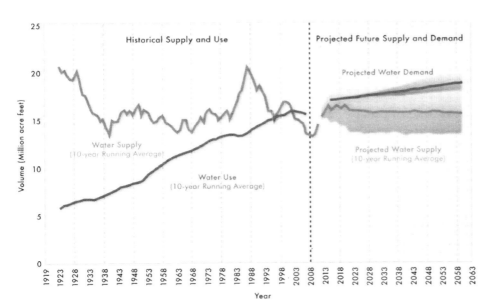

Figure 6.15: Projected 21st-century supply-demand imbalance for the use of water from the Colorado River. The Colorado drains roughly 15% of the continental United States, and is relied upon for municipal and agricultural use by over 35 million people in seven states. (See Teacher-Friendly Guide website for a full color version.)

7. West

7.1 Description

The sun rises in Las Vegas, Nevada—part of the Western US—approximately three hours after it rises in West Quoddy Head, Maine, and about thirty minutes after it rises in Denver, Colorado. The Western US consists of Washington, Oregon, California, and Nevada, and is the only region within the continental US that borders the Pacific Ocean. It also shares a border with both Canada and Mexico, as well as the Northwest Central and the Southwestern US.

7.2 Present Climate

Because of its wide latitudinal range, the proximity of the Pacific Ocean, and the presence of long, north-south mountain ranges, the Western States have an enormous variety of climatic areas. These include hot, dry deserts in the Basin and Range, a Mediterranean climate along the southern Pacific border, rainforests in the northern Pacific border and Alaska, and tundra in Alaska's far north. Even individual states can have tremendous diversity—depending on which of the many **Köppen system** maps you refer to, the state of Washington alone contains as many as eight different climate types.

With such diverse climate types, the West experiences a wide range of temperatures (*Figure 6.16*). Generally, temperatures tend to decrease northward and farther inland, with cooler temperatures at higher elevations and across the West's north-south mountain ranges. Temperatures in coastal areas are moderated by the Pacific Ocean and, in the northwest, by the Rocky Mountains, which prevent cold Arctic air from reaching the coast. Average lows and highs in Southern California range from 3° to 46°C (37° to 114°F) inland in Death Valley and 9° to 24°C (49° to 76°F) on the coast in San Diego. Statewide

West

Köppen system · *a commonly used system of climate categorization developed by Russian climatologist Wladimir Köppen. It is based on the kinds of vegetation that areas sustain, and defines 12 climate types: rainforest, monsoon, tropical savanna, humid subtropical, humid continental, oceanic, Mediterranean, steppe, subarctic, tundra, polar ice cap, and desert. Updated by Rudolf Geiger, it has been refined to five groups each with two to four subgroups.*

US Regional Climates

jet stream • *a fast-flowing, narrow air current found in the ATMOSPHERE. The polar jet stream is found at an altitude of 7–12 kilometers (23,000–39,000 feet), and the air within can travel as fast as 160 kph (100 mph). Jet streams are created by a combination of the Earth's rotation and atmospheric heating.*

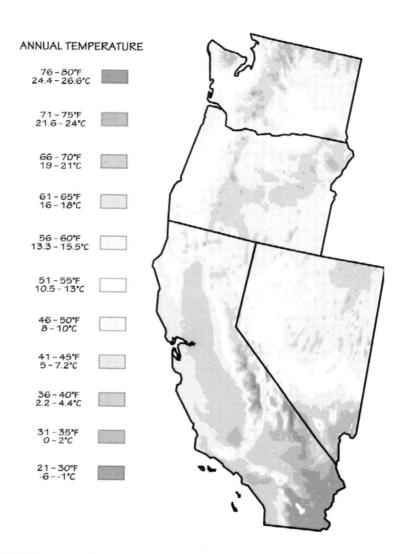

ANNUAL TEMPERATURE

76 – 80°F / 24.4 – 26.6°C	
71 – 75°F / 21.6 – 24°C	
66 – 70°F / 19 – 21°C	
61 – 65°F / 16 – 18°C	
56 – 60°F / 13.3 – 15.5°C	
51 – 55°F / 10.5 – 13°C	
46 – 50°F / 8 – 10°C	
41 – 45°F / 5 – 7.2°C	
36 – 40°F / 2.2 – 4.4°C	
31 – 35°F / 0 – 2°C	
21 – 30°F / -6 – -1°C	

Figure 6.16: Mean annual temperature for the contiguous Western states. (See Teacher-Friendly Guide website for a full color version.)

average lows and highs in Oregon run from -3° to 28°C (26° to 82°F), while in Washington, temperature ranges from -1° to 32°C (29° to 89°F). Nevada experiences temperatures spanning from 4° to 40°C (39° to 104°F).

The West's spectacular mountain ranges run from north to south. These ranges—the Coastal Range, the Cascades, and the Sierra Nevada—create a pronounced east-west precipitation gradient across the Western states. As moist air moves inland from the Pacific Ocean, the mountain ranges force this air upward, which causes its pressure and temperature to drop, creating precipitation. The overall effect is to produce very wet conditions on the western sides of the West's mountain ranges, and very dry rain shadows (*see Figure 6.10*) on the eastern sides. This effect is most pronounced from Northern California up through Washington, since the **jet stream** is often located over this area—especially in winter—and brings moist ocean air inland. As an example of how extreme this precipitation gradient can be, Olympic National Park in Washington receives over 190 centimeters (75 inches) of rain annually on average, whereas communities only 400 kilometers (250 miles) to the east

US Regional Climates

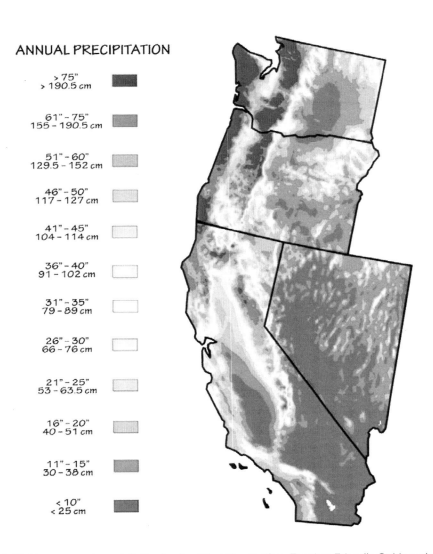

ANNUAL PRECIPITATION

> 75"
> 190.5 cm

61" – 75"
155 – 190.5 cm

51" – 60"
129.5 – 152 cm

46" – 50"
117 – 127 cm

41" – 45"
104 – 114 cm

36" – 40"
91 – 102 cm

31" – 35"
79 – 89 cm

26" – 30"
66 – 76 cm

21" – 25"
53 – 63.5 cm

16" – 20"
40 – 51 cm

11" – 15"
30 – 38 cm

< 10"
< 25 cm

Figure 6.17: Mean annual precipitation for the West Coast. (See Teacher-Friendly Guide website for a full color version.)

in Washington receive only 18 to 20 centimeters (7 to 8 inches) annually. This is almost a full order-of-magnitude difference over a relatively short distance. Strong gradients like this are rarely found on our planet. As the most arid state in the US, Nevada receives only about 24 centimeters (9.5 inches) of rainfall a year (*Figure 6.17*).

climate model • *a computer-generated simulation of the Earth's climate system, projected through time.*

Figure 6.18: Maps showing portions of the cities of Olympia and Seattle, WA that will be inundated if sea level rises by one, two, or three feet. (See Teacher-Friendly Guide website for a full color version.)

7.3 Future Climate

Studies show that the West's climate is changing right now, and that change has accelerated in the latter part of the 20th century. These changes include the following:

- Temperatures in the West have increased in the last 25 years during all seasons.
- Nighttime temperatures in the southwestern part of the West have increased by almost 1.7°C (3°F) since 1900.
- The average annual number of wildfires of over 400 hectares (1000 acres) has doubled in California since the 1970s.
- The freeze-free season in the Northwest is on average 11 days longer for the period of 1991-2010, compared with 1961-1990.
- Heavy downpours have increased by 18% in the Northwest from 1948 to 2006.

Climate models (see Box 6.2) predict that the West's climate will continue to warm, and that the average annual temperature will rise by 2° to 6°C (3° to 10°F) by the end of the 21st century. The oceans are becoming warmer, and warm water expands and leads to sea level rise, a concern for West coast cities such as San Francisco, Seattle, and Olympia (*Figure 6.18*).

Water supply is a critical issue in the West, and communities will need to adapt to changes in precipitation, snowmelt, and runoff as the climate changes (*Figure 6.19*). Models predict that winter and spring storms in Nevada will shift northward, dropping less rain and snow in already arid areas. California will likely be faced with less water flowing in its rivers, declining high elevation forests, and expanding grasslands, along with increased pressure on the water supply for agriculture and cities.

The Northwest is expected to see less summer precipitation and more winter precipitation, and more of the winter precipitation falling as rain rather than

climate gradient • *changes in climate across a distance.*

Figure 6.19: A dry riverbed in California, March 2009.

snow. Over the past 40 to 70 years, the Cascade Range has experienced a 25% decline in snowpack measured on April 1, a trend that is expected to continue. This means less water from snowmelt in the warm season. Spring runoff in Northwestern streams is expected to occur nearly 20 to 40 days earlier during the 21st century.

8. Hawaii

8.1 Description

The sun rises in Honolulu, Hawaii—the southernmost land mass in the US—approximately six hours after it rises in West Quoddy Head, Maine, and over two hours after it rises in Las Vegas, Nevada. Hawaii is far away from the rest of the United States—and from any other major land mass, for that matter. California is more than 2,000 miles away. Japan is nearly 4,000 miles away. Australia is nearly 5,000 miles away. The regional climate of Hawaii, therefore, is quite different from the rest of the US and closely tied to the behavior of the Pacific Ocean.

8.2 Present Climate

The eight main Hawaiian Islands stretch between 19° and 22° north latitude. This places them firmly within the tropics, and also within the belt of persistent northeast trade winds. This geography, combined with the high topography of many Hawaiian peaks, gives rise to large variations in climate across the islands—Hawai'i Island alone has some of the most extreme **climate gradients** of any place on Earth. Additionally, as half of the land area of Hawai'i lies within

US Regional Climates

Hawaii

trade winds • *persistent, large-scale winds in the tropical oceans which blow from the northeast in the Northern Hemisphere and from the southeast in the Southern hemisphere.*

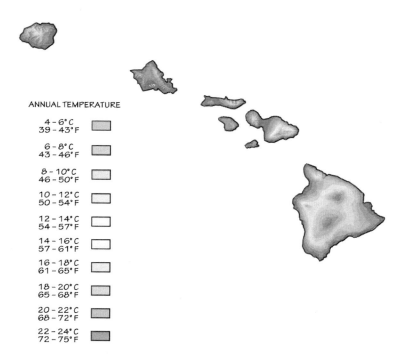

ANNUAL TEMPERATURE

4 – 6°C / 39 – 43°F
6 – 8°C / 43 – 46°F
8 – 10°C / 46 – 50°F
10 – 12°C / 50 – 54°F
12 – 14°C / 54 – 57°F
14 – 16°C / 57 – 61°F
16 – 18°C / 61 – 65°F
18 – 20°C / 65 – 68°F
20 – 22°C / 68 – 72°F
22 – 24°C / 72 – 75°F

Figure 6.20: Mean annual air temperature in Hawai'i. Air temperature is inversely related to elevation, so the temperature variations are closely related to large-scale topographic features. (See Teacher-Friendly Guide website for a full color version.)

eight kilometers (five miles) of the ocean, and the farthest inland you can be on any of the islands is 65 kilometers (40 miles), the ocean is an important control on climate.

Hawai'i is a small archipelago in the center of the world's largest ocean. Water has a very high heat capacity (i.e., a lot of energy is required to raise the temperature of water). This means that the annual temperature variation of the ocean is small. Around the Hawaiian Islands the ocean surface temperature ranges between 24°C (75°F) in winter and 27°C (81°F) in summer. The seasonal variation in land surface temperature for coastal Hawai'i is similar, about 5°C (9°F) from winter to summer. This is very unlike many inland states, which can have large inter-seasonal variations in their temperature (see Section 3 in this chapter on the Midwest).

Another control on the climate of Hawai'i is the high topographic **relief** of the islands. The islands of Hawai'i, Maui, Kaua'i, Moloka'i and O'ahu all have summits that are above 1200 meters (4000 feet) in elevation. On Hawai'i Island the peaks of Mauna Kea and Mauna Loa are each above 4180 meters (13,700 feet). Without these summits, Hawai'i would be a warm and humid place with relatively low rainfall. However, the presence of these huge mountains changes the local climate dramatically, which, in turn, leads to the great diversity of climate zones found in Hawai'i (*Figure 6.20*).

The air above the ocean—the boundary layer—has a high relative humidity because it is in contact with the warm tropical ocean. Northeast **trade winds** carry this moisture-laden air to the Hawaiian Islands. The mountainous islands divert the airflow both around and over the topographic obstructions. Air that rises over the mountains expands and cools, and the moisture carried in

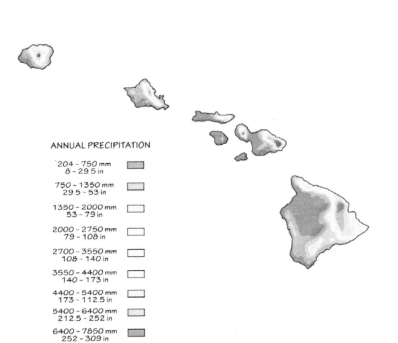

ANNUAL PRECIPITATION

204 – 750 mm 8 – 29.5 in	
750 – 1350 mm 29.5 – 53 in	
1350 – 2000 mm 53 – 79 in	
2000 – 2750 mm 79 – 108 in	
2700 – 3550 mm 108 – 140 in	
3550 – 4400 mm 140 – 173 in	
4400 – 5400 mm 173 – 112.5 in	
5400 – 6400 mm 212.5 – 252 in	
6400 – 7850 mm 252 – 309 in	
7850 – 10,271 mm 309 – 404 in	

windward · *the side of a mountain range or other high landmass which is facing toward the direction the wind is coming. For example, if a wind is coming from the West, the windward side of a mountain range is the western side.*

leeward · *the side of a mountain range or other high landmass which is facing away from the direction the wind is coming. For example, if a wind is coming from the West, the leeward side of a mountain range is the eastern side.*

Figure 6.21: Mean annual rainfall in the Hawaiian Islands. Northeast trade winds combine with topography to create a strongly asymmetrical rainfall distribution. Leeward (west) areas receive little rainfall while windward (east) slopes are some of the wettest places on Earth. (See Teacher-Friendly Guide website for a full color version.)

from the ocean condenses and rains out. The **windward** sides of each island are therefore places with frequent and abundant precipitation (*Figure 6.21*). As the air continues down the **leeward** slopes it is at first compressed, and subsequently warms, and no additional moisture condenses; the leeward island shores are therefore very dry. On most of the Hawaiian Islands, the maximum rainfall occurs at 610–910 meters (2000–3000 feet) above sea level, although the two wettest spots in the islands are slightly higher in elevation. Wai'ale'ale on Kaua'i (1570 meters [5150 feet]) and Big Bog on Maui (1650 meters [5400 feet]) vie with each other for the title of wettest spot in the US, and indeed at about 1000 centimeters (about 400 inches) of annual rainfall they are two of the wettest spots on Earth. Because of the cold temperatures at the highest elevations of the mountains Mauna Kea, Mauna Loa, and Haleakalā, their summits are typically covered in snow in winter.

8.3 Future Climate

Hawai'i stands to be significantly impacted by climate change, with serious potential effects on both its ecosystems and economy. Air temperatures in Hawaii have been warming since 1900, at a rate of 0.06°C (0.11°F) per decade for the last four decades and this trend is expected to continue. These rising temperatures could disrupt the pattern of trade winds, changing rainfall patterns across the islands and creating periods of flooding or drought. Higher temperatures will also place more stress on native plants and animals, enabling the proliferation of invasive species that are better able to withstand temperature extremes.

US Regional Climates

ocean acidification • the increasing acidity, or lowered pH, of ocean waters, caused by absorption of atmospheric carbon dioxide.

Hawai'i is unique among US states in that it is an island state isolated in the Pacific Ocean, and therefore any changes to the Pacific Ocean will impact Hawai'i as well. **Ocean acidification** occurs when excess carbon dioxide in the atmosphere dissolves in the ocean, forming carbonic acid. Both warmer water temperatures and ocean acidification can have devastating effects on coral reefs. Warmer water leads to increased coral bleaching, and more acidic water can damage the shells of marine organisms. Finally, sea level rise could inundate much of Hawai'i's coastline—the worst case scenario of a 2-meter (6-foot) sea level rise would bring Hawai'i's coast a mile inland in some places, submerging or eroding important economic locations like Waikiki Beach and parts of Honolulu.

9. Alaska

9.1 Description

The westernmost point you can reach in the United States is Cape Wrangell, Alaska. The sun rises here almost eight hours after it rises in West Quoddy Head, Maine and, because it is so far north, the sun rises later than it does in Honolulu, Hawaii in the winter months, but earlier than it does in the summer months. Alaska shares a border with Canada, has large coastlines on the Pacific and Arctic Oceans, and is only 55 miles away from Russia. Alaska is twice the size of the second largest state, Texas, and larger than the smallest 21 states combined. It contains both the westernmost point in the US—Cape Wrangell—and the northernmost point—Point Barrow—and the distance between these points is larger than the distance between Los Angeles, California and Houston, Texas or the distance between Denver, Colorado and Washington, D.C.

9.2 Present Climate

Alaska's climate, like that of other parts of the Western US, is influenced by its mountain ranges and its proximity to the ocean. Statewide averages range from a low of -17°C (2°F) in January to a high of 17°C (63°F) in July. (*Figure 6.22*). North of the Brooks Range, Alaska has a cold, dry, polar climate with frequent winter blizzards. Temperatures on the coast are moderated somewhat by the Arctic Ocean. Central Alaska has a dry continental climate, with a large variation between summer and winter temperatures. For example, the town of Takotna in Alaska's interior has an average low temperature of -27°C (-17°F) in January and an average high of 22°C (72°F) in July.

A third climate region exists in the Alaskan southeast, south coast, and southwestern islands, and in west-central Alaska in the summer. These areas have moderate temperatures—an average annual temperature of about 7°C (45°F)—and high precipitation. Some areas are home to lush rainforests and receive around 500 centimeters (200 inches) of rain a year (*Figure 6.23*). The climate in west-central Alaska is influenced by a phenomenon that is unique in the United States: the seasonal presence of sea ice. In the winter when sea ice covers the Bering Sea, this area loses the moderating effect of open water and has a continental climate. When the sea ice melts in summer, the climate returns to a warmer, more humid maritime state.

US Regional Climates

ANNUAL TEMPERATURE

7 – 11°C (45 – 52°F)	
5 – 7°C (41 – 45°F)	
2 – 5°C (36 – 41°F)	
0 – 2°C (32 – 36°F)	
-1 – 0°C (30 – 32°F)	
-2 – -1°C (28 – 30°F)	
-4 – -2°C (25 – 28°F)	
-5 – -4°C (23 – 25°F)	
-8 – -5°C (18 – 23°F)	
-12 – -8°C (10 – 18°F)	
-20 – -12°C (-4 – -10°F)	

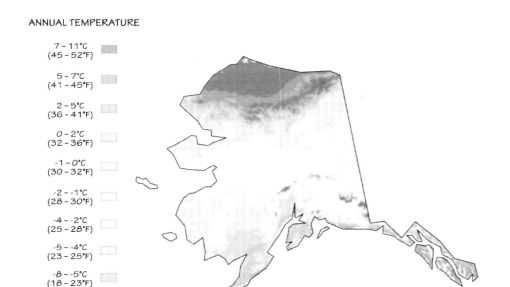

Figure 6.22: Mean annual temperature for Alaska. (See Teacher-Friendly Guide website for a full color version.)

ANNUAL PRECIPITATION

194 – 250 mm (8 – 10 in)	
250 – 360 mm (10 – 14 in)	
360 – 415 mm (14 – 16 in)	
415 – 470 mm (16 – 18.5 in)	
470 – 525 mm (18.5 – 21 in)	
525 – 585 mm (21 – 23 in)	
585 – 695 mm (23 – 27 in)	
695 – 915 mm (27 – 36 in)	
915 – 1360 mm (36 – 53.5 in)	
1360 – 2135 mm (53.5 – 84 in)	
2135 – 3635 mm (84 – 143 in)	
3635 – 16,000 mm (143 – 630 in)	

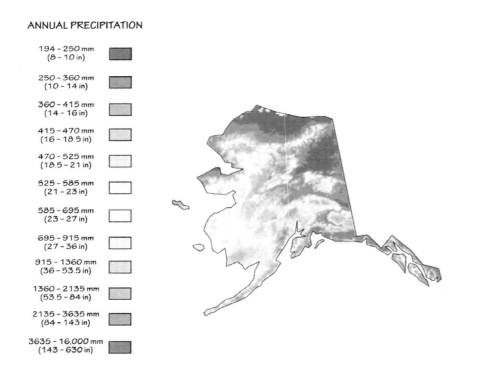

Figure 6.23: Mean annual precipitation for Alaska. (See Teacher-Friendly Guide website for a full color version.)

US Regional Climates

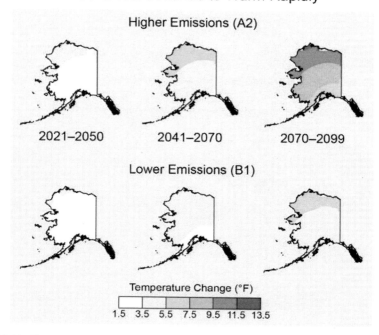

Figure 6.24: Northern latitudes are warming faster than more temperate regions, and Alaska has already warmed much faster than the rest of the country. Maps show changes in temperature, relative to 1971-1999, projected for Alaska in the early, middle, and late parts of this century, if heat-trapping gas (also known as greenhouse gas) emissions continue to increase (higher emissions, A2) or are substantially reduced (lower emissions, B1). (See Teacher-Friendly Guide website for a full color version.)

9.3 Future Climate

Nearly one-third of Alaska lies within the Arctic Circle, which is warming much faster than the global average temperature under climate change. In addition, nearly 80% of the land within Alaska lies above a layer of frozen permafrost, which under a warming climate is thawing. This, combined with rising sea levels and coastal erosion, has already resulted in buildings falling into the ocean and "drunken forests," where trees growing in thawing permafrost are tilted sideways.[8] All of these trends are expected to accelerate in the future, and present an imminent threat to Alaska's infrastructure (buildings, roads, and pipelines).

Statewide average temperatures in Alaska have already increased, with winter temperatures increasing the most: up 3.2°C (5.8°F) from 1949 to 2011. By the middle of the 21st century, temperatures in Alaska are expected to rise by 2° to 4°C (3.5° to 7°F) relative to the late 20th century (*Figure 6.24*). These increased temperatures lead to a whole host of effects, including drier soils from more evaporation, the increased likelihood of drought and fires, and more rain (rather than snow) in the winter.

Climate models (see Box 6.2) project that Alaska will receive more precipitation, but that soils will actually become drier due to increased evaporation from

---

[8] Learn more about "drunken forests" here: http://news.nationalgeographic.com/news/2014/04/140417-drunken-trees-melting-permafrost-global-warming-science/

warmer air temperatures. Summers are expected to support a longer growing season, and also to see more drought and wildfires. Invasive insects that damage Alaskan trees will be better able to survive warmer winters, and will therefore increase and spread. Sea ice will cover the ocean for shorter portions of the year, possibly changing the distribution of plankton blooms, a part of the marine food chain upon which Alaska's fisheries depend.

US Regional Climates

Resources

US Climate Data and Maps

Köppen-Geiger maps, including an animation showing how they evolve with predicted future climate: http://koeppen-geiger.vu-wien.ac.at/

Third National Climate Assessment (2014): http://nca2014.globalchange.gov/ . National Climate Assessments have been published in 2000, 2009, and 2014, with interim assessments in between. Additional assessments are expected approximately every four years.

NOAA/NESDIS Technical Reports - Regional Climate Trends and Scenarios for the US National Climate Assessment. These reports contain historical and projected climate data for all regions of the United States. http://www.nesdis.noaa.gov/technical_reports/142_Climate_Scenarios.html

Temperature and precipitation data, graphs, and maps in your region and much more are available from your NOAA Regional Climate Center (https://www.ncdc.noaa.gov/customer-support/partnerships/regional-climate-centers). The length of the data records available varies by location, but some data go back to the late 19th century.

Historical climate data for the US, on NOAA's Climate at a Glance website: http://www.ncdc.noaa.gov/cag/. Here you can generate maps and time-series plots of temperature, precipitation, and drought data for a broad choice of regions and time periods. Data are also available for cities, from two reliable sources: either the Global Historical Climatology Network or the US Historical Climatology Network.

Summaries of Regional Climate Trends and Scenarios (prepared for the Third National Climate Assessment): https://scenarios.globalchange.gov/node/1155

Information about regional climate change and its impacts: http://climatenexus.org/learn/regional-impacts

Climate Explorer, an interactive map that shows assets and climate threats and interactive graphs of historical temperature and precipitation at weather stations across the US: https://toolkit.climate.gov/tools/climate-explorer

Information about climate change and its impacts in the US, including regional summaries: https://www.epa.gov/climatechange

US Climate Projections

Future Climate chapter of the Third National Climate Assessment: http://nca2014.globalchange.gov/highlights/report-findings/future-climate. This chapter contains maps which show projected change in temperature, precipitation, soil moisture, and more in the US at the end of the 21st century for two different emissions scenarios.

1001 Blistering Future Summers: a tool to see what future temperatures of many cities could be: http://www.climatecentral.org/news/summer-temperatures-co2-emissions-1001-cities-16583

Climate Data US, a site to explore NASA temperature and precipitation projections on a map: http://www.climatedata.us/

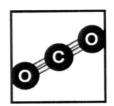

Chapter 7:
Climate Change Mitigation

1. What is Mitigation?

Human activities, especially burning **fossil fuels** for energy, are increasing the concentrations of **greenhouse gases** in our atmosphere, which results in a warmer planet and other changes in our climate. We can address this issue in several ways. One way, explored in Chapter 9: Climate Change Adaptation, is to prepare for how to live with these changes. The other, explored in this chapter, is to reduce the sources of greenhouse gas emissions, thereby reducing the potential impacts. This latter approach is called climate change mitigation.

Mitigation is a human intervention, and as such it involves the complex intersection of science, ethics, economics, politics, social equity, population growth, and industrial and land development. In addition, because greenhouse gases mix throughout the Earth's atmosphere, mitigation actions require international cooperation. Different countries and communities may take different actions, but ultimately we're all in this together.

1.1 Mitigation and Adaptation in Parallel

The Earth's climate system changes slowly, and the greenhouse gases that we have already emitted are going to change the climate over the next decades and centuries even if we stop emitting all greenhouse gases tomorrow. This is why **adaptation** strategies are necessary. Mitigation strategies, on the other hand, ultimately are intended to reduce the severity of climate change impacts by reducing future emissions of greenhouse gases. Future adaptation will be much harder if we don't reduce greenhouse gas emissions today.

Mitigation and adaptation strategies can sometimes conflict and sometimes go hand-in-hand. For example, one strategy to adapt to the more intense heat waves that much of the US can expect is to expand the use of air conditioning to protect people from heat-related illness. But more air conditioning means more energy use, which releases more heat-trapping greenhouse gases (if our power plants are the conventional, fossil-fuel burning ones we use predominantly today). On the other hand, we could adapt to more extreme heat by keeping buildings cooler through the use of insulation and reflective roofs. This could keep people cooler without using more air conditioning. In this example, the "green" building practices accomplish both adaptation and mitigation.

See Chapter 9: Climate Change Adaptation for more on adaptation strategies.

fossil fuel • a non-renewable, carbon-based fuel source like OIL, NATURAL GAS, or COAL, developed from the preserved organic remains of fossil organisms.

greenhouse gas • a gas that absorbs and re-radiates energy in the form of heat; carbon dioxide, water vapor, and methane are examples.

adaptation • in the context of climate change, action taken to prepare for unavoidable climate changes that are currently happening or are projected to happen in the future.

CHAPTER AUTHOR

Ingrid H. H. Zabel

Climate Change Mitigation

Addressing climate change is going to require parallel efforts that implement both adaptation strategies and mitigation strategies simultaneously. We will need to help vulnerable populations (e.g., those at the lowest levels of income, and those living on ocean coasts) adapt to the changes that are already happening. We will also have to help the major emitters of greenhouse gases reduce (that is, mitigate) their emissions in order to limit future warming. We

Box 7.1: Exercise: evaluating analogies to describe climate change mitigation and adaptation, and their relationships

Below are two analogies to describe responses to climate change. Evaluate the strengths and weaknesses of these analogies. Can you think of others?

Analogy 1: credit card debt

Imagine climate change adaptation and mitigation to be like dealing with credit card debt. We've already put a lot of charges on our card, and we're going to have to take some action to pay this off, that is, adapt to the situation. We might have to earn more money or spend less. If we keep making charges to the card without mitigating the situation by paying down the charges that have built up, it's going to be harder to pay it off in the future. We might have to take on a second job or severely alter our lifestyle to cut expenses. If, on the other hand, we pay off some of the debt and we charge less to the card in the future, it will be easier to pay off the remaining debt.

Analogy 2: laundry

Climate change adaptation and mitigation are like doing the laundry. If you let the laundry pile up for a while, you'll have to adapt by maybe not wearing your favorite shirt if it's not clean, or re-wearing clothes that are only a bit dirty. But if you don't mitigate the problem, that is, if you continue to insist on not doing the laundry, eventually you'll be left with some unpleasant choices: wear dirty, smelly clothes, wear no clothes, or go buy yourself an entirely new wardrobe. On Earth, of course, we can't just buy another planet.

On the other hand, if you do the laundry pretty consistently, you may still have to adapt sometimes if your favorite shirt isn't clean or you run out of detergent. But for the most part your adaptive actions and decisions will be small, and you can more easily get back to having enough clean clothes to wear.

Mitigation is taking action to do the laundry regularly. Adaptation is coming up with solutions to when the laundry isn't done. Right now we've let the laundry pile up, and we've got to start cleaning up our act.

Climate Change Mitigation

cannot rely on adaptation alone because the ultimate impact of unmitigated emissions of greenhouse gases will be very severe, and we cannot rely on mitigation strategies alone because historical greenhouse gas emissions are already changing our planet and impacting people around the globe.

anthropogenic • *made by humans, or resulting from human activity.*

1.2 What We're Up Against

Mitigation efforts currently face an uphill battle, because the trends in **anthropogenic** greenhouse gas emissions (i.e., emissions resulting from human activities) show a continued increase in the last few decades. Below is a summary of these trends.[1]

- Global annual anthropogenic greenhouse gas emissions have increased from 27 $GtCO_2eq$ in 1970 to 49 $GtCO_2eq$ in 2010 (see Box 7.2 for an explanation of the unit $GtCO_2eq$).
- Most of the anthropogenic greenhouse gas emissions (78%) during this time period came from fossil fuel combustion and industrial processes.
- About half of cumulative anthropogenic CO_2 emissions between 1750 and 2010 have occurred in the last 40 years.
- CO_2 is the main greenhouse gas emitted from human activities, making up 76% of the total in 2010. It is followed by CH_4 (16%), N_2O (6.2%), and fluorinated gases (2%).[2]
- In 2010, direct anthropogenic greenhouse gas emissions came mainly from electricity and heat production (25%), agriculture, forestry, and other land uses (24%), and industry (21%), followed by transportation (14%), other energy sector activities besides electricity and heat production (9.6%), and buildings (6.4%).

Box 7.2: What do the units $GtCO_2eq$ mean?

The "G" stands for the unit prefix giga, which represents a billion (10^9). The "t" stands for tonne, which is a metric ton or 1,000 kg. CO_2 is carbon dioxide, and "eq" stands for equivalent.

The unit of $GtCO_2eq$ is used to describe a quantity called the Global Warming Potential (GWP) of a greenhouse gas. The GWP is a way to measure the relative warming effects of different greenhouse gases, and it tells you how much warming a certain mass of a greenhouse gas would lead to in a given time period, compared to warming from CO_2. The typical time period used by climate scientists for calculating GWP is 100 years, though some argue that it is important to consider shorter time scales when considering effects of highly potent, short-lived (on the order of a decade) greenhouse gases such as methane (CH_4). For the sake of clarity, we will use the term GWP_{100} when considering a 100-year time horizon.

Example: Assume that nitrous oxide (N_2O) has a GWP_{100} of 280. This means that emissions of one ton of N_2O is equivalent to emissions of 280 tons of CO_2 over the next 100 years.

---

[1] These data come from the latest report (as of this writing) from the Intergovernmental Panel on Climate Change: IPCC, 2014, Summary for Policymakers, In: Climate Change 2014, Mitigation of Climate Change. Cambridge University Press: NY.

[2] These numbers represent percentages of the total 2010 emissions of 49 $GtCO_2eq$.

Climate Change Mitigation

carbon sinks • *a system or part of a system which absorbs carbon.*

IPCC • *the Intergovernmental Panel on Climate Change, a large, international group of climate scientists working to understand climate change and to present reliable climate data and information to policy-makers and the public at large.*

The statistics listed above are global. In the US, the recent picture gives reason for encouragement. According the 2014 US National Climate Assessment,

> *Over recent decades, the US economy has emitted a decreasing amount of carbon dioxide per dollar of gross domestic product. Between 2008 and 2012, there was also a decline in the total amount of carbon dioxide emitted annually from energy use in the United States as a result of a variety of factors, including changes in the economy, the development of new energy production technologies, and various government policies.*[3]

The economic changes referred to are likely associated with the recession following the 2008 financial crisis, and achieving emissions reductions as a by-product of an economic downturn is not a desirable path. But the encouraging aspects are that we *can* achieve emissions and energy use reductions through technology innovations, policies, and behavior changes.

Recent regulatory efforts and advancements in technology and efficiency are reducing the amount of greenhouse gases that developed nations emit each year, but even the most technologically advanced and environmentally conscientious nations (e.g., Germany) are still emitting greenhouse gases every year. Ultimately, to prevent climate change, we may need to develop methods and technologies that can remove greenhouse gases from the atmosphere. There are many current proposals for these methods and technologies that can serve as **carbon sinks** or negative emissions, but they have unknown risks and potentially huge financial and environmental costs, and none currently can be implemented at a large scale.

> See Chapter 8: Geoengineering to learn more about potential ways to remove CO_2 from the atmosphere.

1.3 Mitigation Pathways and Stabilization Wedges

Mitigation pathways are different combinations of technological and behavioral solutions that lead to different levels of greenhouse gas reductions, and have different impacts on society. Pathways with larger and faster emissions reductions lead to smaller global temperature increases in the future, which will make adaptation to unavoidable change easier. These pathways may, however, be harder to implement for political and economic reasons. The Intergovernmental Panel on Climate Change (**IPCC**), a large, international group of scientists considered to be the most authoritative source of information on global climate change, has concluded that the mitigation pathways needed to keep the increase in the world's temperature to less than 2° C (3.6° F) above the pre-industrial temperature (see *Box 7.3*) by the end of the 21st century will likely require large scale changes in the world's energy supply systems.

For example, one potential mitigation pathway is to immediately cease all further emissions of greenhouse gases. This would require that we produce no more power, consume no additional fossil fuels, and basically shut down

---

[3] This analysis comes from Jacoby, H. D., Janetos, A. C., Birdsey, R., Buizer, J., Calvin, K., Chesnaye, F. D., . . . West, J. (2014). Ch. 27: Mitigation. Climate Change Impacts in the United States: The Third National Climate Assessment. US Global Change Research Program. doi:10.7930/J0C8276J

Box 7.3: Why is 2° C considered the limit of acceptable warming for our planet?

The idea of an average surface warming of 2° C (3.6° F) above pre-industrial temperature as the upper limit of acceptable warming was born in the 1970s and grew in acceptance over the next few decades.[4] The temperature number came out of scientific considerations of the temperature conditions under which human societies developed and the impacts of increased warming, including drought and heat waves that would decrease the world's food supply, sea level rise that would flood coastal cities and lead to large-scale refugee migrations, and extreme weather events that would lead to loss of life and damage to infrastructure.

Scientists and policymakers have questioned the 2° C limit and continue to debate it. At the most recent United Nations Climate Change Conference (Paris, 2015), a group of countries pushed for actions to limit warming to 1.5° C (2.7 °F).

modern society. While this would stop all greenhouse gas emissions, and leave us only to adapt to the changes that we have already committed to, this mitigation pathway would shatter industries, collapse economies, and cause social, economic, and political havoc. While this could be considered the ultimate mitigation pathway, it is not a realistic pathway. On the other extreme, we could decide to not mitigate, and hope that our ability to adapt to any future changes will be enough. We could wait until someone somewhere invents some future technology that would cheaply and easily remove greenhouse gases from our atmosphere, thereby solving the issue. While this may be an alluring strategy, it is a risky one. What if it turns out we cannot adapt to the amount of climate change occurring before a large-scale removal technique is found? What if there is no magic bullet technology? Clearly, we need to come up with a combination of mitigation and adaptation strategies and implement them in parallel.

The actions in some mitigation pathways can have adverse side effects. For example, nuclear power plants emit far fewer greenhouse gases than do fossil fuel-burning power plants, but nuclear power plants also produce radioactive waste that is difficult to dispose of and raise serious concerns about catastrophic accidents. Mitigation pathways can also have co-benefits, that is, they can produce results that are beneficial beyond reducing greenhouse gas emissions. For example, strategies that reduce air particulate pollution improve the health of people and ecosystems, and create energy systems and communities that are more sustainable. These pathways are sometimes referred to as "win-win" pathways.

Another way to think about mitigation pathways is through the concept of "stabilization wedges." *Figure 7.1* shows a plot of carbon emissions over time. Historical emissions have increased at a rapid rate in the 20th century and early 21st century, and if emissions continue at the rate of this current path they will lead to dangerous warming. If instead emission rates are flat in the future, it will be easier to adapt to climate change. The area between the dashed

---

[4] For a discussion of the politics behind the 2°C limit, see an article in The Economist: The Economist explains the 2°C limit on global warming, Dec. 6, 2015, http://www.economist.com/blogs/economist-explains/2015/12/economist-explains-4.

Mitigation Strategies

renewable · *able to be naturally replenished on a short time scale. While FOSSIL FUELS come from natural sources (the fossilized remains of plants and animals), they are not renewable on human time scales because they take many millions of years to form.*

wind energy · *electrical energy derived from the mechanical energy of a TURBINE which moves due to the action of the wind.*

hydropower · *electric power derived from the kinetic energy of falling or moving water.*

geothermal energy · *heat energy found below the surface of the Earth.*

biomass energy · *energy produced by burning plants, wastes, or their derivatives.*

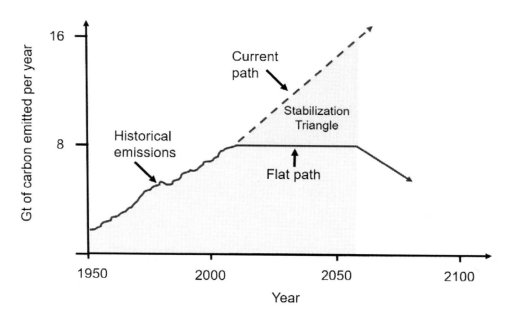

Figure 7.1: Carbon emissions over time, including historical emissions and two future paths, one following the current trend and one that remains flat and eventually decreases. The area between these paths is called the Stabilization Triangle, and represents the future emissions we will need to avoid to move from the current path to the flat path. (See Teacher-Friendly Guide website for a full color version.)

line (current path) and the flat path is called the Stabilization Triangle, and it represents the future carbon emissions we need to avoid in order to stay on the flat path.

How do we move from the current path to the flat path? In other words, how do we reduce carbon emissions represented by the area of the Stabilization Triangle? Like many big problems, the solution can be broken into parts, and we can undertake a variety of strategies. These are represented by Stabilization Wedges (*Figure 7.2*), which together can reduce the emissions of the entire Stabilization Triangle. Examples of these strategies are increasing energy efficiency in all sectors of the economy (using less energy), using **renewable** energy (**wind, solar, hydropower, geothermal, and biomass**), using nuclear energy, replacing coal-burning power plants with natural gas-burning power plants, carbon capture and storage, and increasing natural carbon sinks through forestry and agricultural practices. These strategies are addressed in the remainder of this chapter.

2. Mitigation Strategies

Mitigation strategies vary, and they can involve different levels of effort and scope, from broad-ranging actions taken at the government level to actions by specific industries or companies, and to behavior changes made by individuals. A successful mitigation pathway will likely involve combinations of these strategies.

Climate Change Mitigation

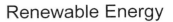

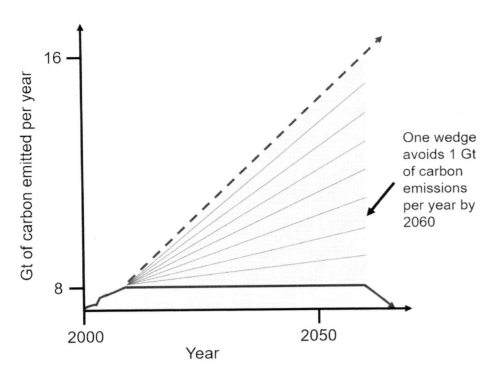

One wedge avoids 1 Gt of carbon emissions per year by 2060

Figure 7.2: Carbon stabilization wedges: triangles representing carbon emissions reduced by different mitigation strategies. Used together, all these strategies could move emissions from their current path to a flat path. (See Teacher-Friendly Guide website for a full color version.)

2.1 Renewable Energy

Renewable energy is energy that comes from sources that are naturally replenished. In 2015, renewable energy accounted for about 13% of US energy generation and 10% of energy consumption, and it comes in many forms (*Figure 7.3*). Consumption of wind and solar energy has increased dramatically in the last decade (*Figure 7.4*), and businesses and governments are discovering new methods of capturing, storing, and distributing renewable energy.

One of the attractions of renewable energy is that, because it is naturally replenished, it has the potential to be sustainable. It also holds promise for climate change mitigation because, compared with fossil fuels, many renewable energy sources emit far fewer greenhouse gases. Renewable energy at a large, commercial scale is not without environmental costs, however. A mitigation pathway that combines renewable energy production and *less* energy use is ideal.

Biomass *(Figure 7.5)* has many thousands (if not millions) of years of history as an energy source and it is still the largest renewable source of energy. Wood and wood products still account for just over half of US commercial biomass energy production, but it is now nearly equaled by biofuels (ethanol and biodiesel). *Estimates of amount of wood used for commercial energy do not take into* account home heating provided by wood burning. Energy from waste, including landfill gas, is also included as biomass. Landfill gas is a mixture of methane and other gases produced by microorganisms breaking down biomass within a landfill.

Climate Change Mitigation

U.S. renewable energy supply

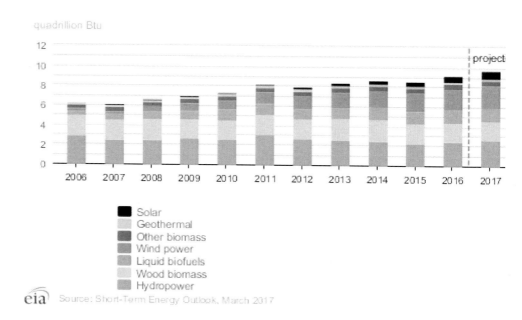

Figure 7.3: US renewable energy supply, for 2006-2016 (actual) and 2017-2018 (projected). (See Teacher-Friendly Guide website for a full color version.)

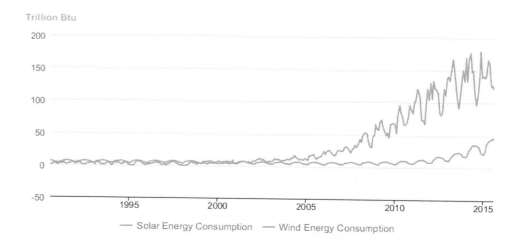

Figure 7.4: Changes in US consumption of wind and solar energy from August 1990 to August 2015. (See Teacher-Friendly Guide website for a full color version.)

Climate Change Mitigation

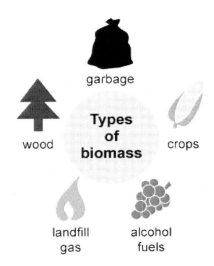

Figure 7.5: Types of biomass used for energy production.

The burning of biomass, like fossil fuels, yields carbon dioxide and often other emissions, although the carbon emitted into the atmosphere during the burning of biomass is balanced out by the carbon removed from the atmosphere during the growth of the biomass itself. This is because growing plants take in carbon dioxide from the atmosphere through photosynthesis. Recent studies suggest, however, that the net effect of biomass burning is warming.[5] This is because biomass burning releases soot and other particles— also known as black and brown carbon — that reduce sunlight-blocking cloud cover and make icy and snowy surfaces absorb more heat, warming the Earth.

Geothermal, hydropower, solar, and wind energy installations produce zero or almost no carbon emissions once they are up and running. The main carbon emissions associated with these sources of energy are in the production, transport, and maintenance of materials and installations.

Hydropower is the longest established renewable energy source used for electricity production, and still accounts for the largest portion of renewable electric generation in the US. The world's first commercial-scale hydropower plant began operation at Niagara Falls, New York, in 1881. Hydropower accounts for about 7% of US electricity use, and because most substantial river systems have already been dammed for electricity use or their damming has been deemed too environmentally costly to pursue, there is little likelihood that the US can obtain much more energy from traditional hydropower.[6] The environmental costs include habitat destruction from flooding of gorges or valleys typically required for hydropower generation. Indeed, many hydropower plants have been removed in recent decades because of their impact on wildlife, particularly fish migration.

---

[5] These studies include Bond, T. D. (2013). Bounding the role of black carbon in the climate system: A scientific assessment. Journal of Geophysical Research: Atmospheres, 118(11), 5380–5552 and Jacobson, M. Z. (2014). Effects of biomass burning on climate, accounting for heat and moisture fluxes, black and brown carbon, and cloud absorption effects. Journal of Geophysical Research: Atmospheres, 119, 8980-9002.

[6] An article that discusses this is Manahan, M., & Verville, S. (2005). FERG and dam decommissioning. Natural Resources and Environment, 19(3), 45-49.

Climate Change Mitigation

Renewable Energy

turbine • *a machine that converts rotational mechanical energy into to electrical energy. In its simplest form, a turbine consists of a shaft with a rotor with blades on one end and an electric generator on the other end. Water, wind, or steam pushes the blades and causes the rotor to rotate. Inside the generator, a coil of metal wire sits inside a large magnet. When the shaft rotates it spins the metal coil in a magnetic field, producing electric current by induction.*

Figure 7.6: Aerial view of the Grand Coulee Dam taken in 2016, on the Columbia River in Washington.

Hydropower works by converting the kinetic energy of falling water into mechanical energy to operate a **turbine**, which then generates electricity. Most hydropower is produced at large dams such as the Grand Coulee Dam in Washington (*Figure 7.6*), but hydropower generation is possible on a small scale from undammed streams and rivers. The calculation in *Box 7.4* gives an estimate of the power generated in a large dam.

Wind power generation in the US at large-scale facilities (i.e., utilities) grew by a factor of ten from 2005 to 2014. Wind power generation is not uniformly distributed across the country: in 2013, 80% of the US's wind power was produced by just twelve states (Texas, Iowa, California, Oklahoma, Illinois, Kansas, Minnesota, Oregon, Colorado, Washington, North Dakota, and Wyoming). Wind power works by using the force of wind to rotate turbine blades (*Figure 7.7*), and the turbine converts rotational mechanical energy to electrical energy. The physics and economy of wind turbines favors the construction of large diameter blades. This brings permanent structures to rural landscapes that are scores to hundreds of feet high. Although impacts upon bird populations appear smaller than initially believed, current designs of turbines could have substantial impacts on bat populations.

Geothermal both provides direct heat and generates electricity, using Earth's internal heat as an energy source. It has long been used on a small scale for heating where the heat release is high—at hot springs, for example. In recent decades, capturing Earth's heat for power production has grown substantially, but it remains a small part of the global energy portfolio. Such deep geothermal energy systems sometimes use hydraulic fracturing to increase the flow of water through the rock, which regulates heat and controls energy production. Also in the last few decades, small-scale, relatively shallow (less than 300 feet, or 91 meters) geothermal heat pumps have been effectively used to preheat air in winter or cool it in summer, thus reducing heating and air conditioning

Climate Change Mitigation

![Box icon] **Box 7.4: Physics connection: hydropower generation**

Suppose the hydropower station at the Grand Coulee Dam has a flow rate of 2800 m³/s. That is, 2800 cubic meters of water flow through the station's turbines in one second. If the height of the dam is h=170 m and the turbines are 100% efficient (an idealization), how much power does the station generate? Note: 100% efficiency means that we are ignoring energy losses due to friction in the turbines.

Ignoring frictional energy losses as the water drops down from the top of the dam, the kinetic energy of the water when it enters the turbines at the bottom of the dam is equal to the gravitational potential energy of the water at the top of the dam. One cubic meter of water has a mass m = 1000 kg. For one cubic meter of water, this potential energy is

$mgh = (1000 \text{ kg}) \times (9.8 \text{ m/s}^2) \times (170 \text{ m}) = 1.67 \times 10^6 \text{ J}$

(g is the acceleration due to gravity at the Earth's surface).

The kinetic energy of the water is used to do work, and power is the rate of doing work. A flow rate of 2800 m³/s would generate a power of

$P = (2800 \text{ m}^3/\text{s}) \times (1000 \text{ kg/m}^3) \times (9.8 \text{ m/s}^2) \times (170 \text{ m}) = 4.7 \text{ GW (gigawatts)}.$

Follow-up question: How many homes can this dam power? Students will have to estimate the electricity use of a typical home.

Figure 7.7: Wind turbines in California.

Nuclear Energy

rare earth metals • *one of a group of seventeen chemical elements with similar properties and often found together in the Earth. Rare earth metals include the fifteen lanthanides, scandium, and yttrium.*

fission • *the process of bombarding atomic nuclei with neutrons, splitting the nuclei into those of lighter elements and more neutrons, and also resulting in the release of energy.*

costs in homes and other buildings. These systems take advantage of nearly constant temperature (approximately 50–60°F) below the surface and do not require fracturing bedrock. Globally, geothermal electricity production grew 44% from 2004 to 2014, but its total contribution is still comparatively small at 12.8 GW (gigawatts) of installed electric generating capacity in 2014.

Solar power works in two ways: solar thermal uses the sun for heat, and photovoltaic cells (PV) convert light into electric current. Both types are growing rapidly, with global PV generating capacity growing from 2.6 to 177 GW between 2004 and 2014. Both solar thermal and PV systems can range in scale from very small household systems to very large power plants. Further, passive solar building design coupled with good insulation and control of airflow can eliminate or practically eliminate the need for heating systems. Solar energy produces no emissions once systems are installed, but there are concerns about the manufacture and disposal of photovoltaic solar cells, and related to the mining practices, particularly outside the US, of **rare earth metals** used in PV and battery production. Whether a commercial-scale solar energy installation generates heat or electricity, it must cover and industrialize considerably more physical area compared to other kinds of power plants that generate the same amount of energy, although smaller-scale solar energy systems can be roof-mounted, reducing these concerns.

2.2 Nuclear Energy

Carbon emissions from nuclear energy are very low compared with fossil fuel sources, and are comparable to those from renewable energy technologies such as solar and wind.[7] As with those technologies, most of the emissions come from processes that occur ahead of operating a power plant, i.e., from extracting and transporting raw materials and constructing the plant.

Nuclear power is produced by the **fission** ("splitting") of the nuclei of relatively heavy atoms, such as uranium (*Figure 7.8*). Typically, the method for electricity production from nuclear fission is similar to that from fossil fuel power plants—the energy from nuclear reactions (rather than fossil fuels) is used to boil water that produces steam to turn turbines. In 2015 nuclear power accounted for 20% of US electricity generation.

Nuclear power has only been a commercial source of electricity since 1957 and its substantial growth stopped (or paused) in the United States in the late 1970s as a result of a combination of prohibitive economic costs and environmental concerns, highlighted by the 1979 accident at Pennsylvania's Three Mile Island nuclear generating station, and the long-term handling of nuclear waste. Unlike in later catastrophic nuclear power plant accidents at Chernobyl, Soviet Union and Fukushima, Japan, there were no documented deaths associated with the US's best-known nuclear accident.

There are very serious concerns about nuclear power, especially related to accidents and the long-term management of highly toxic waste material. While

---

[7] It is important to consider the greenhouse gas emissions across all stages of a method's or product's life cycle when making comparisons. The US National Renewable Energy Laboratory (NREL) provides a comparison of life cycle greenhouse gas emissions for different types of electricity generation in this handout: http://www.nrel.gov/docs/fy13osti/57187.pdf.

Climate Change Mitigation

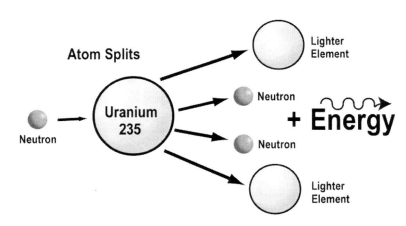

Figure 7.8: Diagram of the process of nuclear fission. A neutron is fired into the nucleus of a uranium atom, which then splits into nuclei of lighter elements and additional neutrons. Energy is released in this process. The additional neutrons then collide with other uranium nuclei and the process repeats in a chain reaction.

accidents in the nuclear industry are rare, the ones that have happened have been extremely dangerous. While technological advances have drastically cut the amount of radioactive waste used by newly designed nuclear power plants, there are still many costs and environmental concerns.

Humans are not always good at analyzing and comparing risks at different scales. For instance, would you rather live near a nuclear power plant that produces 100% clean energy, but has a one-in-a-million chance of having a meltdown, or would you ban all nuclear power plants, but rely on fossil fuels that are changing the entire planet's climate? This is a difficult problem to quantify and compare: the risk of a nuclear meltdown is catastrophic for the people who live nearby, while the risk of burning fossil fuels is applied around the world, gradually over time.

Box 7.5: There's no such thing as a free megawatt[8]

One large nuclear plant produces the same amount of electricity as 3,000 large wind turbines or 130 square kilometers (50 square miles, the equivalent of 24,200 football fields) of photovoltaic cells. It is not a simple question to determine the most environmentally benign energy source, and the answer can vary depending on local contexts. There is no such thing as a free megawatt, which is why efforts to increase our energy efficiency are so important. The environmental impact of an energy source is a complicated issue, and although it is clear that some energy sources are more environmentally friendly than others, all commercial-scale energy production has negative environmental impacts. For any energy source, there is a wide range of factors to consider and those factors should be considered not in isolation but in contrast to current or likely future energy practices.

---

[8] This title comes from a presentation by Don Duggan-Haas, published in the Journal of Sustainability Education Vol. 8, Jan. 2015, and freely available online here: http://www.jsedimensions.org/wordpress/content/theres-no-such-thing-as-a-free-megawatt-hydrofracking-as-a-gateway-drug-to-energy-literacy_2015_01/ .

energy efficiency · *methods which enable machines to perform functions while minimizing energy loss or using less energy than previously.*

energy conservation · *an approach to processes and activities that results in using less energy, on scales ranging from individual to industrial to national and global.*

green infrastructure · *structures that use plants, soil, and other natural features to perform functions such as providing shade, absorbing heat, blocking wind, or absorbing and filtering stormwater.*

Climate Change Mitigation

2.3 Energy Efficiency and Conservation

Energy efficiency and **conservation** measures may be the most important and effective mitigation actions we can take. Energy production and use are by far our biggest contributors to greenhouse gas emissions. According to the 2013 data from the US Energy Information Administration (eia.gov),

> *In the United States, greenhouse gas (GHG) emissions come primarily from the burning of fossil fuels in energy use. Fossil fuels supply 82% of the primary energy consumed in the United States and are responsible for 94% of total carbon dioxide emissions.*[9]

Our success in mitigating climate change will depend on finding ways to use less energy and different energy. This section explores strategies for using less energy.

2.3.1 Buildings

Buildings are one of the sectors with the biggest potential for energy savings. Buildings use energy for heating, cooling, lighting, and other electrical systems, and, according to the US Energy Information Administration, residential and commercial buildings accounted for 40% of the US's total energy consumption in 2013.

One large-scale mitigation initiative that addresses energy use in buildings is the 2030 Challenge (http://architecture2030.org). Launched by a group of architects, the 2030 Challenge asks the building design and construction community to set a series of goals for new buildings and major renovations. The final goal is to design buildings so that by the year 2030 they use no fossil fuel energy to operate. Strategies for doing this include innovations in design that reflect heat away from buildings in the summer or trap heat in the winter, generating power on-site using renewable sources, or purchasing renewable energy (up to a 20% limit). Many cities, including large ones such as Seattle, Pittsburgh, Denver, Dallas, Cleveland, and Los Angeles, have set up "2030 Districts" within their boundaries where they have committed to meeting their goals.

The use of **green infrastructure** is a mitigation strategy for buildings and communities. Green infrastructure refers to structures that use plants, soil, and other natural features to perform functions such as providing shade, absorbing heat, blocking wind, or absorbing stormwater (*Figure 7.9*). Green infrastructure can also help us *adapt* to climate change hazards such as heat waves and heavy rainfalls. As a mitigation tool, green infrastructure helps to reduce energy use.

Anyone who has walked through a neighborhood with tree-lined streets on a hot summer day has felt the cooling effect of plants. Trees reduce the need for air conditioning by providing shade. Trees and other plants also cool the air itself

---

[9] These data and more can be found on the United States Energy Information Administration's website. This particular statistic came from What are greenhouse gases and how much are emitted by the United States? (2014), Retrieved February 12, 2015, from Energy in Brief: http://www.eia.gov/energy_in_brief/article/greenhouse_gas.cfm

Climate Change Mitigation

Figure 7.9: Green roof on an urban building.

evapotranspiration • a combination of evaporation of liquid water on plant leaves and in the soil around the plant and transpiration, the transfer of water from a plant's roots to its leaves and then to water vapor in the air. Evapotranspiration cools the air because it takes heat from the air to convert liquid water to water vapor.

wastewater • water that has been used in residential or commercial activities and which needs to be treated before being released back into the environment.

through **evapotranspiration**. Studies have shown that the presence of mature trees in a suburban neighborhood can have a cooling effect of 4 to 6°F (2 to 3°C). Another energy-saving type of green infrastructure is a green roof – a roof with a layer of plants growing on it. The plants shade the underlying roof and the layer insulates the building, reducing energy costs for cooling and heating. Green infrastructure can also save energy when it is used to conserve water, recharge groundwater, and prevent sewer system overflows during storms, because managing water uses energy. In most cities electric water pumps are the largest portion of municipal electric use; the exceptions are cities with electrified mass transit, which uses a lot of energy. A Congressional Research Service Report[10] found that estimates for water-related electric use ranged from 4% to 13% of US electric generation, depending on different factors included in the analyses, and demand varies substantially with geography. According to the EPA, the activities of drinking water and **wastewater** utilities in the US result in about 116 billion pounds of CO_2 emissions annually (*Box 7.6*).

Certification and ratings systems can be very useful for architects and builders as well as for consumers in figuring out how to save energy in buildings. LEED (Leadership in Energy & Environmental Design) is a green building certification program that provides guidance and recognition for those wanting to create energy-efficient buildings. ENERGY STAR ratings (see *Box 7.7*) help consumers choose appliances such as dishwashers, refrigerators, computers, and furnaces that use less energy. The US EPA reports that between 1993 (when the ENERGY STAR program began) and 2012, the program has prevented the emission of 1.9 $GtCO_2eq$ of greenhouse gases.

---

[10] The report, titled Energy-Water Nexus: The Water Sector's Energy Use, can be found at https://fas.org/sgp/crs/misc/R43200.pdf.

Climate Change Mitigation

As stated above, the activities of drinking water and wastewater utilities in the US result in about 116 billion pounds of CO_2 emissions annually. For cars, burning one gallon of gasoline releases 19.64 pounds of CO_2.

Assume a car is driven 10,000 miles annually and has a gas mileage of 25 miles per gallon (mpg). For this car,

the number of gallons of gas used per year is 10,000 miles/25 mpg = 400 gallons.

This car thus releases 400 gallons x 19.64 lbs. CO_2/gallon = 7,856 pounds of CO_2 in one year. The equivalent of CO_2 released from water utilities, expressed in terms of CO2 released through driving cars, is

116 billion pounds / 7856 pounds per car = 14.8 million cars.

In other words, the annual CO_2 emissions from US water and wastewater utilities are equivalent to that of about 15 million cars.

Box 7.7: How to read an energy guide label

The US Federal Trade Commission runs a program that provides Energy Guide labels for many types of appliances, to help consumers make purchasing decisions that lead to energy savings. Below is an example of an Energy Guide label for a refrigerator.

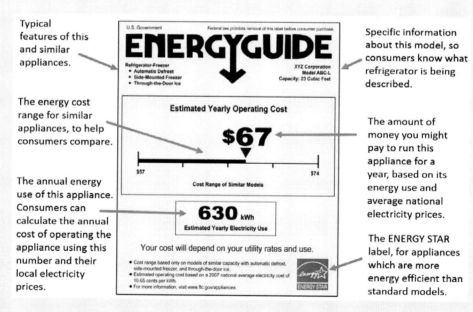

2.3.2 Transportation

After electric power generation, the transportation sector is the second biggest contributor to the US's energy-related greenhouse gas emissions, accounting for 25% of the total. The transportation sector also is a primary source of

Climate Change Mitigation

other kinds of emissions that degrade air quality and threaten human health. Reducing transportation emissions will both mitigate future climate change *and* improve air quality and human health. Such benefits that go beyond reducing emissions are sometimes referred to as a **co-benefits**. Increasing efficiency and reducing emissions in the transportation sector has tremendous potential.

We can save energy at the individual level by driving less: carpooling, combining errands into fewer trips, and walking, biking, or taking public transportation instead of cars. The vast majority of adult Americans drive to work alone, as illustrated in this visualization: http://flowingdata.com/2015/01/20/how-americans-get-to-work . We can also choose to buy products that involve less transportation, such as buying locally- or regionally-grown produce instead of imported fruits and vegetables. When we do drive, we can use less energy by not idling, driving at lower speeds on the highway (see *Box 7.8*), keeping tires properly inflated, and doing regular maintenance. We can choose to buy more fuel-efficient cars. Sometimes we can choose to live in neighborhoods where employers, services, and activities are close by and require less driving. Sometimes some of us can choose to work from home.

co-benefit • *sometimes called multiple benefit, is an improvement or positive outcome from an action that was not the primary one intended. For example, a person might choose to use a highly energy-efficient appliance in order to reduce energy use and thus carbon emissions, and saving money might be a co-benefit of this choice.*

Box 7.8: Physics connection: why does driving at lower speed on the highway save energy?

In the 1970s, highway speed limits around the US were set to 55 mph in order to save energy. This has since changed, but it can be instructive to consider why this speed limit was set.

One of the main reasons is that cars are designed to perform optimally in a range of speeds, and pushing to high speeds beyond that range can reduce their efficiency. Friction from the air around the car also makes a difference. Aerodynamic drag is the force of air on a moving object. The drag force on a moving car resists the car's motion, and the car has to use energy to overcome it. The faster the car goes, the higher the drag force. In fact, the drag force is proportional to the square of the relative velocity between the car and the air:

F_{drag} is proportional to v_{rel}^2.

Calculate how much higher the drag force is for a car traveling at 75 mph than for a car traveling at 55 mph. Note: this is a simple, "back-of-the-envelope" calculation that doesn't account for all the complexities of the drag force on a car and all the differences between driving 55 and 75 mph. But, it can give students an idea of the issues involved.

Solution: The ratio of drag forces on a car traveling at 75 mph compared to that at 55 mph is

$F_{drag,75} / F_{drag,55} = (v_{75}/v_{55})^2 = (75mph/55mph)^2 = 1.86$.

That is, the drag force on a car traveling at 75 mph is 1.86 times higher than the drag force on a car traveling 55 mph. It costs energy to fight the drag force, and thus it is more energy efficient to drive at 55 mph than at 75 mph.

Climate Change Mitigation

On a larger scale, we can make societal decisions to reduce our transportation energy use. For example, cities can choose to build public transportation networks so we use less energy driving individual cars, or cities can build infrastructure that makes it easier to ride a bicycle (*Figure 7.10*).[11] Communities can choose to develop neighborhoods where jobs and stores are close to where people live. Businesses can create incentives and mechanisms for employees to telecommute and carpool. Governments can set fuel efficiency standards for vehicles. Most of these changes, both on the small and large scale, not only reduce energy demand and therefore emissions, but also contribute to good health and save money.

Figure 7.10: Roadway jammed with cars, with space available in an adjacent bike lane.

Box 7.9: Discussion: commuting to school and work

What could adults learn from kids and from the way kids get to school, in terms of saving energy and reducing carbon emissions?

What constraints do adults have that might limit them from using the same methods as kids?

What are some solutions, and how can we implement them?

[11] Cities such as Minneapolis, MN, San Francisco, CA, and Portland, OR, are often at the top of lists of bike-friendly cities, because they have built infrastructure to make bike riding easier.

Climate Change Mitigation

Box 7.10: Exercise: what difference do vehicle fuel efficiency improvements make?

Compare a car that gets 28 miles per gallon and a light truck that gets 23 miles per gallon. If each is driven 10,000 miles per year,

the car uses 10,000 miles/28 mpg = 357 gallons of gas in a year and

the truck uses 10,000 miles/23 mpg = 434.

In 2013, US auto dealers sold 7.9 million new light duty trucks and 7.6 million new cars.[12] Assuming that these vehicles have the gas mileages above, the new light trucks would burn about 482 million more gallons of gas than the new cars. That releases about 9.5 billion pounds more CO_2 into the air, and that difference is just from new vehicles sold in one year in the US.

Many technologies exist today that can increase the fuel efficiency of vehicles. One example is turbocharging, where engine exhaust is re-used to run a fan that blows compressed air back into the engine's cylinders. Combustion requires air and fuel, and the addition of more fuel together with the compressed air results in combustion that generates more power with each explosion in the car's cylinders. The US Energy Information Administration estimates that with existing and soon-to-be-available technologies a gasoline-powered midsize passenger car could achieve a fuel efficiency of 53 miles per gallon by the year 2025, about a 50% increase from 2014. This would come with a 10% increase in the price of the car.[13]

Other vehicle options that use significant energy but may produce less greenhouse gas emissions include electric and hybrid gas-electric cars (*Figure 7.11*). The emissions reductions depend not only on the energy used while driving, but the emissions from generating electricity that the car needs for charging. If an electric car uses electricity generated at a coal-fired power plant, the net emissions may not be significantly less than a conventional gasoline-powered vehicle. But if the electric car uses electricity from a lower-emissions source, the emissions reductions can be significant. You can learn about the impact of electric power sources on vehicle emissions at the Alternative Fuels Data Center website, which allows you to enter your zip code and find out the types of energy sources in your area and the impact on vehicle emissions: http://www.afdc.energy.gov/vehicles/electric_emissions.php#wheel .

An interesting future technology to consider when discussing reduced energy use in transportation is driverless cars. Driverless cars on a smart transportation network might use less energy for several reasons. Because they remove human error they presumably wouldn't require as many safety features and could be built out of lighter materials, and a lightweight car needs less energy to run than a heavier one. They can be programmed to drive in ways that

---

[12] You can find this vehicle data and more at the National Automobile Dealers Association website, https://www.nada.org/nadadata/.

[13] Information about fuel economy improvements was published by the United States Energy Information Administration in 2014: Significant fuel economy improvement options exist for light-duty gasoline vehicles. United States Department of Energy. Retrieved February 25, 2015, from http://199.36.140.204/todayinenergy/detail.cfm?id=17111.

Climate Change Mitigation

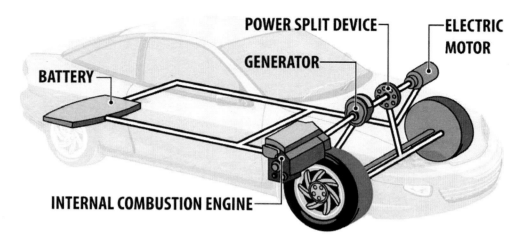

Hybrid electric vehicles combine the benefits of gasoline engines and electric motors. Typically, the wheels are powered by an electric motor, and in some cases, the internal combustion engine assists. Hybrid electric vehicles do not need to be plugged in to charge the battery because they are charged by an onboard generator.

Figure 7.11: Diagram of a hybrid gas-electric car.

minimize energy use, unlike human drivers. Groups of driverless cars could take advantage of aerodynamic advantages like drafting, where cars following close behind a lead car benefit from reduced air resistance. Driverless cars also have the potential to reduce the demand for everyone to own their own vehicles, not only reducing the energy use for vehicle production, but also allowing the conversion of parking spaces to other uses. On the other hand, people might use driverless cars more than they use conventional cars because of the benefits and conveniences, and this could cancel out energy savings.[14] It remains to be seen whether driverless car networks will come into existence and what their energy impact will be.

2.3.3 Industry

Industrial production is energy-intensive. Industries use energy for processes that students learn about in chemistry and physics classes: driving reactions, producing heat, and doing mechanical work.[15] The industrial sector has potential for reducing energy use. According to the IPCC,

> *The energy intensity of the industry sector could be directly reduced by about 25% compared to the current level through the wide-scale upgrading, replacement and deployment of best available technologies.*

[14] This dilemma is sometimes called Jevon's Paradox. For a discussion of this, see https://en.wikipedia.org/wiki/Jevons's_paradox.

[15] An extensive review of industrial processes and the potential for lowering their energy use and emissions is found in the IPCC's report: Edenhofer, O., Pichs-Madruga, R., Sokona, Y., Farahani, E., Kadner, S., Seyboth, K., . . . (eds.), J. M. (2014). *Climate Change 2014: Mitigation of Climate Change. Contribution of Working Group III to the Fifth Assessment Report of the Intergovernmental Panel on Climate Change.* Cambridge University Press: NY.

Climate Change Mitigation

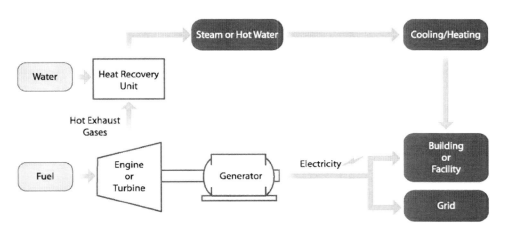

combined heat and power
• *an approach that uses a single fuel source to generate both electricity and usable heat. Combined heat and power systems are typically located near where the energy is consumed, and they use the heat which is wasted in traditional electrical power generation processes.*

Figure 7.12: Diagram of a combined heat and power system: gas turbine or engine with heat recovery unit.

Industries and businesses are motivated to reduce energy use because this reduces their energy costs. They may be deterred by upfront costs for more energy efficient systems and not enough information about options. Examples of industrial systems with potential for energy efficiency improvements are electrical motors and systems that produce steam and heat.

One example of an industrial energy efficiency improvement is the use of on-site **combined heat and power** (CHP). Conventional electricity generation produces heat that is simply wasted, released to the atmosphere. With an on-site CHP system, a facility produces its own electricity instead of buying it from the grid, and it uses the heat generated instead of wasting it. The heat can be used to produce steam or hot water to drive industrial processes or heat and cool buildings.[16] The energy efficiency gain, and thus energy savings, can be tremendous: from about 50% efficiency for a conventional system to over 80% efficiency for a CHP system. The diagram in *Figure 7.12* shows an example of a CHP system.

Finally, industrial processes can produce greenhouse gases not only through their energy use but from the processes themselves. One example is the production of cement, where limestone is heated, breaking down calcium carbonate and releasing CO_2. Worldwide, about 5% of CO_2 emissions come from cement production. Carbon emissions have risen dramatically since the beginning of industrialization, and changes in the industrial sector — in the way we produce things — are an important part of climate change mitigation. We may need to find different ways to product cement, or find other materials to use instead.

2.4 Carbon Capture and Storage (CCS)

Imagine a coal-fired power plant or oil refinery where CO_2 was removed from the final waste products. After removal, the CO_2 could be stored away or reused for other purposes. A technological solution that could achieve this for power plants would be a huge step, because energy production is the world's largest source of greenhouse gas emissions.

---

[16] It may seem obvious to students how steam can heat a building, but not how steam can cool a building. To learn more, students can research steam turbine chillers and/or steam absorption chillers.

Climate Change Mitigation

flue gas separation • *a process which uses a liquid solvent to chemically remove CO₂ molecules from a gas as the molecules make their way through a flue.*

oxy-fuel combustion • *burning a fuel in pure or enriched oxygen instead of in air.*

pre-combustion • *taking place before burning.*

This solution, carbon capture and storage (CCS), exists today although it is mostly used in fossil fuel refining and extraction. It is not in wide use in power plants for economic and environmental reasons. The world's first large-scale, coal-burning power plant with a CCS system — the Boundary Dam plant in Saskatchewan, Canada — began operations in October, 2014. This plant has a new CCS facility, built at the cost of about $1.1 billion (US dollars), which is expected to emit about 90% less CO_2 than the other parts of the plant that don't use CCS technology.

The CCS process can work in several ways, and each way has a financial and an energy price tag. For a power plant, the energy cost is taken out of the output and can be substantial. For example, a coal-fired power plant might need to use 20 to 30% of its electrical output to power its CCS system.

 Box 7.11: Chemistry connection: chemical recations in carbon capture systems

There are three main methods of capturing carbon in a CCS system. A post-combustion method called **flue gas separation** uses a liquid solvent to chemically remove the CO_2 molecules as they make their way through a column. The chemical reaction with the solvent monoethanolamine is shown below.

$$C_2H_4OHNH_2 + H_2O + CO_2 \rightarrow C_2H_4OHNH_3^+ + HCO_3^-$$

In the next step, the solvent passes through a unit where it is heated and the reaction runs in reverse, releasing condensed water vapor, the original solvent (to be reused), and concentrated CO_2. This CO_2 can then be compressed for storage or reuse.

A second method of carbon capture, **oxy-fuel combustion**, burns the fossil fuel in pure or enriched oxygen instead of in air. This results in mostly CO_2 and H2O as combustion products, instead of a waste gas that contains only 3 – 15% CO_2. Condensing out the water vapor leaves behind CO_2, which can then be compressed and stored or reused. This process still requires a lot of energy to separate gases, but the separation takes place on incoming air before combustion — to produce the pure or enriched oxygen — instead of in the flue after combustion.

The third method, **pre-combustion**, captures CO_2 before burning the fossil fuel. With coal, the process begins with gasifying the coal by reacting it with oxygen and steam at high pressure and temperature, producing a gas of mostly CO and H_2. The next step uses water to react with the CO to produce CO_2 and more H_2.

$$CO + H_2O \rightarrow CO_2 + H_2$$

In the final step, the CO_2 is captured and the H_2 is used as fuel for a turbine, to generate electricity.

Climate Change Mitigation

2.4.1 Carbon Capture Costs and Benefits

The IPCC reports that carbon capture technologies can reduce CO_2 emissions from new power plants by 81 – 91%, depending on the method.[17] This reduction comes at a cost, however, ranging from a 33 to 57% increase in the cost of electricity production and a 37 to 76% increase in the capital cost. While these seem like significant costs that will lead to higher energy costs, this may be a more realistic representation of the actual cost of using energy that emits CO_2. Economists often refer to this as "internalizing the externalities." These numbers do not include any costs associated with transporting and storing the CO_2 after it has been captured. The tradeoffs between emissions reductions, financial costs, and environmental costs need to be evaluated when deciding whether CCS makes sense as a mitigation option.

2.4.2 Carbon Storage

Storing the captured CO_2 involves transporting it to a site where it can be injected into the Earth to be trapped under an impermeable rock layer, injected into the ocean where it would either dissolve in seawater or form a slowly-dissolving CO_2 lake at the sea floor, or injected together with water into rock such as basalt where it would mineralize and remain underground. All of these methods have environmental concerns and require more research. Storage under an impermeable rock layer has the risk of leakage, especially with seismic activity. It would require long-term monitoring (and the associated costs) to test whether leaks are occurring. Dissolution in the ocean only adds to the problem of ocean acidification that is taking place from atmospheric CO_2 dissolving in the ocean, affecting aquatic life. Carbon mineralization is appealing in that once completed there's no risk of leakage, but it requires large amounts of water.

2.4.3 Carbon Reuse

Carbon reuse is an alternative to carbon storage, and one example already taking place on an industrial scale is a process called Enhanced Oil Recovery. In this process, captured CO_2 is injected underground into an oil reservoir in which the oil is difficult to extract through other means. The CO_2 mixes with or dissolves in the oil and makes it flow more readily. A full-cycle analysis of Enhanced Oil Recovery is necessary to determine whether it is a mitigation option, since the end product is a fossil fuel which, when burned, releases more CO_2.

Other ways to reuse captured CO_2 are under research or are viable at a small scale. One example comes from the lab of Cornell University professor Geoffrey Coates, whose research group is working on creating polymers from CO_2 and limonene, an extract found in orange peels and other plants (*Figure 7.13*). These polymers can be used to make plastic, a product typically made from **petroleum**. Other research groups are exploring synthetic photosynthesis, a

petroleum • *a naturally occurring, flammable liquid found in geologic formations beneath the Earth's surface and consisting primarily of hydrocarbons. Petroleum, also called OIL, is a fossil fuel, formed when large masses of dead organisms (usually algae or plankton) are buried underneath sediments and subjected to intense heat and pressure.*

---

[17] For more detail see Working Group III of the Intergovernmental Panel on Climate Change, M. B. (2005). IPCC Special Report on Carbon Dioxide Capture and Storage. Cambridge University Press: NY.

[18] For a news article on some of this research, see Yarris, L. (2015, April 16). Major Advance in Artificial Photosynthesis Poses Win/Win for the Environment. Retrieved December 10, 2015, from Berkeley Lab News Center: http://newscenter.lbl.gov/2015/04/16/major-advance-in-artificial-photosynthesis/.

7

Land Use

Climate Change Mitigation

Figure 7.13: Polymers created using carbon dioxide and limonene oxide derived from orange peels.

way to produce energy and materials in a laboratory using sunlight and CO_2, mimicking the process occurring naturally within a leaf.[18]

2.5 Land Use: Forests, Soils, and Agriculture

Plants and soils sequester (hold) carbon when left untouched by large-scale human activity. Plants take in carbon through photosynthesis, release some to the atmosphere through respiration and some to the soil through their roots, and store the remainder in their tissues. A tree's dry weight is almost half from carbon.[19] The soil takes in carbon when plants die and decompose. When people burn forests or till soil, carbon is released into the atmosphere. The practices we use in managing forests and land can have a big impact on carbon emissions.

2.5.1 Forests

The story of human impacts on the world's forests over time has mainly been one of deforestation. Even the Northeastern United States, whose forests have grown back significantly after a period of extensive deforestation in the 18th and 19th centuries, is not covered with as much forested land as it was before European settlement. Today, tropical forests in the Amazon River basin, Indonesia, and central Africa are being cut and burned at a rapid rate.

Some forestry options for mitigating the release of carbon are afforestation, reforestation, reducing deforestation, and planting forests that grow rapidly. Afforestation is the process of planting trees on land that was not previously covered by a forest, or was only covered by a forest a long time ago. Reforestation is the rebuilding of forests that have recently been cut down. As with any land use, people make assessments and calculations of the value of using the land for forest versus some other use. Some forestry projects are supported through carbon offset programs: systems set up so that actions that release carbon into

---

[19] For more information on carbon stored in trees and an exercise on calculating how much carbon one tree stores, see activities from the Science Education Resource Center at Carleton College: A) Trees – the Carbon Storage Experts (http://serc.carleton.edu/eslabs/carbon/1a.html) and B) Carbon Storage in Local Trees (http://serc.carleton.edu/eslabs/carbon/1b.html).

Climate Change Mitigation

Box 7.12. Exercise: Discussion of Carbon Offset Programs

Air travelers may see signs at airports offering purchase of carbon offsets to offset the carbon emissions associated with air travel (which are large!). Some people think this is a good idea, because the money from these purchases goes to real actions to mitigate climate change, like establishing forests and setting up renewable energy installations. Others think that these carbon offset programs just encourage people to fly more, increasing their carbon emissions, because travelers feel they can buy their way out of environmental responsibility.

What do you think? What would be required of a carbon offset program to really make it have the intended effect of reducing carbon emissions?

Box 7.13. Exercise: Locking Up Carbon in Biomass

An idea for removing carbon from the atmosphere is to grow a lot of trees, cut them down, put the biomass from these trees into buildings or structures that will be around for decades or centuries, and then grow more trees. How many trees would be required to make a difference? What might be the impact on total carbon uptake of replacing larger mature trees with smaller young ones? What are some other ways you can think of to "lock up" carbon?

---

the atmosphere (such as air travel or industrial production) are offset by paying to support actions that take in carbon, such as reforestation (see *Box 7.12*).

2.5.2 Soils

Soils lose carbon from natural processes such as weathering, erosion, and leaching over very long time scales. Soils that have been exposed over many thousands of years contain much less carbon than younger soils. For example, the soils of the northern Great Plains and Northeastern US are relatively young, having been scraped away by continental ice sheets and redeveloped since retreat of glaceris about 14,000 and 11,000 years ago. In contrast, the soils of the southern Appalachian Mountains have been not been stripped away by glaciers, so have been in a constant state of erosion and renewal by new weathering over spans of millions of years. The northern Great Plains soils contain about 4 to 7% organic matter (that is, materials that were carbon-containing organic tissues of organisms), whereas soils in the southern Appalachian Mountains typically contain less than 1% organic matter.

Human activity depletes soil carbon at a much faster rate than natural processes do. Most soils in the Midwest retain only 50 to 70% of the carbon that they contained before people began building farms on the prairie. Tilling the soil exposes organic matter to the air where it can oxidize, releasing carbon. Carbon is also lost through wind erosion, leaching, and water runoff, processes that are accelerated when the soil is disturbed from agricultural practices.

Agricultural practices also can play a role in returning carbon to the soil. For example, instead of leaving a field fallow over the winter, farmers may plant a cover crop: a crop of rye or some other plant that will prevent erosion of exposed soil and loss of carbon through water runoff. The crop adds carbon to the soil through its roots, and in the spring the crop is killed and plowed

Waste Management

pyrolysis • *a method of decomposing organic material by heating it at high temperatures in the absence of oxygen.*

pre-consumer • *created before being used by a consumer. For example, pre-consumer recycled items are recycled before they have been used.*

post-consumer • *created after use by a consumer, and not involving production of any new material.*

Figure 7.14: Field windbreaks in North Dakota to protect the soil against wind erosion.

under the soil, adding more carbon. *Figure 7.14* shows the practice of planting trees around fields as windbreaks, which slow the wind locally and reduce wind erosion of soil.

Other ways of sequestering carbon in soil include planting deep-rooted grasses and adding biochar to soils. Deep-rooted grasses can remove more carbon from the atmosphere simply by moving carbon deeper into the soil than shallower-rooted plants. Biochar is a solid byproduct of **pyrolysis** of plant wastes, similar to charcoal. The main products of the pyrolysis of plant wastes are liquid and gaseous biofuels. The biochar can also be used as a fuel, but if instead it is returned to the soil, improving the soil for new plant growth, biochar restores about 50% of the carbon in the soil where the plants originally grew.[20] The advantages of this process are that it produces renewable biofuels and sequesters carbon.

2.6 Waste Management

Garbage is something most people would rather not think about, and yet the ways we manage waste products in society have significant environmental impacts, including on greenhouse gas emissions. Wastes generated by human activity are classified as **pre-consumer** or **post-consumer**. Our household garbage is an example of post-consumer waste. Water use also leads to post-consumer waste that needs to be treated at wastewater facilities. Pre-consumer wastes include those from manufacturing, energy production, agriculture, and forestry.

---

[20] For more on carbon sequestration using biochar see Lehmann, J. (2007). Biochar for mitigating climate change: carbon sequestration in the black. Forum Geookul., 18(2), 15-17.

Climate Change Mitigation

Post-consumer waste accounts for less than 5% of global greenhouse gas emissions. Although this is a small fraction of total greenhouse gas emissions, pursuing proper waste management makes sense because technologies exist today to mitigate much of the emissions, and mitigation has co-benefits such as reducing pollution that is harmful to human health and providing renewable energy. Landfills, which produce methane and carbon dioxide, are the main source of greenhouse gas emissions from waste. The second largest source is wastewater, particularly from sewer systems, which can emit methane and nitrous oxide.

A direct way to reduce greenhouse gas emissions from waste is landfill gas recovery. This technique focuses on capturing and using the methane generated from bacterial anaerobic decomposition of landfill waste. Over a few decades, a landfill gas recovery project can cut methane emissions from a landfill by 60 to 90%. The captured methane can be burned to produce heat or electricity, avoiding use of fossil fuels for these needs. Although the process of burning methane produces CO_2, it is a far less potent greenhouse gas than methane. A landfill gas recovery project that produces electricity can use some of the electricity to power the system and sell the rest to help pay for the required technology and infrastructure.

Waste management techniques that mitigate climate change indirectly include recycling and material reuse. These techniques avoid waste generation and avoid greenhouse gas emissions from the energy used to produce new materials. They also have the co-benefits of preventing degradation of land that often accompanies obtaining new raw materials such as metals. *Table 7.1* shows data on some of the energy and resource savings from recycling.

Composting organic matter rather than landfilling it also reduces greenhouse gas emissions. When bacteria in a landfill decompose food scraps and plant matter anaerobically, they generate methane. Organic matter in a well-tended

Table 7.1: Energy and resource savings from recycling.[21]

Material and amount	Energy saved by recycling (KWh)	Resource savings from recycling	Landfill space saved (cubic yards)
1 ton aluminum	14,000	40 barrels of oil	10.0
1 ton newsprint	601	1.7 barrels of oil and 7,000 gallons of water	4.6
1 ton office paper	4,100	9 barrels of oil and 7,000 gallons of water	3.3
1 ton plastic	5,774	16.3 barrels of oil	30.0
1 ton steel	642	1.8 barrels of oil	4.0
1 ton glass	42	5 gallons of oil	2.0

---

[21] These data come from a nice summary of the benefits of recycling from the Stanford University Buildings and Grounds Maintenance department: Frequently Asked Questions: Benefits of Recycling. Retrieved Dec. 9, 2015, from http://bgm.stanford.edu/pssi_faq_benefits.

life cycle analysis • *a way of determining the total environmental impact of a product, including all steps from beginning (extraction of raw materials) to end (disposal, recycling, or reuse) and quantifying all inputs and outputs.*

compost pile, with access to oxygen, will decompose aerobically and produce carbon dioxide instead of methane. In an accounting of greenhouse gas emissions this carbon dioxide is balanced by the carbon dioxide taken in to grow the organic matter, resulting in net zero emissions. In practice, compost piles can emit methane and nitrous oxide, formed in parts of the pile that are low in oxygen and high in nitrogen, respectively. The amounts are small compared with the methane that would have been generated from the organic matter in a landfill.

When considering the carbon footprint of any process, one needs to conduct a detailed and full **life cycle analysis**. This accounts for the energy use and carbon emissions from all parts of the process, including things like transportation and packaging. For composting, the sources of emissions include: transporting the organic material to the composting site; using water and running equipment to set up and maintain the site; and running equipment to transport and apply prepared compost. On the other side of the equation are: the reduction in emissions compared with landfilling; carbon sequestration in the soil when compost is used; and less use of synthetic fertilizers and herbicides, resulting in less emissions associated with their production.

Another way of managing waste to reduce carbon emissions is through waste incineration for heat and electricity generation, often called "waste-to-energy." This process reduces carbon emissions by avoiding the use of fossil fuels for heating and electricity production. Modern waste-to-energy plants are a far cry from the household backyard burning seen in some areas. They involve sophisticated systems to efficiently generate heat and electricity and to prevent toxic air pollution. As such, they are currently expensive and are used in developed countries that have the means to build and operate them. Sweden incinerates about 50% of household waste in waste-to-energy plants, and has recently become so successful at reducing waste through recycling and reuse that it needs to import waste from other countries to burn in its plants. While waste-to-energy has certain advantages over landfills or recycling, it does produce carbon emissions and ash that must be disposed of.

2.7 Social Innovation

The way we go about our everyday lives within our cultural norms has an impact on our energy use and greenhouse gas emissions. For example, 76% of Americans drove to work alone in 2013.[22] Changing this behavior is one way to help mitigate climate change, though behavior is not the only factor. Change will also require changes in transportation systems, such as more public transportation options, and in workplace practices, such as scheduling that would allow for carpooling.

Energy savings from social innovation can be significant. For energy consumption in buildings, for example, the IPCC estimates that "for developed countries, scenarios indicate that lifestyle and behavioural changes could reduce energy demand by up to 20% in the short term and by up to 50% of

[22] These data came from a summary of US auto commuting statistics: McKenzie, B. (2015, August). Who Drives to Work? Commuting by Automobile in the United States: 2013. Retrieved December 10, 2015, from www.census.gov: https://www.census.gov/hhes/commuting/files/2014/acs-32.pdf

[23] See the source in note 15.

present levels by mid-century."[23] One example of social innovation for reducing energy use in buildings is Japan's "Cool Biz" campaign, starting in 2005. This campaign aimed to reduce air conditioning use in buildings by encouraging office workers to wear cool clothing instead of business suits. It involved changing cultural norms of how people dress at work. The campaign has been viewed as successful, and official estimates for the resulting reduction in carbon dioxide emissions per year range from 0.9 million tons (2005) to 2.2 million tons (2012).[24]

Another aspect of social innovation to mitigate climate change involves dietary choices in food consumption, and gives added weight to the old call to "eat your veggies." Transporting food leads to greenhouse gas emissions, but recent research has shown that by far the largest contribution to greenhouse gas emissions comes from food production, which is 83% of the average American household's food consumption carbon footprint. Red meat and dairy production are the most greenhouse gas emission-intensive. A 2008 study found that "shifting less than one day per week's worth of calories from red meat and dairy products to chicken, fish, eggs, or a vegetable-based diet achieves more GHG reduction than buying all locally sourced food."[25] Switching from a meat-eating diet to an entirely plant-based (vegan) diet would reduce dietary-based greenhouse gas emissions by about 50%.[26]

Sadly, about 30% to 40% of the US post-harvest food supply is wasted[27], which has not only ethical and economic impacts but also consequences for greenhouse gas emissions. Food that ends up in landfills contributes to methane emissions. Food production uses water and energy, and researchers estimate that about 25% of the water used in agriculture goes into wasted food.[28] Irrigation and water treatment systems use energy, which leads to greenhouse gas emissions, so using water for wasted food is simply releasing greenhouse gases into the atmosphere for no reason. Similarly, approximately 300 million barrels of oil are used each year in US production of food that is eventually wasted. As individuals we can reduce food waste with better planning and food management (for example, freezing leftover food to eat later). As a society, we can support programs that help food producers, markets, and restaurants donate more food to those in need.[29] For food that is not eaten, we can prevent it from entering landfills by composting, feeding it to animals, or using it to generate energy though biomass burning (*Figure 7.15*).

---

[24] For more information about this campaign, see Yotsumoto, J. (2015, May 1). Cool Biz Campaign Heats up. Retrieved December 10, 2015, from NHK (Japan Broadcasting Corporation) World: http://www3.nhk.or.jp/nhkworld/english/news/onbusiness/20150501.html

[25] The results of this research are published here: Weber, C. L., & Matthews, H. S. (2008). Food-Miles and the Relative Climate Impacts of Food Choices in the United States. Environ. Sci. Technol., 42, 3508–3513

[26] See Scarborough, P., Appleby, P. N., Mizdrak, A. B., Travis, R. C., Bradbury, K. E., & Key, T. J. (2014). Dietary greenhouse gas emissions of meat-eaters, fish-eaters, vegetarians and vegans in the UK. Climatic Change, 125(2), 179-192.

[27] Food that is edible but is not consumed is considered wasted. Food is wasted in many ways, such as in not using all that could be used in cooking, in being allowed to get moldy or eaten by pests before people can eat it, or in not being stored properly so its spoils and becomes inedible.

[28] A study that gives details on food waste in America is Hall, K. D., Guo, J., Dore, M., & Chow, C. C. (2009). The Progressive Increase of Food Waste in America and its Environmental Impact. PLoS One, 4(11), e7940. doi:10.1371/journal.pone.0007940 .

[29] Learn more about national efforts to reduce food waste here: http://www.epa.gov/sustainable-man-agement-food.

Climate Change Mitigation

Figure 7.15: A hierarchy of options for using uneaten food.

3. Summary

The decisions made by humans over the past few centuries have already committed us all to unavoidable climate consequences. We are going to have to adapt to these consequences, which we explore in detail in Chapter 9. However, this does not mean that we are committed to the most catastrophic climate change scenarios. We have the capability to mitigate the factors that could lead to the worst climate changes by reducing our greenhouse gas emissions and thereby taking responsibility for the future of our planet and all the living things—include us—that live on it.

These dual efforts—adaptation and mitigation—must occur concurrently if we are to both manage the changes that are already in the pipeline and prevent the most catastrophic possibilities for our future. Climate change mitigation efforts are occurring across a wide range of systems: energy, infrastructure, transportation, industry, land use, waste management, and society. Many of the strategies for non-energy sectors are of comparable magnitude to historical technological revolutions, such as the invention of distributed electricity, or the invention of the internet. It should be noted, however, that these two examples have contributed to—and are currently dependent upon—fossil fuel based greenhouse gas emissions.

Climate Change Mitigation

On a geological timescale, humans have been using fossil fuels for only a short amount of time. Coal and peat have been used in modest quantities (compared to today) in China and Europe for several thousand years, and coal use accelerated in Europe (especially England) from the 1500s to 1700s. It wasn't until the invention of the steam engine and industrial revolution in England the late 1700s that coal because a primary energy source.[30] In the US, it was around 1885 when coal began to produce more energy than wood combustion, and only around 1950 that petroleum products produced more energy than coal. To avoid catastrophic climate change over the next century and beyond, we are going to need to transition away from coal and petroleum fossil fuel products towards a renewable- and/or nuclear-powered future.

---

[30] A readable account of the history of coal use can be found in Barbara Freese's 2003 book Coal: A Human History, Penguin Books: NY.

Climate Change Mitigation

Resources

Mitigation

For a comprehensive overview of climate change mitigation in many sectors of the economy, see the Intergovernmental Panel on Climate Change (IPCC) report. The latest IPCC report as of the writing of this guide (2017) was published in 2014: http://www.ipcc.ch/report/ar5/wg3/.

Links to information from the US Environmental Protection Agency (EPA) on US greenhouse gas emissions, the EPA's efforts to reduce emissions, and what you can do: https://www3.epa.gov/climatechange/reducing-emissions.html.

Energy

A useful resource for teaching about energy is *Energy Literacy: Essential Principles and Fundamental Concepts for Energy Education:* http://energy.gov/eere/education/energy-literacy-essential-principles-and-fundamental-concepts-energy-education.

The US Department of Energy's website (http://energy.gov/) has information about energy, including education resources: http://energy.gov/science-innovation/science-education.

A vast amount of information, data, and graphics on energy production, energy use, greenhouse gas emissions, and more is available from the US Energy Information Administration Independent Statistics and Analysis: http://www.eia.gov/.

The National Energy Education Project website contains teaching resources, information for students, and more: http://www.need.org/.

Renewable Energy

US Department of Energy Office of Energy Efficiency and Renewable Energy: http://energy.gov/eere/office-energy-efficiency-renewable-energy.

Information on microhydropower: http://energy.gov/eere/energybasics/articles/microhydropower-basics.

The Wind Prospector: An interactive mapping tool to assess potential wind energy resources in the US. https://maps.nrel.gov/wind-prospector/.

A video on how geothermal heat pumps work: https://energy.gov/eere/education/videos/energy-101-geothermal-heat-pumps.

The Geothermal Prospector: An interactive mapping tool to assess potential geothermal energy resources in the US. https://maps.nrel.gov/geothermal-prospector/.

Climate Change Mitigation

Map of solar energy potential in the US (zoom out to see Alaska and Hawaii): https://energy.gov/maps/solar-energy-potential.

Information on What Individuals and Schools Can Do

Carbon Footprint Calculators

- One geared towards secondary school students: http://web.stanford.edu/group/inquiry2insight/cgi-bin/i2sea-r2a/i2s.php
- http://www.nature.org/greenliving/carboncalculator/
- https://www3.epa.gov/carbon-footprint-calculator/

A Few Websites/Documents on Energy Use in Schools

- https://www.energystar.gov/buildings/tools-and-resources/datatrends-energy-use-k-12-schools
- https://www.epa.gov/sites/production/files/2015-08/documents/k-12_guide.pdf
- https://www.ase.org/projects/powersave-schools

Chapter 8:
Geoengineering

1. Counteracting Climate Change

Geoengineering, or climate intervention, is a large-scale technological effort to change the Earth's climate. It differs fundamentally from **climate change mitigation**, because instead of aiming to slow warming by decreasing carbon emissions, it involves either removing carbon dioxide from the atmosphere or decreasing heat received from the sun. Such methods could be used to supplement climate change mitigation, or used even while carbon emission rates continue increasing. Many scientists and policymakers are wary of geoengineering for this reason, because they are concerned that climate intervention will be seen as a magic bullet or easy solution that allows us to go on with business as usual, releasing more and more carbon. Geoengineering would be anything but easy, however, and could have tremendous financial and environmental cost. Intervening with Earth's climate systems also has great uncertainty at our current level of understanding, and could have harmful unintended consequences.

In a report on geoengineering from The Royal Society in the U.K., the world's oldest scientific association, the authors discuss the nature of this uncertainty:

See Chapter 7: Climate Change Mitigation for more information about efforts to reduce carbon emissions.

> When analysing potential problems associated with geoengineering in relation to long-term climate change, the language of 'risk' is often used, implying some knowledge about both potential outcomes of geoengineering technologies and their probabilities. But so embryonic are geoengineering technologies that there is commonly little knowledge yet about the nature of (potentially unwanted) outcomes and still less knowledge of probabilities. This is a situation of 'indeterminacy' (or 'ignorance') rather than risk.[1]

Given the concerns about geoengineering, why consider it at all? Some scientists view climate intervention as an undesirable but important method of last resort that deserves study. Others think that geoengineering methods that remove carbon dioxide (CO_2) from the atmosphere could contribute to emissions reduction efforts, and some methods may even cost less than certain types of mitigation. Other interventions which effectively block sunlight from reaching the Earth could theoretically begin to cool the climate within a few years of deployment, so they could be emergency options. If the climate

---

[1] The Royal Society's report, Geoengineering the climate: science, governance and uncertainty. London, UK (2009), is an extensive review of geoengineering methods.

[2] These studies include the Royal Society report mentioned in (1) and two reports from the US National Research Council: Climate Intervention: Carbon Dioxide Removal and Reliable Sequestration (2015), and Climate Intervention: Reflecting Sunlight to Cool Earth (2015), The National Acadamies Press, Washington, D.C.

geoengineering • a large-scale technological effort to change the Earth's climate, typically either by removing carbon dioxide from the atmosphere or by blocking incoming solar radiation.

climate change mitigation • actions taken to limit or eliminate emissions of greenhouse gases in order to reduce future climate warming.

CHAPTER AUTHOR

Ingrid H. H. Zabel

Geoengineering

greenhouse gas • *a gas that absorbs and re-radiates energy in the form of heat; carbon dioxide, water vapor, and methane are examples.*

ocean acidification • *the increasing acidity, or lowered pH, of ocean waters, caused by absorption of atmospheric carbon dioxide.*

approached a tipping point—a threshold beyond which the Earth would enter a vastly different climate state—then emergency measures would likely garner more serious attention. Major studies of geoengineering[2] conclude that while research into climate intervention is prudent in order to be prepared for the worst, it is most important that we focus on reducing carbon emissions quickly.

1.1 Types of Climate Intervention

Geoengineering methods fall under two classes: 1) Carbon dioxide removal (CDR), which removes CO_2 from the atmosphere, and 2) solar radiation management (SRM), which reflects sunlight back into space. The advantage of carbon dioxide removal is that, together with conventional emissions reduction, it could potentially reduce atmospheric CO_2 down to lower, even pre-industrial, levels. Carbon removal may be necessary even if we stopped emitting all **greenhouse gases** today, because of the cumulative effects of the greenhouse gases we've already emitted. CDR also addresses the critical problem of **ocean acidification**, which results from atmospheric CO_2 dissolving in sea water and which could have catastrophic effects on ocean ecosystems. Disadvantages of CDR are that to be effective it may need to take place on vast spatial scales, and it would take decades after implementation to see the effects.

An advantage of the second class of methods, solar radiation management, is that it could work relatively quickly after deployment—within a few years. Disadvantages of SRM are that it does nothing to address the underlying problem of increasing CO_2 in the atmosphere, so ocean acidification would only get worse without serious mitigation efforts. It would also require maintaining a tricky balance between incoming sunlight and atmospheric CO_2, and if systems failed or were turned off the climate could quickly revert to a much warmer state because of all the remaining CO_2 in the atmosphere.

Both CDR and SRM would be expensive to different degrees, could require large amounts of energy to run and maintain, and would likely harm the environment in various ways. Both would require international cooperation and run the risk of unknown consequences if a single country or even a wealthy individual or business decided to act on their own. The following sections are not a comprehensive overview of all types of geoengineering proposals, but they discuss examples of several geoengineering methods most commonly promoted and concerns about their implementation.

2. Examples of Carbon Dioxide Removal (CDR) techniques

2.1 Enhanced Chemical Weathering

Nature already has several ways of removing carbon from the atmosphere, including chemical weathering of rocks (*Figure 8.1*). For example, a chemical reaction describing weathering of albite (a variety of the most common kind of silicate mineral in the crust, plagioclase feldspar) is as follows:

Geoengineering

CO$_2$ Removal

fossil fuel • *a non-renewable, carbon-based fuel source like OIL, NATURAL GAS, or COAL, developed from the preserved organic remains of fossil organisms.*

Figure 8.1: Hawaii's famous red dirt: chemically weathered rock (basalt) on the island of Kauai, HI.

$$2NaAlSi_3O_8 + 2CO_2 + 11H_2O \rightarrow Al_2Si_2O_5(OH)_4 + 2Na^+ + 2HCO_3^- + 4SiO_2 + H_2O$$
silicate minerals + carbon dioxide + water → clay minerals + cations + bicarbonate + silica + water

In this example, the weathering of plagioclase feldspar results in sodium, bicarbonate ions, and silica ions in solution, and the clay known as kaolinite. These products are eventually washed to the ocean or become part of the soil. For each molecule of albite, a CO$_2$ molecule is used up from the atmosphere. Natural weathering processes such as these take a long time to remove carbon from the atmosphere, on the order of tens to hundreds of thousands of years. This is much slower than the rate at which **fossil fuel** burning is adding carbon dioxide to the atmosphere.

Geoengineering techniques aim to enhance or accelerate the rate of natural chemical weathering by exposing more rock to weathering. One way to do this is to mix a silicate mineral such as olivine into soil, exposing it to weathering. While the approach seems simple, it could be expensive and energy-intensive, and it would need to operate on a scale similar to the energy systems which are currently responsible for CO$_2$ emissions:

> Large quantities of rocks would have to be mined and ground up, transported, and then spread over fields. It is estimated that a volume of about 7 km^3 per year (approximately twice the current rate of coal mining) of such ground silicate minerals, reacting each year with CO$_2$, would remove as much CO$_2$ as we are currently emitting.[3]

---

[3] The Royal Society, Geoengineering the climate: science, governance and uncertainty. London, UK (2009).

Geoengineering

Enhanced chemical weathering could also take place by replicating natural weathering processes in a factory setting, for example, capturing CO_2 from a fossil fuel-burning power plant and reacting it with ground up silicate rock. Another approach would be to heat limestone (the carbonate rock made of $CaCO_3$) to the point where the limestone releases CO_2, capture this CO_2, and react it to form lime ($Ca(OH)_2$). In both approaches, the product of the reaction would be added to the ocean. Adding lime to the ocean would increase its alkalinity, which in turn would promote absorption of CO_2 from the atmosphere.[4] A third approach is to grind and deposit powdered calcium carbonate directly into the ocean, reducing the acidity of the ocean and enhancing CO_2 absorption from the atmosphere. This would be a very slow process: by adding 4 billion tons of calcium carbonate to the ocean per year it would take 200 years to reach a rate of atmospheric CO_2 absorption of about 1 Gt per year.[5] To put this in perspective, our fossil fuel burning worldwide released around 32 Gt of CO_2 into the atmosphere in 2014.

What are the environmental costs of enhanced chemical weathering? Land degradation and pollution from large-scale mineral mining and transportation projects are concerns. Enhanced weathering in an industrial setting would require energy, which would lead to further release of CO_2 if it came from fossil fuel sources. Finally (and critically), the chemical, biological, and ecological consequences of releasing minerals into the ocean or changing the ocean's alkalinity are not well understood.

> **Box 8.1: Exercise to examine the mass scales involved in one type of enhanced chemical weathering[6]**
>
> Assume that 32 Gt of CO_2 are released into the atmosphere in a year from fossil fuel burning. If all of this CO_2 is to be reacted to form calcium carbonate ($CaCO_3$) that would be stored in the ocean, how much calcium carbonate would result? The reaction under consideration is:
>
> $$CO_2 + CaSiO_3 \rightarrow CaCO_3 + SiO_2.$$
>
> Using the molar masses of CO_2 (44 g/mole) and $CaCO_3$ (100 g/mole), one finds that the ratio of mass of $CaCO_3$ to CO_2 is approximately 2.3. Using up 32 Gt of CO_2 in one year through storage in $CaCO_3$ would result in 2.3 × 32 Gt = 74 Gt of calcium carbonate. For comparison of mass, this is about ten times the mass of coal mined worldwide in 2014,[7] and would require tremendous resources to process and transport.

---

[4] Carbonate chemistry can be counterintuitive: the formation of $CaCO_3$ releases CO_2 and its dissolution removes CO_2 ($Ca_2^+ + 2HCO_3^- <-> CaCO_3 + CO_2 + H_2O$). Shifts in alkalinity and pH change the relative ratios of the ions that make up the aqueous carbonate system (CO_2^g, H_2CO_3, HCO_3^-, CO_3^{2-}), which changes the partial pressure of CO_2^g in the water, and whether the ocean takes up or releases CO2 into the atmosphere.

[5] More detail on this can be found in: Harvey, L. 2008. Mitigating the atmospheric CO_2 increase and ocean acidification by adding limestone powder to upwelling regions. Journal of Geophysical Research Oceans, 113, C04028.

[6] This exercise was derived from a similar calculation in US National Research Council, Climate Intervention: Carbon Dioxide Removal and Reliable Sequestration (2015), The National Acadamies Press, Washington, D.C.

[7] Data on coal mining come from a webpage of the World Coal Association: https://www.worldcoal.org/coal/coal-mining, retrieved 3/17/2016.

2.2 Ocean Fertilization

Another of Nature's ways of removing CO$_2$ from the atmosphere is through **photosynthesis** by **phytoplankton** at the surface of the ocean (*Figure 8.2*). These organisms eventually die or are eaten by other organisms that die or release fecal material, and these wastes and dead organisms sink to the bottom of the ocean. Bacteria in the deep ocean consume most of this organic matter and re-release CO$_2$ through respiration. As the ocean circulates this carbon is eventually brought back to the surface and released, but the ocean's waters turn over slowly, on time scales from decades to millenia. A small percentage of the organic matter becomes buried in sediments, potentially storing carbon for up to millions of years. The process from surface photosynthesis to deep ocean respiration, often referred to as a "biological pump," effectively takes carbon from the atmosphere and stores it deep in the ocean.

photosynthesis · *a chemical process in plants and other organisms which converts light energy and carbon dioxide into chemical energy (sugars that provide fuel) and oxygen.*

phytoplankton · *one-celled photosynthetic algae that float near the surface of bodies of both marine and freshwater.*

Figure 8.2: *A pale brown plume of dust swept out of Argentina's Pampas, a heavily farmed grassland, and split into two plumes over the South Atlantic Ocean. The wide arc and subtle curls within the dust plume complement the patterns visible in the ocean beneath it. Peacock-colored, the South Atlantic Ocean was in full bloom: a display of blue and green streaks and swirls peek from beneath the dust storm. The wind-blown dust also carries iron and other nutrients that fertilize already fertile ocean waters. The surface-dwelling phytoplankton color the ocean, contributing to the brilliant color seen in the image. Sediment from the Rio de la Plata may also be contributing to the ocean color. The southern edge of the brown, sediment-filled estuary is visible along the top of the image. Like dust, sediment from river plumes also adds nutrients to the ocean, further supporting phytoplankton blooms.*

Figure 8.3: Diatoms (a type of phytoplankton) seen through a microscope. These specimens were living between crystals of annual sea ice in McMurdo Sound, Antarctica.

Scientists have proposed enhancing this process by "fertilizing" the ocean: adding nitrogen, phosphate, or iron to seawater to boost phytoplankton growth near the surface. Iron fertilization has been the preferred approach since phytoplankton produce much more carbon per mole of iron than they do per mole of nitrogen or phosphate. Researchers have focused on the Southern Ocean as a candidate location for iron fertilization. Phytoplankton growth there is currently limited by relatively little iron in surface waters, but the water is rich in nitrogen and phosphorus which could feed phytoplankton growth once it is stimulated by adding iron to the water. *Figure 8.3* shows a close-up view of some types of phytoplankton found in the Southern Ocean.

Estimates are that global-scale iron fertilization of the oceans would remove less than 1 Gt of carbon per year from the atmosphere. By comparison, fossil fuel burning worldwide released around 9 Gt of carbon into the atmosphere in 2014. There are concerns and unknowns about it as well. The success of CDR through accelerating the ocean's biological pump depends partly on ocean circulation taking a long time to bring carbon in the deep ocean back up to the surface. One of the problems with this method is that climate change which has already begun will likely change ocean circulation patterns in ways we don't fully understand. These changes could reduce the effectiveness of ocean fertilization.

As with any large-scale intervention in Earth's systems, iron fertilization may harm ecosystems. Increased iron and increased phytoplankton growth could affect fish, birds, and other organisms, and indeed the entire marine food web. Iron fertilization could lead to changes in nutrient supplies and oxygen levels (through increased respiration of more organic material). It could also alter the ocean's biogeochemistry in other ways, such as producing increased release of the greenhouse gas nitrous oxide (N_2O) from marine microorganisms.

3. Examples of Solar Radiation Management (SRM) Techniques

SRM techniques involve reducing solar heating of the Earth by increasing the Earth's or the atmosphere's reflectivity (albedo), or blocking sunlight before it reaches the Earth. Since these techniques do not remove any greenhouse gases from the atmosphere, they do nothing to address the problem of ocean acidification. These techniques are so controversial, poorly understood, and risky that a recent report published by the US National Academy of Sciences recommends quite definitively that "albedo modification at scales sufficient to alter climate should not be deployed at this time."[8] The report does recommend studying SRM, however, in the event that there is pressure to use it as an emergency option or that it is attempted by an individual nation or organization. Research connected to SRM can also further climate science, especially if it leads to a better understanding of the role of clouds, **albedo**, and **aerosols** in Earth's climate system.

3.1 Marine Cloud Brightening

The ocean covers most of the Earth, and absorbs more sunlight per unit area than land, **sea ice**, and **ice sheets**. Low clouds, however, cover from 20 to 40 percent of the ocean surface. These clouds reflect sunlight, and several proposals have looked at ways to enhance the brightness of these clouds so that they reflect even more sunlight. This could be done by spraying particles—maybe small grains of salt produced by evaporating sea water—into the clouds from airplanes or ships. The salt particles would serve as **nucleation sites** for water droplets, and these additional water droplets in the clouds could reflect additional sunlight away from the Earth.

Advantages of marine cloud brightening using salt spray are that the raw material (sea water) is readily available and the salt particles that would eventually fall as rain would not pollute the ocean. Further, if problems arose the process could be stopped quickly. Disadvantages are the cost (and fossil fuel use) of deploying machinery to spray particles into the atmosphere, the uncertainty of how cloud brightening could affect local and regional weather and ocean currents, and the uncertainty of the basic efficacy of the method. We know from satellite observation that trails of exhaust from ocean-going ships form bright clouds; the particles in the exhaust act as cloud nucleation sites. *Figure 8.4* shows a satellite image of ship tracks in the Pacific Ocean. We don't know whether cloud brightening methods work reliably, and even if they did, whether cloud brightening could be done economically on a large enough scale to produce substantial cooling.

3.2 Stratospheric Aerosol Distribution

People have observed over centuries that volcanic eruptions can have a rapid, dramatic effect on climate. The sulfur dioxide (SO_2) particles released into the

---

[8] US National Research Council, Climate Intervention: Reflecting Sunlight to Cool Earth (2015), The National Acadamies Press, Washington, D.C.

SRM Techniques

albedo • the fraction of solar energy that a surface reflects back into space.

aerosol • the suspension of very fine solid or liquid particles in a gas.

sea ice • frozen seawater at the surface of the ocean.

ice sheet • a mass of glacial ice that covers part of a continent and has an area greater than 50,000 square kilometers (19,000 square miles).

nucleation sites • suspended particles in the air which can serve as "seeds" for water molecules to attach to, in the first step in the formation of clouds. See also CONDENSATION NUCLEI.

8 Geoengineering

SRM Techniques

stratosphere • *the second layer above the Earth's surface in the ATMOSPHERE. The stratosphere reaches to about 50 kilometers (30 miles) above the Earth's surface.*

infrared • *electromagnetic radiation in the part of the spectrum with wavelengths from 750 nanometers to 1 millimeter. People sense infrared radiation as heat.*

ozone • *a molecule (O_3) found in the STRATOSPHERE which absorbs ultraviolet light. When found near the surface of the Earth, ozone is considered a pollutant because it is a component of smog and can cause lung irritation.*

"ozone hole" • *a region of ozone depletion in the STRATOSPHERE above Antarctica, caused by destruction of ozone from ANTHROPOGENIC chemicals released into the ATMOSPHERE.*

volcanic sulfates • *sulfate molecules in the atmosphere formed from chemical reactions with sulfur dioxide released in volcanic eruptions.*

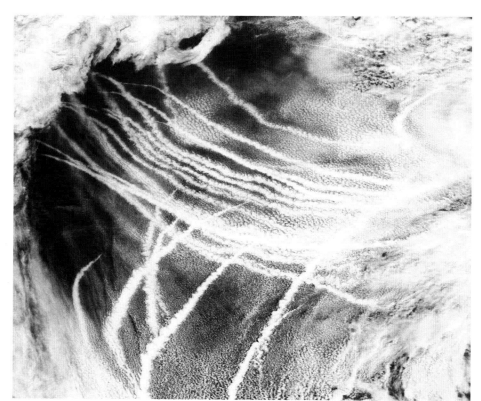

Figure 8.4: Bright linear clouds—ship tracks—formed from the exhaust trails of ships south of Alaska.

stratosphere from large volcanic eruptions reflect away incoming sunlight, cooling the Earth for up to a few years. The most recent example was the 1991 eruption of Mount Pinatubo in the Philippines (*Figure 8.5*), which led to an almost 0.6°C (1°F) decrease in average global temperatures over 15 months.[9] A temporary and substantial decrease in rainfall over land has also been attributed to the eruption of Mount Pinatubo.[10]

A geoengineering proposal that seeks to mimic this cooling effect involves injecting aerosols such as sulfur dioxide into the stratosphere continuously over the course of decades or centuries. If the particles are the right size they will reflect incoming sunlight back to space without scattering outgoing **infrared** radiation (i.e., heat) back towards the Earth. This technique could work very quickly, reducing Earth's temperature within a year of deployment.

Injecting aerosols into the stratosphere has substantial unknowns about how it would affect temperature, precipitation, and weather patterns regionally and globally. In addition, it carries the risk of changing **ozone** concentrations in the stratosphere. Ozone in the atmosphere protects life on Earth from damaging ultraviolet rays, and after an "**ozone hole**" (a region of depleted ozone) was detected over Antarctica there was a major international effort to ban substances that lead to ozone depletion. **Volcanic sulfates** in the atmosphere can undergo chemical reactions that lead to ozone depletion. After the eruption of Mount Pinatubo, ozone concentrations decreased in the Northern Hemisphere and

---

[9] A summary of the effects of Mt. Pinatubo's eruption ten years afterward can be found here: http://earthobservatory.nasa.gov/IOTD/view.php?id=1510 .

[10] See Trenberth, K. E., & Dai, A. (2007). Effects of Mount Pinatubo volcanic eruption on the hydrological cycle as an analog of geoengineering. Geophysical Research Letters, 34, L15702.

Geoengineering

carbon cycle • *the exchange and recycling of carbon between the geosphere, hydrosphere, atmosphere, and biosphere.*

Figure 8.5: Ash cloud of Mt. Pinatubo during 1991 eruption.

increased in the Southern Hemisphere. These changes have been attributed to changes in the movement of global air masses due to temperature effects from the eruption. Our understanding of the complex interactions that link aerosols, atmospheric chemistry, and global weather patterns is far from complete, and must be improved before we consider injecting aerosols into the atmosphere as a geoengineering technique.

3.3 Surface Albedo Alteration

Another way to reflect more sunlight away from the Earth is to alter the Earth's surface itself. This could include planting crops or grasslands that have a higher albedo than other plants, covering large areas of desert with reflective material, or painting roofs white. Most of the Earth's surface is covered by the ocean, which has a lower albedo than land or ice (see *Figure 8.6*), and some proposals suggest producing bubbles near the ocean's surface to increase its reflectivity. These options have not been studied thoroughly, and preliminary analyses suggest that their costs would far outweigh their effectivity. As with other geoengineering proposals, they raise questions of environmental and societal impact. For example, how would we balance the need to plant crops or grasses that have higher albedo with the need to grow certain plants for food and biofuels? What damage would occur to desert ecosystems if we covered large areas of land with reflective materials? How would surface bubbles in the ocean affect phytoplankton, an important part of the **carbon cycle**?

Geoengineering

Figure 8.6: Map of the albedo of the Earth's land surfaces for the month of March, 2016, measured by Moderate Resolution Imaging Spectroradiometer (MODIS) sensors on NASA's Aqua and Terra satellites. The lighter colors seen in areas covered by ice, snow, and sand indicate high albedo, and the darker colors seen in forest-covered areas indicate low albedo.

Box 8.2: Exercise to estimate the costs of painting roofs white to increase reflectivity[11]

Assume that the cost of painting roofs white is $0.30 per square meter per year (including materials and labor and factoring in repainting every 10 years). Assume that the paintable roofs covered 1% of the Earth's *land* surface. What would be the total annual cost for this endeavor?

One can look up that the Earth's total surface area is about 197×10^6 square miles, and that about 30% of that surface area is land. This means that the Earth's land surface area is approximately:

$$0.30 \times 197 \times 10^6 \text{ mi}^2 = 59 \times 10^6 \text{ mi}^2.$$

Convert this to square meters:

Earth's land surface area = $59 \times 10^6 \text{ mi}^2 \times (1609 \text{ m/mi})^2 = 1.5 \times 10^{14} \text{ m}^2.$

The annual cost for painting roofs in 1% of this area is then:

$$\$0.30/\text{m}^2/\text{year} \times 0.01 \times 1.5 \times 10^{14} \text{ m}^2 = \$4.5 \times 10^{11}/\text{year}.$$

In other words, $450 billion per year!

Estimates of the effectivity of roof painting conclude that the net effect would reduce the radiative impact of a doubling of CO_2 in the atmosphere by only about 0.25%.

---

[11] This exercise is based on an estimate in The Royal Society, Geoengineering the climate: science, governance and uncertainty. London, UK (2009).

4. Geoengineering Choices

This section did not review all geoengineering proposal discussed in the literature. Omissions include reflective structures in space to block sunlight before it even reaches Earth's atmosphere, technologies that can remove CO_2 directly from the air, and biofuel production and use combined with carbon capture and sequestration technology. Several of the footnotes in this chapter give references which provide more detail on these methods.

Geoengineering proposals have varying but generally high degrees of uncertainty in their effectivity and impacts. They must be evaluated based on financial cost, land area used, energy required, potential for environmental degradation, effectivity, time scales for implementation and effect, and social and political barriers. For many approaches, their implementation has risks that we don't currently know how to evaluate. For these reasons, almost all reviews of geoengineering methods emphasize that our primary focus today should be on reducing greenhouse gas emissions.

See Chapter 7: Climate Change Mitigation.

Geoengineering

RESOURCES

An article about an innovative approach to climate intervention that could also simultaneously produce biofuels and food: *Marine Microalgae: Climate, Energy, and Food Security from the Sea* by C.H. Greene et al., *Oceanography* 29(4):10–15 (2016). https://tos.org/oceanography/assets/docs/29-4_greene.pdf.

Two 2015 reports on climate intervention from the US National Research Council, along with links to media coverage of their release: https://nas-sites.org/americasclimatechoices/other-reports-on-climate-change/climate-intervention-reports/.

The website of the Oxford Geoengineering Programme at Oxford University, UK, contains brief overviews of geoengineering methods: http://www.geoengineering.ox.ac.uk/.

Chapter 9:
Climate Change Adaptation

The Earth's average surface temperature has risen 0.8°C (1.4° F) since 1880,[1] largely as a result of human-caused emissions of carbon dioxide (CO_2). These emissions spread evenly throughout the atmosphere and interact with the oceans, rocks, and plants and animals in a complex system we call the **carbon cycle**. Most of the CO_2 that we emit will remain in the Earth system—and continue to raise the Earth's temperature—for hundreds or thousands of years. According to the Intergovernmental Panel on Climate Change (IPCC, see Box 9.1),

> *Most aspects of climate change will persist for many centuries even if emissions of CO_2 are stopped. This represents a substantial multi-century climate change commitment created by past, present and future emissions of CO_2.*[2]

Even if we could instantly prevent any future CO_2 emissions—which we cannot do—we will have to deal with the ultimate impacts of the CO_2 that we have already emitted. These impacts are often described as being "in the pipeline," meaning that we are already committed to these changes and while we can't stop them, we can adapt to them. It is imperative that we continue to expand our mitigation efforts to limit the amount of human-caused global warming, but we also need to find ways to adapt to these climate impacts that are "in the pipeline." This chapter explores existing and proposed adaptation strategies

carbon cycle • the exchange and recycling of carbon between the geosphere, hydrosphere, atmosphere, and biosphere.

Box 9.1: The Intergovernmental Panel on Climate Change (IPCC)

The IPCC, founded in 1988 by the World Meteorological Organization and the United Nations Environment Programme, is a group of scientists from 195 countries who assess the state of the world's climate, climate science, impacts and risks of climate change, and options to respond to it. Over three thousand scientists are involved in writing and reviewing the IPCC's climate assessments approximately every six years, and these assessments are considered by many to be the authoritative source of information on climate change science. The assessments do not include policy suggestions, but they are intended to provide information to help government officials develop sound, research-based climate change policies.

See Chapter 7 on efforts to mitigate climate change.

---

[1] This and other data on climate change can be found on a NASA website, Global Climate Change: Vital Signs of the Planet, http://climate.nasa.gov/.

[2] The IPCC publishes in-depth technical reports on climate change science, impacts, and mitigation. They also publish summaries for policymakers. The most recent summary of climate change science (as of this writing) can be found here: http://www.ipcc.ch/report/ar5/wg1/.

CHAPTER AUTHOR

Ingrid H. H. Zabel

Climate Change Adaptation

Adaptation Cost

> **greenhouse effect** • *the influence of GREENHOUSE GAS molecules in the Earth's atmosphere to retain heat (infrared radiation) radiating from the Earth's surface that would otherwise escape into space.*

> **storm surge** • *a large volume of ocean water pushed onto land by offshore winds during a storm.*

for a variety of climate hazards and examines some of the challenges these strategies present.

1. How Much Does Adaptation Cost?

Many climate hazards come from processes that change very slowly over time, but are extremely difficult to stop. For example, as the atmosphere warms due to the **greenhouse effect**, so does the surface of the ocean. Surface water mixes slowly with the rest of the ocean, and it will take hundreds of years for the ocean to absorb and mix the additional heat we are introducing to the system. Warmer water takes up more volume than colder water, so the ocean is expanding and sea level is rising. Rise by 2100 due to this influence is expected to be between 15 and 30 centimeters (6 to 12 inches), depending on the level of future carbon emissions.[3]

> For more on systems and ocean circulation, see Chapter 3: What is Climate?

This presents a challenge to economists and policy makers who try to determine the cost of any particular adaptation strategy. For example, many large cities are located on ocean coasts and sit at or just above sea level. As these cities make plans for the upcoming decades they have to decide how they will deal with the sea level rise that is "in the pipeline." City infrastructure such as airports, sea ports, roads, bridges, and subway systems and people living in coastal cities will be affected by rising sea levels, and they will need to plan for how to adapt.

Cities can select a variety of potential strategies. They can build sea walls or levees, or enhance shorelines with plants and natural structures that can absorb water and break waves. They can develop building requirements that mandate new structures be built at higher elevations. They can develop plans to raise the elevation of sea ports and airports that are at risk. All of these options come with a cost—some much larger than others—but city planners also have to weigh these costs against the cost of inaction. If you are creating a city budget for the next year, future sea level rise may not seem like much of a threat. You may decide to do nothing and leave the sea level rise problem for future planners. You also may decide to build protective structures—at a high cost—and to justify these costs to the taxpaying public.

To make things even more difficult, many of these adaptation strategies and decisions have to be made in the face of uncertainty. How much will protective infrastructure cost? Who should pay for it? How high will the sea level rise? What type of **storm surge** should one prepare for? Are the frequency or severity of storm surges going to change in a warming climate? What should we do if sea levels start to rise quicker than we initially thought? What would happen if we did nothing?

---

[3] This cause of sea level is different than that caused by melting glaciers. The IPCC reports that from 1993 to 2010, thermal expansion contributed to sea level rise at a rate of 1.1 mm/yr, melting from glaciers contributed at a rate of 0.76 mm/yr, and melting of the Greenland and Antarctic ice sheets contributed at rates of 0.33 and 0.27 mm/yr, respectively. For melting glaciers there is a somewhat shorter time lag than for thermal expansion, and a feedback between a warmer atmosphere and glacial melting.

Climate Change Adaptation

Every adaptation strategy has its own set of uncertainties and potential trade-offs. One example of a way to think about adaptation strategies and the potential costs and benefits comes from the US Department of Transportation:

> *Actions taken to adapt transportation systems to climate change have both costs and benefits. Costs can include increased construction cost associated with designing a bridge to be able to withstand more frequent and intense storms, training costs associated with process or equipment changes, or the increased cost of labor and materials if operation and maintenance activities change or occur more frequently. Costs can also include broader effects (whether positive or negative) on the economy and jobs.*

> *The benefits of adaptation are the adverse impacts that are avoided; the more effective adaptation is, the greater the benefits. Benefits could include savings from avoiding the need to repair/replace assets. Benefits could also include impacts on quality of life from reduced traffic delays, avoided risks to human safety, avoided disruption of the flow of goods, etc.[4]*

Costs assessments can be done from "bottom-up," where one constructs detailed inventories of systems and their components, and the costs of specific adaptation methods applied to them. Another approach is "top-down," where one uses aggregate data on a system and makes assumptions about the additional costs needed to apply adaptation techniques to the system. Benefits such as improvements to quality of life can be hard to quantify, but economists attempt to define and assign values to measurable quantities such as delays avoided, lives saved, health improved, jobs created, repairs deferred, and **ecosystem services** maintained. A cost-benefit analysis compares the costs and benefits of an action, with the goal of finding actions where the benefits outweigh the costs. This is a difficult exercise, because in addition to estimating monetary values of costs and benefits, one has to factor in the likelihood of the action being adopted and the time frame on which the costs and benefits will be realized (see *Box 9.2*).

2. Types of Adaptation Strategies

Table 9.1 lists examples of different types of adaptation strategies.[5] It does not address every possible hazard associated with climate change and is not meant to be comprehensive. Rather, it is meant to give examples of a range of strategies which communities, governments, and businesses can use to adapt to climate change. Some strategies are "win-win" or "no-regrets," that is, they have benefits beyond adapting to climate change and should probably be done anyway. Others can be seen as more drastic.

ecosystem services • *the numerous benefits that healthy ecosystems provide to people, such as food, medicine sources, raw materials, erosion control, waste decomposition, filtering pollutants out of air and water, and recreation opportunities.*

---

[4] These examples came from a 2013 US Department of Transportation report, Assessment of the Body of Knowledge on Incorporating Climate Change Adaptation Measures into Transportation Projects: Assessing Costs and Benefits of Adaptive Strategies.

[5] Examples of climate change adaptation strategies can be found on many federal and state websites. Examples in Table 9.1 were drawn mainly from Rosenzweig, C., Solecki, W., DeGaetano, A., O'Grady, M., Hassol, S., Grabhorn, P., & (eds), Responding to Climate Change in New York State: The ClimAID Integrated Assessment for Effective Climate Change Adaptation, Technical Report (2011), Albany, NY, New York State Energy Research and Development Authority (NYSERDA) and Denver Climate Resiliency Committee, City and County of Denver Climate Adaptation Plan (2014), Denver, CO Department of Environmental Health.

Climate Change Adaptation

Table 9.1: Example adaptation strategies.

Adaptation Strategy: Relocate and retreat
Sea Level Rise
Climate Hazard: *Coastal flooding, permanent inundation of coastal areas*
Adaptation Strategy: *Relocate homes and infrastructure to higher elevations*
Heavy Downpours
Climate Hazard: *Increasing flood risk*
Adaptation Strategy: *Implement phased withdrawal of infrastructure from flood-prone areas*

Adaptation Strategy: Make changes in built infrastructure
Heat Waves
Climate Hazard: *Decreasing dairy productivity due to heat stress in cows*
Adaptation Strategy: *Alter livestock barns to increase cooling capacity*
Sea Level Rise
Climate Hazard: *Coastal flooding and property damage*
Adaptation Strategy: *Build structures to attenuate waves and storm surges*
Extreme Storms
Climate Hazard: *Damage to power and communication lines*
Adaptation Strategy: *Relocate lines underground where possible*

Adaptation Strategy: Renew and conserve natural systems
Sea Level Rise
Climate Hazard: *Coastal erosion and loss of wetlands*
Adaptation Strategy: *Renourish beaches and restore wetlands*
Heavy Downpours
Climate Hazard: *Riverbank erosion and river flooding*
Adaptation Strategy: *Stabilize riverbanks by planting deep-rooted, native plants*
Temperature Change
Climate Hazard: *Shifts in range of animal species*
Adaptation Strategy: *Maintain habitat connectivity and migration corridors*

Adaptation Strategy: Make land use changes
Sea Level Rise
Climate Hazard: *Permanent inundation of coastal land*
Adaptation Strategy: *Build up portions of low-lying cities*
Heavy Downpours
Climate Hazard: *Increased flood risk and flood damage*
Adaptation Strategy: *Buy out land or perform land swaps to encourage people to move out of flood-prone areas*

Adaptation Strategy: Modify management and operations
Temperature Change
Climate Hazard: *Changing growing season and crop productivity*
Adaptation Strategy: *Alter planting cycles, crop variety, and crop type*
Extreme Storms
Climate Hazard: *Reduced bridge and roadway safety*
Adaptation Strategy: *Plan to reduce/suspend traffic during extreme storm events*
Heat Waves
Climate Hazard: *Heat-related illness and death*
Adaptation Strategy: *Increase power supply for air conditioning, provide cooling centers for vulnerable populations*

Climate Change Adaptation

Table 9.1: Continued.

Adaptation Strategy: Diversify to increase resilience

Temperature Change

Climate Hazard: *Reduced crop productivity at higher temperatures*

Adaptation Strategy: *Innovate and develop new crop types and farming methods*

Reduced Snowfall

Climate Hazard: *Loss of wintertime tourism (skiing, snowmobiling)*

Adaptation Strategy: *Shift and innovate other recreational and tourist activities*

Adaptation Strategy: Social innovation

Heat Waves

Climate Hazard: *Heat-related illness and death*

Adaptation Strategy: *Foster community networks that find and help at-risk populations*

Drought

Climate Hazard: *Stress on water supply*

Adaptation Strategy: *Influence consumer water conservation behavior with the use of smart meters and pricing*

Reduced Snowpack

Climate Hazard: *Reduced snowpack runoff and water supply*

Adaptation Strategy: *Encourage landscaping and gardening practices that use drought-resistant plants and eliminate need for irrigation*

Adaptation Strategy:Risk management

Extreme Weather

Climate Hazard: *Energy supply disruptions*

Adaptation Strategy: *Increase distributed electricity generation (electricity from multiple small sources)*

Extreme Storms

Climate Hazard: *Damage to transportation systems*

Adaptation Strategy: *Create mutual insurance pools to share risks*

Heat Waves

Climate Hazard: *Heat-related illness and death*

Adaptation Strategy: *Create systems to predict threats and alert at-risk populations*

Adaptation Strategy: Policy changes

Extreme Coastal Storms

Climate Hazard: *Damages to coastal property*

Adaptation Strategy: *Update building codes to promote storm-resistant structures*

Sea Level Rise

Climate Hazard: *Loss of coastal wetland habitat*

Adaptation Strategy: *Protect coastal wetlands with rolling easements (recognize nature's right-of-way to advance inland as sea level rises)*

Drought

Climate Hazard: *Lack of water for hydropower plants*

Adaptation Strategy: *Adjust reservoir release policies to ensure sufficient summer hydropower capacity*

Climate Change Adaptation

tidal floods · *a flood occurring during high tides.*

nuisance flooding · *flooding which leads to inconveniences such as road closures and overflowing storm drains, but which does not cause severe damage.*

aquifers · *a water-bearing formation of gravel, permeable rock, or sand that is capable of providing water, in usable quantities, to springs or wells.*

storm surge · *a large volume of ocean water pushed onto land by offshore winds during a storm*

Box 9.2: Classroom exercise on cost-benefit assessment

A high school is in a region that is experiencing more intense heat waves, especially during June when classes are wrapping up and students are taking final exams. The school has inadequate cooling systems, and people are concerned about heat-related illness affecting the staff and students. Several students have already been taken to the hospital, suffering from heat stress.

The administration is considering several options to deal with extreme heat. Evaluate the costs and benefits of each option, and come up with a recommendation for what action(s) to take based on this analysis. You can add options that are not listed here.

Adaptation options:

1. Install a building-wide central air conditioning system

2. Install window air conditioners in classrooms, staff offices, the library, and the gym, but not elsewhere in the building

3. Provide ice water stations in the hallways for students to use in between classes

4. Shorten winter break and spring break so that school can end earlier in May, when heat waves are less likely

5. Start school two hours earlier, to avoid the afternoon heat

6. Avoid the afternoon heat by ending the school day earlier, but add school on Saturday to make up for the lost time

3. Adaptation to Different Climate Hazards

This section presents examples of adaptation responses to different hazards from a changing climate.

3.1 Rising Sea Level

Coastal communities sometimes experience flooding during high tides. These **tidal floods** (*Figure 9.1*) provide a view of the future with rising seas, when today's tidal floods become the future's everyday floods. In addition to **nuisance flooding**, a rising sea level can lead to coastal erosion, property damage, saltwater intrusion into freshwater **aquifers** and ecosystems, and permanent flooding of coastal land and infrastructure. When coastal storms with intense winds produce **storm surge**—a rising sea pushed onto land—higher sea levels lead to higher storm surge and more storm damage and risk to human lives.

Sea level rise affects billions of people worldwide. In 2010, 80% of the world's population lived within 60 miles of a coast. 75% of all large cities are located

Climate Change Adaptation

Figure 9.1: Tidal flooding in the Brickell neighborhood of downtown Miami, FL in October, 2016.

on or near an ocean coast. In the US, Florida has the most cities at risk, but other American cities such as New York, Boston, Charleston, New Orleans, San Francisco, and many smaller cities are also vulnerable to sea level rise. Sea level rise also affects estuaries far upstream from the ocean. As sea level rises, salt water gets pushed further up into the freshwater region of an estuary, putting ecosystems and water resources for people at risk.

Strategies to protect coasts and communities from sea level rise include building structures that break or attenuate waves, maintaining and enhancing natural protective coastline features, setting restrictions and rules on whether and how coastal land can be developed, and relocating infrastructure and communities to higher ground. Building hard structures such as seawalls, levees, storm surge barriers, and breakwaters was common in the mid-20th century, but more recently organizations such as the Army Corps of Engineers have favored nature-based approaches such as building dunes and nourishing (i.e., adding sand to) beaches. Other nature-based approaches include maintaining and enhancing wetlands, coastal forests, barrier islands, and oyster reefs. These natural features help to prevent erosion, break waves offshore, and reduce the energy of incoming waves. They also serve other functions such as absorbing stormwater and providing habitat for commercially important fish and shellfish species. Some adaptation projects have used nature-based engineering, for example, they have created artificial oyster reefs or other structures that replicate natural ones (*Figure 9.2*).

Policies, regulations, building codes, and flood preparedness and insurance programs all play a role in adapting to rising seas. Communities can set restrictions on where buildings can be built, limiting development extremely close to the coast where beaches and buildings are at greatest risk (*Figure 9.3*). Communities can also create building codes that require new construction to be more storm-resistant, built on stilts, or made with the capacity to float. They can define "rolling easements" on property, which recognize that wetlands and beaches will migrate inland, regardless of whether properties will be eroded or flooded. Flood insurance rates for coastal properties can be set to reflect the reality of the risk in coastal zones, which is high. Finally, communities need to create effective flood and storm warning and preparedness programs, to keep residents safe in place or to evacuate them when necessary.

Climate Change Adaptation

Figure 9.2: Artificial oyster reefs parallel to the shoreline provide a way to slow the rate of coastal erosion by reducing incoming wave energy.

Figure 9.3: Beaches houses on the western side of Misquamicut Beach, Westerly, Rhode Island.

Some communities will need to consider relocation. This is already happening in places such as the village of Shishmaref, AK, where residents voted in 2016 to move their entire village away from a barrier island; in Staten Island, NY, where some residents left with no plans to return following devastation from Hurricane Sandy; and in Isle de Jean Charles, LA, where residents received the first ever grant of federal funding to help them relocate because of rising sea level brought on by climate change. Relocation can involve moving critical infrastructure such as hospitals, wastewater treatment plants, and bridges, but it can also involve moving entire communities or neighborhoods farther inland to higher ground. Other proposals have included building up low-lying areas of cities such as Norfolk, Virginia, which face the combined pressures of low elevation, rising seas, and naturally subsiding ground. The financial and social costs of relocation can be enormous, which is why mitigation—taking action to reduce the rate and magnitude of climate change, rather than relying entirely upon adaptation—is critical.

3.2 Heat Waves

Heat waves—defined as a series of consecutive days with exceptionally high air temperatures—can be deadly. During an intensely hot period in July of 1995,

Climate Change Adaptation

733 people died from heat-related illness in Chicago. In 1993, a heat wave in Europe killed nearly 35,000 people, and in 2010, a heat wave in Moscow killed more than 10,000 people. Heat waves often disproportionately affect vulnerable populations: people who don't have enough income to pay for air conditioning at home, elderly people living alone who can't get themselves to cool locations, or people living in crime-ridden neighborhoods who are afraid to open windows.

Heat waves also stress ecosystems, livestock, and infrastructure. Dairy cows produce less milk and crop growth can slow during periods of intense heat, and paved roads can buckle. Energy systems are strained during heat waves when electricity demand for air conditioning rises, sometimes leading to **brownouts** and blackouts. These power disruptions in turn put strain on communications and emergency response systems. Heat waves combined with drought can increase the likelihood of wildfires. Under a warming climate the frequency and length of heat waves has increased in much of the US. This trend has already been noted in recent decades and is expected to continue.

Adaptation efforts to deal with extreme heat are underway, especially in urban areas where pollution, pavement, and the surfaces of buildings magnify localized warming in a phenomenon called the **urban heat island effect**. Strategies to reduce this effect often focus on reducing absorption of sunlight. Approaches include planting trees along city streets and in open spaces, and building living roofs—rooftops covered with living plants instead of asphalt or other materials (*Figure 9.4*). These techniques involving vegetation lead to measurable cooling. Plants can cool a roof or other surface by lightening the surface color (compared with dark asphalt), since light colors absorb less sunlight and radiate less heat than dark colors. A layer of plants can also provide insulation on a roof. Where living roofs are not feasible, painting roofs with reflective paint can help keep buildings cool. Using lighter colored paving materials for streets can also reduce local warming.

In addition, plants can cool the air through evapotranspiration. Evapotranspiration is a combination of evaporation of liquid water on plant leaves and in the soil around the plant and transpiration, the transfer of water from a plant's roots to its leaves and then to water vapor in the air. Evapotranspiration cools the air because it takes heat from the air to convert liquid water to water vapor.

Climate Hazards

brownout • *a situation where available electric power is limited but not eliminated.*

urban heat island effect • *a phenomenon in which an urban area experiences higher temperatures than do surrounding rural areas as a result of pollution, pavement, and the surfaces of buildings magnifying localized heating.*

Figure 9.4: Living roof on a building at the US Air Force Joint Base Andrews, MD.

Climate Hazards

green infrastructure · *structures that use plants, soil, and other natural features to perform functions such as providing shade, absorbing heat, blocking wind, or absorbing and filtering stormwater.*

Climate Change Adaptation

In addition to making structural changes to keep cities cool, communities must develop effective heat warning systems to alert residents to the dangers of extreme heat, and put in place heat response plans to protect residents. These systems and plans must pay particular attention to vulnerable populations such as the elderly, low-income residents, and non-English speakers who may find it hard to get weather and safety information they can understand. The heat response plans might include actions such as using neighborhood social networks to check on elderly residents, opening air-conditioned cooling centers for the public, and providing maps and transportation to these centers.

Agricultural strategies to adapt to more frequent heat waves include using fans, sprinklers, and other cooling methods in livestock barns, and developing new crop varieties that can tolerate heat better. For activities such as transportation, telecommunications, and energy distribution, many of the adaptation strategies for extreme heat involve technological solutions. For example, power lines may need upgrading with wiring and transformers that work well at higher temperatures. Bridge and road materials may also need upgrading, and public transportation systems such as subways and buses may need more and better air conditioning. In addition, if large-scale systems that use energy can be made more energy efficient, it will reduce the strain on electrical systems during heat waves when demand is high.

3.3 Heavy Rainfall

Warmer air can hold more water vapor, so under a warming climate the average global amount of precipitation will increase—although this will not be evenly distributed. Some regions will get more rainfall, and some regions will get less, but heavy downpours have been increasing in most regions of the US, and are expected to continue to increase. *Figure 9.5* shows percent increases in the amount of precipitation falling in very heavy events (defined as the heaviest 1% of all daily events) from 1958 to 2012. A large amount of rain falling in a short time can overwhelm stormwater management and sewer systems and lead to dangerous, destructive flooding and mudslides. It can also wash nutrients from farms and pollutants into sensitive ecosystems and drinking water reservoirs.

One way that cities are addressing the increased risk of heavy rainfall is through the use of **green infrastructure**. Conventional or "gray" ways of managing heavy rainfall in cities involve capturing the rain with gutters and storm sewers and moving it away through pipes to nearby streams, rivers, or lakes. Green infrastructure incorporates soil and plants, and uses them to absorb and filter rainwater. The absorption reduces the amount of stormwater that could potentially flood streets and neighborhoods, and any excess water is cleaner after being filtered.

One example of green infrastructure is a rain garden, typically a basin near a sidewalk or street containing decorative plants (*Figure 9.6*). The garden collects and absorbs rainwater, reducing pollution and preventing flooding. Building and maintaining a rain garden can be an excellent experiential education project for a school (see rain garden resources at the end of this chapter for guidance). A bioswale is a type of rain garden built as a channel along a street or parking lot. Bioswales absorb and filter water, and they also slow water down as it moves along the channel, reducing the risk of flooding. Paved areas such as parking

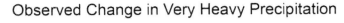
Observed Change in Very Heavy Precipitation

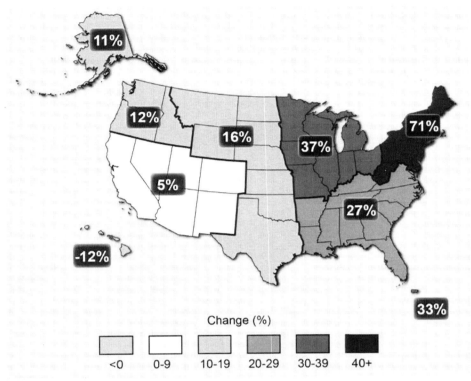

Figure 9.5: The map shows percent increases in the amount of precipitation falling in very heavy events (defined as the heaviest 1% of all daily events) from 1958 to 2012 for each region of the continental United States. These trends are larger than natural variations for the Northeast, Midwest, Puerto Rico, Southeast, Great Plains, and Alaska. The trends are not larger than natural variations for the Southwest, Hawai'i, and the Northwest. The changes shown in this figure are calculated from the beginning and end points of the trends for 1958 to 2012. (See Teacher-Friendly Guide website for a full color version.)

lots can also be built to absorb stormwater, using permeable pavement instead of plants. This type of pavement has small holes that allow water to drain into the soil below (*Figure 9.7*).

Another solution to address heavy rainfall involves upgrading culverts. Culverts are pipes or channels that carry water underneath roads or railroad lines. Most drivers don't give a second thought to culverts, but when they are too small to handle water from a heavy downpour, flooding and severe erosion of the roadbed and surrounding area can occur. Many culverts around the country will need to be redesigned and rebuilt to an appropriate size for the increased heavy rains that climate change is expected to bring.

A final strategy to adapt to the increasing frequency of heavy rainfall is to relocate key infrastructure out of flood-prone areas, and to site new construction away from these areas. An important part of this strategy is having the best possible knowledge of the location of flood zones. The Federal Emergency Management Agency (FEMA) publishes and regularly updates flood hazard maps that can be used for managing floodplain development.

Climate Change Adaptation

Figure 9.6: Rain garden in the High Point neighborhood in Seattle, WA.

Figure 9.7: Permeable pavement in an alley in Chicago, IL.

3.4 Drought

While many parts of the US have experienced drought in the past, the rising temperatures associated with global climate change will likely make droughts more severe. Warmer air leads to more evaporation from soils, lakes, and streams, and moisture loss from plants. These effects can stress agricultural production, ecosystems, and water resources for drinking water and energy production. The dry conditions from drought can also increase the risk of wildfires.

Adapting to more frequent and severe drought can involve monitoring and planning, restricting water use and grazing, improving and upgrading water supply and delivery infrastructure, developing and encouraging the use of drought-tolerant plants for gardens and crops, and educating the public and farmers on water conservation practices.

The National Drought Mitigation Center at the University of Nebraska-Lincoln, in partnership with the US government, produces weekly maps of drought conditions across the country (http://droughtmonitor.unl.edu). This monitoring, together with assessment of water sources and impacts of past droughts, can help communities plan for how to handle drought. Actions that communities can plan for include setting up a drought warning system, making arrangements for alternate water sources during drought events, and setting up irrigation schedules for farmland. An early warning system, for example, can help ranchers make decisions about grazing their cattle sustainably. Pastures may not grow during droughts, and with enough advance warning ranchers can plan to limit grazing, look for alternate sources of feed, or sell off parts of their herd in order to sustain their grazing land and livelihood.

Another important type of monitoring is checking water supply systems for leaks, to minimize wasted water (see *Box 9.3*). This falls under the broader goal of water conservation, which is a wise practice at all times and which can become critical during times of drought. Communities can conserve water by imposing restrictions—limiting water use to firefighting and other emergency or essential use—or through voluntary measures and education. Households can conserve water by eliminating lawn watering and planting gardens with drought-tolerant plants, buying low-water-use dishwashers and clothes washers and using them only when full, fixing leaks and drips promptly, building driveways with permeable pavement to allow rain to filter into the ground, and capturing and reusing rainwater or other household water. Farmers can conserve water by using planting practices that reduce erosion, slow water runoff, and maximize water absorption in soil, irrigating different areas at different times to spread the use of water over time and land area, and capturing rainwater.

Ecosystems also experience stress during times of drought, but people can take action to help plants and wildlife adapt. One example is by creating fish passages. When streams and rivers dry out because of drought, fish find it much more difficult to travel upstream to spawn. Even if they are able to spawn, low stream flows can threaten the viability of their eggs and young. Fisheries managers can help fish by building channels with sufficient stream flow to allow fish to pass, and by removing barriers such as dams.

Climate Change Adaptation

3.5 Extreme Weather

One of the consequences of climate change is an increase in the frequency and intensity of extreme weather events such as heat waves, drought, hurricanes, winter storms, and coastal storm surges. Some of these are driven by the ability of warmer air to hold more moisture while others are the result of climate change and the response of the interconnectivity of the atmosphere, the oceans, the biosphere, and the land. Extreme weather can be highly destructive and life threatening, and poses a difficult adaptation challenge.

Adaptation strategies for drought, heat waves, and heavy rainfall are addressed in other sections of this chapter, so the focus of this section will be on storms that bring heavy winds, snow and ice, and storm surge. The more intense a hurricane, the higher the risk of damaging winds and storm surge. Storm surge occurs when offshore winds push a great volume of ocean water onto land. Sea level rise—another consequence of climate change due to warmer, expanding oceans and melting ice sheets—exacerbates the risk associated with storm surge because it means the sea is higher relative to land to begin with.

See *Box 6.5* in Chapter 6: Regional Climates for a discussion of climate change and extreme weather.

Adapting to storm surge is a difficult challenge for those who live on the coast, especially since storm surges can rise over 30 feet in an intense hurricane. Houses can be raised above the land surface by being built on piles (vertical structures), which allow water to flow beneath the house. The piles are built with deep foundations to prevent erosion of and damage to the piles. Communities can set regulations that require new buildings to be set back from flood-prone areas. They can also protect and revitalize natural features that provide buffers against storms surges, such as dunes and beach vegetation.

Adaptation strategies for high winds include using building practices that strengthen structures, designing building sites with high winds in mind (*Figure 9.8*), protecting power lines and other infrastructure, and providing education on safety in the face of severe winds. Building practices can be voluntary or made mandatory through building codes, and they include things like using extra nails when applying roof shingles, putting steel bracing around tall chimneys, and anchoring structures to permanent foundations. Site design considerations include incorporating natural wind breaks such as trees, designing features to

Climate Change Adaptation

Figure 9.8: Hurricane clips, shown circled above, help anchor roofs to the main structure to prevent detachment due to severe wind. These clips can be found at many hardware stores, and are an inexpensive way to mitigate home damage from hurricanes. The home above kept its lid on during the severe winds brought by Hurricane Katrina, even though construction of the house had not been completed.

direct wind away from buildings, and using ventilation systems to control the flow of air in and out of buildings. Power and telecommunication lines can be placed underground for protection, and regular tree trimming can help prevent damage to over-ground lines.

Education plays a big role in making sure communities are prepared for storms with high winds. Examples from the Federal Emergency Management Agency (FEMA) include:

- informing residents of shelter locations and evacuation routes;
- educating homeowners on the benefits of wind retrofits such as shutters and hurricane clips;
- ensuring that school officials are aware of the best area of refuge in school buildings;
- instructing property owners on how to properly install temporary window coverings before a storm; and
- educating design professionals to include defense against strong winds as part of building design.

Winter storms can include high winds and storm surge (if along the coast), but they bring the additional hazards of snow, ice, and cold temperatures. A loss of power following a winter storm can lead to lack of heat for buildings, putting people at risk and causing water pipes to freeze and burst. Implementing and enforcing building codes can help reduce the risk of weak roofs that collapse under heavy snow, and can reduce heat loss through the use of insulation. Utilities lines can be protected from ice and snow damage through similar measures as described above for protection from high winds, and communities can install snow fences or rows of trees to prevent snow from drifting and building up on roads. As with other weather hazards, education is critical for preventing loss of life. People need to learn: how to drive on icy roads (and when to avoid driving); how to prevent death from carbon monoxide poisoning by venting generators to the outside, installing detectors, and not sitting in a snow-covered car with the engine on; and to check on elderly and other vulnerable neighbors who may have lost power.

snowpack • *snow accumulated over time, often in mountainous areas that have a long cold season. When snowpack melts it feeds streams and rivers.*

Climate Change Adaptation

3.6 Reduced Snowfall and Snowpack

Although climate change is expected to bring more intense winter storms, many parts of the country have experienced a reduction in overall snowfall and **snowpack**. Snowpack is an important water resource, and less snow in the winter means less meltwater in the spring, reducing the flow of streams and rivers and depleting water supplies. People depend on this water supply for household use and agriculture, and ecosystems depend on it to sustain fish and other wildlife populations. The snow itself is an important part of tourist industries such as skiing and snowmobiling, and trout fishing tourism depends on streams with cold meltwater from snowpack. In addition to less snowpack, climate change is expected to bring earlier springs and earlier flows of meltwater.

Adapting to changes in snowpack and snowmelt is largely a question of water management. Communities may need to expand or build additional reservoirs to store more water in preparation for times of low snowmelt. They may also need to work out arrangements with communities in other watersheds, to purchase water from elsewhere in times of great need. A critical part of adapting to dwindling water resources is to do a much better job of conserving water.

Tourist industries that depend on snowpack can take several steps to adapt to less snow. Ski resorts, for examples, can use snowmaking technology, alter and develop slopes so they require less snow, and diversify their businesses to offer other attractions. These practices come with costs, of course. The recreational trout fishing season may shift to earlier months when streams are cooler, and anglers may switch to fishing for warm-water species such as bass.

4. Equity and Social Justice Considerations

Decisions about responding to climate change cannot be based on science and economics alone. They need to incorporate considerations of humans' relationships and responsibilities to each other, and how groups of people who have more resources to take action can help other groups who have less. Countries vary over orders of magnitude in the total amount of CO_2 they've emitted in the past as a country, how much they emit now, and how much they emit per capita. One of the challenges in creating international agreements on carbon emissions, and in creating domestic support for such agreements, is in resolving the real-world economic implications of decisions that, in principle, might take these sorts of factors into account.

Climate Change Adaptation

Box 9.4: Classroom discussion topic: global environmental justice

In 2011, the five countries that emitted the most CO_2 were:[6]

		percent of global CO_2 emissions
1.	China	28%
2.	United States	16%
3.	European Union	10%
4.	India	6%
5.	Russia	6%

In metric tons of CO_2 emitted per person in 2011, the top five ranked countries were:[7]

		metric tons of CO_2 emitted per person
1.	Saudi Arabia	19.65
2.	Australia	18.02
3.	United States	17.62
4.	Canada	16.24
5.	Russia	12.55

China's and India's per capita CO_2 emissions were 6.52 and 1.45 metric tons per person, respectively.

Potential discussion questions:

1. Given these numbers, what are the responsibilities of different countries for taking action to adapt to and mitigate climate change?

2. Should wealthier nations such as the US pay to help poorer nations respond to climate change? If so, what is a country's balance between spending money to protect its own people and cities and spending money to help people elsewhere?

3. Do developed countries such as the US and Canada bear greater responsibility to address climate change since the current warming comes largely from CO_2 they have emitted in the past, or is China's responsibility greater since it is the largest emitter (total, not per capita)? Note that recent studies suggest China's carbon emissions are slowing down.

4. What are individuals' responsibilities to address climate change? An interesting question to consider is one posed by philosopher Dale Jamieson.[8] He describes a person taking a long airplane flight, which results in a large amount of carbon emissions. These carbon emissions contribute to warming which can lead to extreme weather events that kill people. One could argue then that taking airplane flights can amount to committing murder, but very few people flying on airplanes feel like they are murderers. How does our sense of morality fit with our actions that are causing climate change?

---

[6] For details see https://www.epa.gov/ghgemissions/global-greenhouse-gas-emissions-data#Country.

[7] The Union of Concerned Scientists presents data for these countries and more here: http://www.ucsusa.org/global_warming/science_and_impacts/science/each-countrys-share-of-co2.html#.WJt4aDsrLIU. The original data source is the US Energy Information Administration.

[8] See, for example, Jamieson's book Reason in a Dark Time (Oxford University Press, 2014).

Climate Change Adaptation

Resources

General Adaptation Resources

The US Climate Resilience Toolkit provides a wealth of case studies, tools, maps, and other resources on adaptation to climate change: https://toolkit.climate.gov.

To help identify adaptation efforts across the country, the Georgetown Climate Center has created a map though which one can find state and local adaptation plans: http://www.georgetownclimate.org/adaptation/plans.html.

In 2013 FEMA published a report that outlines actions communities can take to reduce the risk from natural hazards and disasters, many of which are exacerbated by climate change. The report, *Mitigation Ideas: A Resource for Reducing Risk to Natural Hazards*, can be found here: https://www.fema.gov/ar/media-library/assets/documents/30627.

Adapting to Sea Level Rise

The US Army Corps of Engineers has written a report that provides an overview of different types of approaches to making coastal areas more resilient to climate change impacts. The report is titled *Coastal Risk Reduction and Resilience: Using the Full Array of Measures* and is available here: http://www.corpsclimate.us/ccacrrr.cfm.

After Hurricane Sandy the US Department of Housing and Urban Development launched a design competition called Rebuild by Design to find innovative ways to rebuild coasts that would make them more resilient to future storms. Information about the winning designs and the future of the Rebuild by Design initiative can be found here: http://www.rebuildbydesign.org/.

Restore America's Estuaries, a non-profit conservation organization, has produced a video that explains the concept and benefits of living shorelines for protecting coasts: https://vimeo.com/140113632.

Adapting to Extreme Heat

This US Environmental Protection Agency webpage provides a concise overview of the ways in which plants can help keep cities cooler: http://www.epa.gov/heat-islands/using-trees-and-vegetation-reduce-heat-islands.

Talking Trees: An Urban Forestry Toolkit for Local Governments provides overviews, details, and case studies on the benefits of planting trees in cities. https://www.nyclimatescience.org/catalog/n255?DocId=vitroIndividual:http://www.nyclimatescience.org/individual/n255.

Many cities and counties have plans for excessive or extreme heat, including warning systems, information on how to avoid heat illness, maps of cooling center locations, and information about water and power conservation. Some examples can be found at:

- https://www1.nyc.gov/site/em/ready/extreme-heat.page (New York City)
- https://www.cityofchicago.org/city/en/depts/fss/provdrs/emerg/svcs/city_cooling_centers.html (Chicago)
- https://beta.phila.gov/services/safety-emergency-preparedness/natural-hazards/excessive-heat/ (Philadelphia)
- https://www.stlouis-mo.gov/government/departments/health/news/heat-advisory-until-8-pm-tuesday.cfm (St. Louis)
- http://www.ci.minneapolis.mn.us/health/preparedness/extremeheat (Minneapolis)
- http://lacoa.org/ht_extreme%20heat.htm (Los Angeles)

Adapting to Heavy Rainfall Events

The internet contains many excellent resources on how to design, install, maintain a rain garden. These are just a few examples:
- http://www.12000raingardens.org/build-a-rain-garden/schools/
- http://www.raingardennetwork.com/benefits-of-planting-rain-gardens/
- http://nemo.uconn.edu/raingardens/
- http://water.rutgers.edu/Rain_Gardens/RGWebsite/RainGardenManualofNJ.html

The US EPA has an informative website on managing stormwater with green infrastructure: https://www.epa.gov/green-infrastructure.

The University of Idaho has a webpage with information about the benefits, history, and technical details of green roofs: https://webpages.uidaho.edu/larc380/new380/pages/greenRoof.html.

The Nature Conservancy produced a video on the role of well-designed culverts in adapting to climate change, both for protecting fish and human communities: https://www.youtube.com/watch?v=vWtVFsOOFW8.

The Chicago Green Alley Handbook gives examples of ways in which small urban streets can be redesigned to handle the impacts of climate change: http://www.chicagoclimateaction.org/filebin/pdf/greenalleyhandbook.pdf.

Chapter 10:
Obstacles to Addressing Climate Change

1. Controversial Issues and Complex Systems

"The first principle is that you must not fool yourself and you are the easiest person to fool."
— *Richard P. Feynman*

"A new scientific truth does not triumph by convincing its opponents and making them see the light, but rather because its opponents eventually die, and a new generation grows up that is familiar with it."
— *Max Planck*

A third or more of Americans reject the scientific consensus that human-induced climate change is real and a serious threat to our economy and environment,[1] in spite of abundantly clear evidence to the contrary. Some people in leadership positions believe, or behave as if they believe, anthropogenic climate change is a hoax, confounding the problem. The question of whether climate change is real has become so politically polarizing that in some areas of the US it can be uncomfortable to discuss the subject in the classroom. How do we broach such a controversial topic with our students, and in fact how do we help create a generation of students more comfortable having meaningful dialogues than those of our current adult generation?

Responses to sociopolitically controversial topics, both those involving science (such as climate change, energy extraction, and evolution), and others such as the nature of K-16 education itself, have some patterns in common. These commonalities provide an opportunity to create some general rules of thumb for approaches in education to addressing controversial issues (see *Table 10.1*). The primary goal of this chapter is to uncover the shared roots of challenges to public acceptance of certain well-evidenced findings, to seek both deeper understandings of each problem and empathy for those with whom we disagree, in order to be more effective educators.

Part of the challenge in all controversial issues is that (1), the academic topics themselves (for example, the climate system and climate change) are generally interdisciplinary and complex, and (2), key findings from research on

---

[1] In a March 2017 Gallup poll, about 68% of Americans "believe global warming is caused by human activities" and 45% "worry a great deal about global warming." These numbers are among the highest recorded in the past two decades, thus public opinion may be changing. Half in US Are Now Concerned Global Warming Believers, by Lydia Saad, Gallup Politics, March 27, 2017, http://www.gallup.com/poll/207119/half-concerned-global-warming-believers.aspx.

CHAPTER AUTHOR

Don Duggan-Haas

Addressing Climate Change

Table 10.1: Rules of thumb for teaching controversial issues.

1. **Be nice (but there are limits).** Treating those who disagree as either idiots or evil people is unlikely to convince them that you're correct.
    a. **Know your audience.** "Nice" has different meanings with different audiences.
    b. **For the most part, people aren't lying.** They largely believe what they say. Default to the expectation that the people you are interacting with believe what they are saying unless you have good evidence to the contrary.
    c. **Advocacy *may* deepen convictions more than understanding.** Evangelism turns on people who agree with you and turns off many who don't. Being certain and being right aren't the same thing, and they aren't all that closely related. Put more faith in people and institutions that are pretty sure than those that are certain.
    d. **Don't let the bastards get you down.** Working on nurturing public understanding of controversial issues will make people angry, and angry people say and do nasty things. Have a support system you can turn to.

2. **Complexify the seemingly simple.** As educators (and like journalists and politicians), we are driven to simplify the seemingly complex. It's often important, but we do it *too* often. The world is complex.
    a. **Move from debate to discussion.** There are often ways to reframe away from false dichotomies.
    b. **Controversial issues are always interdisciplinary.** Pay attention to the tools and strategies of the most centrally related disciplines.
    c. **Don't forget the importance of the simple.** While acknowledging the issue's complexity is important, there are often simple ideas illuminated within that complexity.

3. **Evidence matters, but evidence alone is not enough.** All of us hold beliefs for which ample conflicting evidence exists.
    a. **Learn about cognitive biases (including your own)** and how to communicate more effectively in light of them. Warn learners in advance to avoid biased reasoning.[2]
    b. **State evidence clearly and directly, identifying a small number of key points.** Too many different points cloud the issue.
    c. **Mathematics matters.** Scale plays a central role in many controversial issues, and understanding really large or really small numbers brings special challenges. "Social math"[3] uses familiar examples to show volume, mass, or relative number.
    d. **Call out logical fallacies, and hold people accountable for (mis)using them.** There's a taxonomy of problematic argument types. Get to know it and put it to use.

---

[2] This article by Keith Stanovich has more information on decoupling prior beliefs: Stanovich, Keith E., Richard F. West, and Maggie E. Toplak. "Myside Bias, Rational Thinking, and Intelligence." Current Directions in Psychological Science 22, no. 4 (2013): 259–264.

[3] National Center for Injury Prevention & Control. (2008). Adding Power to Our Voices: A Framing Guide for Communicating About Injury (p. 40). Atlanta, GA. Retrieved from http://wwwn.cdc.gov/NCIPC-SuccessStory/Social_Math_Resources.html.

Table 10.1: Continued.

4. Persistence matters. Beliefs related to controversial issues are often closely tied to worldviews, and such beliefs do not change quickly or easily.
    a. **People do change their minds on things that matter.** A broad modern example is the change in acceptance of gay marriage. A more personal scale example is divorce.
    b. **Piling on evidence can bring beliefs to a tipping point.** Of course, not always.
    c. **Reflect on big changes in your own beliefs.** Chances are, it took either a long time or an immersion in the issue.
    d. **Social media may be a better venue for this than classrooms** because connections last more than a semester or a year.

5. Use one's place in the world as a starting point to engage in critical inquiry of the forces working to shape that place (geology, ecology, capital flows, law, etc.).

those topics have implications for equally complex societal systems (such as economic, energy, and political systems). It is common to say that a system such as the world energy system is "broken," because the system delivers problematic outcomes. But another perspective is that many systems still work more-or-less as originally intended – when developed decades or centuries ago – but yield numerous and substantial unintended consequences. Alternatively, they may "work" in a different sense in that they function as self-replicating systems, continuing to operate not because they satisfy their original goals, but rather they persist because they suit the system in some other way.

For example, the structure of the economy is not grounded in research on climate change. The economy took its basic form long before climate science became robust. Energy choices were made based on availability of known energy sources and the price per unit of energy long before the economics of environmental and health consequences were known. Some impacts of energy use became (relatively) quickly known at local scales, such as decline of air quality from coal burning in cities such as London and Pittsburgh, but awareness of global impacts by those making political and economic decisions remained a century away. Likewise, development of today's global coordination of extraction and distribution of fossil fuels did not take into account the eventual enormous cumulative environmental impacts and associated costs. The energy system to a large extent achieves its fundamental goals of making energy widely available and profiting those employed in the industry, and in this sense it doesn't need to be "fixed" so much as it needs to be re-envisioned to fulfill a broader set of goals. By analogy, jet planes did not originate from the improvement or repair of canal boats. Likewise, wind farms are not repaired coal power plants. If the wider ramifications of the interactions of human-made and natural systems had been understood from the start, some decisions about the construction of human-made systems *may* have been different and the world might look very different today.

In isolation and in hindsight, the idea of burning hundreds of millions of years of fossil fuels in just a few hundred years seems insane. After all, the chemical properties of carbon dioxide are well known, and evidence is strong that atmospheric carbon dioxide concentration has strongly influenced the temperature of other planets (e.g., Venus) and past Earth climates. And we

Addressing Climate Change

can quantify the amount of organic carbon sequestered in sedimentary rocks, of which a substantial fraction has been burned, well enough to know that it is significant relative to the amount of carbon in the atmosphere as carbon dioxide. It would, based on these observations, be quite surprising if the Earth's climate were *not* changing after burning so much organic matter, which had taken about a million times longer to accumulate over geologic time than the time it has taken to burn it.

But the infrastructure that makes possible heating our homes, transporting us, and creating large amounts of electricity was well-formed before and while these scientific understandings were developing. The lives of billions of people are now partially dependent on these big human constructs -- the infrastructure has grown to such a size and familiarity, that it has become nearly impossible to build new systems while the old ones are still running.

2. Creating Meaningful Dialog

The infrastructure of energy is tightly tied, of course, to our economic and political systems, and to the quality of our lives. How we prioritize jobs, rights to land and resources, degree of political control, importance of environmental protection, weighting of local versus global and national versus international concerns, among many other considerations, determines how we might react to recognizing human-induced climate change as a valid issue, and whether we should adopt policies to counter it. Our feelings about these issues are deeply rooted in our worldviews. Given this, how can we begin to productively relate to, and to teach, students with diverse and different views?

2.1 Developing Empathy

One way potentially to develop empathy for folks we disagree with is to identify areas of our own lives in which we might make assumptions or arguments about activities or beliefs in which we're immersed. For example, one area that most people reading this *Teacher-Friendly Guide* will have in common is teaching within the traditional educational system: schools organized into classes of about 20 students, sitting in a series of 50 minute classes of various subjects, about 40 weeks a year, for 13 years or so. If asked if the system works, most of us would defend it, even if we know it has flaws. It is the way we were taught, the way many of us were taught to teach, and, in most cases, the structure available to us for teaching (no matter what we might dream would be ideal). With time, we develop strategies within the system we use and recognize constraints that would make it difficult to achieve our most idealistic (or research-based) aspirations, and we grow weary of new "reforms" that we know will be hard to implement within the constraints of the existing system.

Given these constraints, it becomes difficult to enact a next generation of educational systems that results not merely in improvements to schools and classrooms, but rather in the replacement of these structures with something fundamentally different and better. How do we work effectively toward a new system that we can scarcely imagine? In this sense, might we sometimes be like climate change deniers, resistant to pushing for change because we are immersed in social groups whose goals have long been to excel within the current system, and inconvenienced and perhaps offended by pushes for change from outside. (It's not a perfect analogy – for example, most climate change deniers are not climate scientists, while teachers are actively immersed in doing science education.)

2.2 Asking Deep Open-Ended Questions

Part of changing the culture of discussion may be asking questions that are rich and open-ended and seeking new solutions with common ground, instead of questions focused on "right" or "wrong," "do" or "don't." For example, arguments about permitting high volume hydraulic fracturing – a.k.a. "fracking" – are often framed around about whether to frack or not. Of course, that's a worthy question, but it fails to take into account that all *large scale* energy generation is bad for the environment. Therefore, worthier questions include, "By what combination of energies, in different times and places, can we get the energy we need with the least environment impact" and, even more importantly, "How can we use a lot less energy?"[4] Likewise, when we discuss the *Next Generation Science Standards* (NGSS), the question typically asked seems to be either, "Will the NGSS succeed or fail?" or, "How can we make the NGSS work?" where "work" is poorly defined. Again, these are worthy questions, but not nearly as important as, "How can we change schools (and science education) so that they prepare individuals for the responsibilities of citizenship?" With respect to climate change, rather than ask, "Is climate change happening?" or "How do we cut carbon emissions in our current activities," we might ask instead "How do we change the way we build communities in order to decrease the energy we need and take into account the climate change that is expected to occur?"

2.3 Resistance to Change is not Equivalent to Lack of Education

Research by Dan Kahan suggests that deeper knowledge often facilitates stronger polarization regarding these issues rather than broader acceptance.[5] Kahan has written that those with the highest degrees of science literacy were not necessarily the most concerned about climate change, but that these individuals on average were more culturally polarized. Thus one reason so many people in the public do not accept climate change is not lack of knowledge, but rather, according to Kahan, the presence of a "conflict of interest: between the personal interest individuals have in forming beliefs in line with those held by others with whom they share close ties and the collective one they all share in making use of the best available science to promote common welfare." Thus it's important to recognize that, while access to abundant and accurate evidence is necessary for an understanding of climate change, for many individuals this evidence is not by itself sufficient for them to accept human-induced climate

---

[4] See "Chapter 9: Teaching about the Marcellus Shale" in Duggan-Haas, R.M. Ross, & W. D. Allmon. Ross. 2013. The Science beneath the Surface: A Very Short Guide to the Marcellus Shale. Paleontological Research Institution, Ithaca, New York Special Publication No. 43, 252 pp. See also the Prezi by Don Duggan-Haas, There's No Such Thing as a Free Megawatt, https://prezi.com/em-or03bprhy/theres-no-such-thing-as-a-free-megawatt-hydrofracking-as-a-gateway-drug-to-energy-literacy/?webgl=0.

[5] Dan M. Kahan, Maggie Wittlin, Ellen Peters, Paul Slovic, Lisa L. Ouellette, Donald Braman & Gregory Mandel, The polarizing impact of science literacy and numeracy on perceived climate change risks, Nature Climate Change advance on line publication, http://www.nature.com/doifinder/10.1038/nclimate1547 (2012).

Addressing Climate Change

change. This is because individuals make choices on what they accept using a variety of criteria, most especially the views of the peers with whom they associate and their own pre-existing world views. Thus it's important to know each other and our students as multidimensional people with social pressures, not merely as dispassionate analysts of data. All of us are susceptible to a wide variety of cognitive biases associated with these external pressures and other factors, including how our brains work, that impact our perspectives and what we accept as true.

3. Factors That Influence How We Think

"The most erroneous stories are those we think we know best – and therefore never scrutinize or question."

- Stephen J. Gould

Research in cognitive sciences has helped to distinguish many ways in which our thinking is influenced by a combination of factors in our environment (such as influence of our culture generally and peer groups specifically), plus the way our brains give priority to certain kinds of information and stimuli. **Cognitive biases** and **logical fallacies** lead us to believe things to create a worldview and social dynamics that are internally consistent. *Most everyone holds as true things that are clearly and demonstrably false;* because we are wrong about these things, we cannot see that we are wrong. These aspects of human nature drive us to believe certain things that are demonstrably false falls under the umbrella of **identity-protective cognition.** Familiarity with some of the kinds of common biases is helpful when considering and teaching about controversial issues.

The common phenomenon, discussed above, of additional evidence alone being insufficient to change understandings and associated beliefs, can be a precondition to the backfire effect.[6] The **backfire effect** causes beliefs to become stronger when they are challenged with conflicting evidence.[7] The backfire effect is in part a response to identity protective cognition, the status quo bias, and allegiance to community norms, each of which are powerful forces that resist change. The **status quo bias** is an emotional bias and a preference for the current state of affairs. The current baseline (or status quo) is taken as a reference point, and any change from that baseline is perceived as a threat or loss.

Myside bias or **confirmation bias** is the tendency to seek out information that agrees with one's existing prior opinions, and to ignore established evidence that might conflict with those opinions. A common occurrence of this bias is reading only media likely to align with one's existing views. More subtle subconscious confirmation biases can occur, however, even in research in selective choice

---

[6] Scientists often prefer to use the term "accept climate change" rather than "believe in climate change," as a way to distinguish evidence-based conclusions (accepting evidence) as opposed to faith-based conclusions (belief). In this article and this book, we often follow this convention, but do use the terms "believe" and "beliefs" when we feel the intended meaning is not likely to be misinterpreted.

[7] People may be more likely to consider another position when they do not feel challenged or threatened. See Horowitz, Eric. "Want to Win a Political Debate? Try Making a Weaker Argument." Pacific Standard, August 23, 2013. https://psmag.com/want-to-win-a-political-debate-try-making-a-weaker-argument-446f21de17a1.

Addressing Climate Change

of data to analyze and literature to reference. One function of the peer-review process in scientific publication is to insure that researchers have taken into account all available credible evidence for and against their hypotheses.

The sunk-cost fallacy, spending good money (or time, or other resources) after bad, is the tendency to pour resources into a system in part to justify the resources already used. Such reasoning makes it difficult to abandon existing infrastructure or long held practices. If, however, putting resources into new solutions is more likely to lead to better outcomes than maintaining an existing system, the amount already invested in the existing system logically should not factor into decision-making.

Solution aversion refers to the idea that claims (such as the influence of climate change) might be rejected because the implication of accepting those claims would be accepting solutions that require sweeping (and therefore challenging) changes to the systems and cultures in which one lives and works.

The **availability heuristic** pushes us to rely on immediate examples rather than information grounded in extensive data or research. The understanding of cause and effect within complex systems over long-intervals is thus challenging in part due to delays in feedback. Examples include attributing individual weather observations to support for climate change (an extreme weather event) or against it (a cold and snowy day), even though climate change by definition refers to long-term averages.

Objections to climate change are also commonly in the form of narratives of good and evil. This is addressed in Chapter 11, Perspective.

4. How Do People Change Their Minds?

Changing a closely held worldview is not about changing understandings of isolated concepts, but rather remaking that worldview. What goes into such a large change? Changing one's mind about deeply held beliefs requires reaching a tipping point. Ultimately, to release an idea people have clutched tightly, they divorce themselves from it. The word "divorce" is not chosen lightly. For some individuals and communities, separating from such ideas may mean divorcing from other individuals and communities that are central to identity. That separation may be as painful as divorce from a marriage, or a conversion of faith.

Some ideas are hard to swallow because they imply that we or our sociocultural group have been contributing to something harmful. We may strongly identify as a "good" person who makes decisions based on what we think is best for our families, communities, and country, and other good people around us may think the same way. Thus if an idea is at conflict with those of our social groups, it is natural to assume there must be something wrong with the arguments of the other side. We select the evidence that maintains the most internal consistency within our worldview. There is an advantage to this in certain contexts – it helps us to maintain important social connections and to protect our identity. It may push us to believe things that are demonstrably false, but some new beliefs are accompanied by a cascade of other implications – beliefs we would need to let go of, and people in our social group with whom we'd be at odds. Thus,

Addressing Climate Change

while maintaining belief in something that appears to be false based on a preponderance of available evidence may, out of context, seem illogical, in the broader scope maintaining our belief may create the least tension, and in that sense may be perceived as a logical choice.

5. How Can We Envision New Systems?

In responding to challenges of climate change, there is a drive to make existing energy-using systems more efficient at what they do. While this makes good intuitive sense, it is focusing on "the right way to do the wrong thing."[8] It focuses upon teaching what we know how to do rather than upon doing what needs to be done. We focus on making specific *existing* processes, strategies, and technologies better. We should do that, of course, but often it is more important to make fundamentally (revolutionarily) *new* processes, strategies, and technologies (*Figure 10.1*). For example, part of the strategy to reduce carbon emissions is making better cars and trucks. There may, however, be a limit to improved efficiency from vehicles that look too much like cars. Ultimately, we may need to make a transportation system that is *better* than cars and trucks.

By analogy, on the route to improving educational outcomes, we need to make better schools, but there's a ceiling effect if we're locked into the systems of traditional schools. Eventually it is likely more important to make an educational system that is better than schooling. This, of course, is a heavy lift. We hope that the approaches and ideas discussed here serve both the existing educational system and whatever educational systems might lie in the future.

For adoption to occur of new system innovations—transportation, energy, education, or otherwise—the new things need to look enough like the old things to be understandable. Successful (broadly adopted) innovations are likely to be "optimally distinct," that is, different enough from current practice to make a difference in outcomes, but not so different as to be outside of cultural or professional norms or too weird to be understood.[9] In a study of journal articles with the highest impact, for example, it was found that found that combining conventional science in unconventional ways is twice as likely to yield higher impact studies than either novelty or conventional science alone.[10] For reforms of systems that make a difference to mitigating climate change, we need to consider how to combine conventional ideas in unconventional and productive ways.

---

[8] To lift a lyric from singer-songwriter, Cheryl Wheeler. See: http://www.cherylwheeler.com/songs/rway.html.

[9] Berger (2016) Berger, Jonah. "The Goldilocks Theory of Product Success." Harvard Business Review, July 7, 2016. https://hbr.org/2016/07/the-goldilocks-theory-of-product-success.

[10] Uzzi et al (2013) Uzzi, Brian, Satyam Mukherjee, Michael Stringer, and Ben Jones. "Atypical Combinations and Scientific Impact." Science 342, no. 6157 (2013): 468–472. http://www.kellogg.northwestern.edu/faculty/uzzi/htm/papers/Science-2013-Uzzi-468-72.pdf.

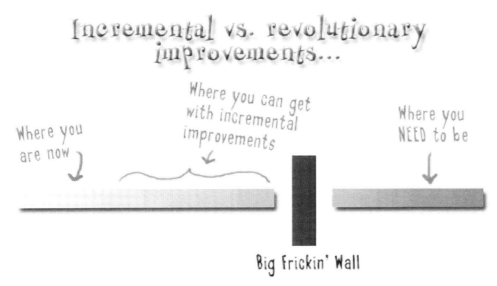

Figure 10.1: Often a barrier ("Big Frickin' Wall") to improvement of a system requires revolutionary improvement, rethinking the system, rather than incremental improvements within the existing system.

Addressing Climate Change

Resources

Online Resources

The website "You Are Not So Smart," by David McRaney, the author of the book of the same name, includes an excellent series of podcasts on logical fallacies. https://youarenotsosmart.com/. McRaney is, as of April 2017, finishing a new book about how people change their minds on important issues.

See the website http://yourlogicalfallacyis.com, which is titled at the top "Thou Shalt Not Commit Logical Fallacy." The site compiles in table form information about many of the best known logical fallacies, and offers this as a poster that can either be downloaded as a pdf or ordered from the site.

The Cultural Cognition Project at Yale Law School offers a large selection of articles written for both academic and popular publications and blog posts on cultural and psychological issues that complicate science communication. Access here: http://www.culturalcognition.net/.

The website for the Yale Program on Climate Change Communication, http://climatecommunication.yale.edu/, includes the various "Six Americas" reports that cluster Americans into six groups based on their attitudes, beliefs, behaviors, policy preferences and risk perceptions related to global warming. The six groups are: Alarmed, Concerned, Cautious, Disengaged, Doubtful, and, Dismissive, and the website includes resources and strategies for effective communication with these different groups. The sister site, Yale Climate Connections (http://www.yaleclimateconnections.org/), "is an online news service providing daily radio broadcasts and original online reporting, commentary, and analysis on the issue of climate change," with readings and 90 second daily podcasts that are readily usable in the classroom.

Chapter 11: Perspective

1. Apocalyptic Tales of Climate Change

In polarizing issues, apocalyptic rhetoric is often found at both poles of the issue in question. The extremes related to **climate change** are destruction of the environment and civilization (or even the entire Earth) at one extreme and destruction of the economy, freedom, and the "American way of life" at the other.

We've been telling stories of apocalypse and of lost Edens as long as we've been telling stories.[1] Such tales are engaging, memorable, instructive, and motivating. Environmental educators and advocates have been telling modern versions of these tales for generations for the same reasons that other folks have told them for millennia. From the Book of Genesis to *The Lorax*,[2] humans are drawn to stories of paradise lost. And they learn from them too.

Rachel Carson's *Silent Spring*[3] helped to usher in an era of environmental apocalyptic writing and reporting, and those stories were fundamental to cleaning up our environment. About the same time predictions were being made by scientists and reported on by the media—predictions that, metaphorically, looked a lot like biblical visions of fire and brimstone from the Book of Revelation. The villainous actions were readily visible: flammable chemical wastes dumped directly into rivers, and black smoke billowing out of smokestacks, rivers catching fire, and cities being shrouded in smog and smoke. A recent example is the fires around Fort McMurray, Alberta (Canada), where forest fires associated with record heat surrounded the strip-mined landscape containing the Athabasca **Tar Sands** and its piles of waste sulfur (see Box: *Real-life Fire and Brimstone*).

Al Gore and Bill Nye are examples of many who point out the urgency and apocalyptic outcomes of rapid climate change. While they've both done great work and deepened the understandings of millions of Americans, they've simultaneously unintentionally deepened the convictions of millions who reject the scientific consensus on climate change. The reasons for these mixed outcomes are complex, but at least one may be the apocalyptic storylines associated with their messages. Al Gore is also seen as a political partisan and is instantly polarizing for many, regardless of what he says (what he says is

---

[1] The loss of a past ideal state and the destruction of the current state are different but sometimes related ways of expressing regret or fear of significant negative change. For the sake of readability, these are lumped together in this chapter as "apocalyptic tales."

[2] The Lorax is a children's book by Dr. Seuss (Theo Geisel) about the destruction of the environment through corporate greed. It was published in 1971 during a rise in public environmental awareness.

[3] Rachel Carson published *Silent Spring* in 1962, about the effects of the widespread use of insecticides (Houghton Mifflin Company: Boston, MA, 368 pp.). The book had an enormous effect on the growth and awareness of environmental sciences.

---

climate change • the current increase in the average surface temperature worldwide, caused by the buildup of greenhouse gases in the atmosphere, and the related changes to other aspects of climate such as precipitation patterns and storm strength. See also GLOBAL WARMING.

tar sand • a mixture of clay, sand, water, and bitumen, a thick oil that can be extracted and refined into liquid oil.

CHAPTER AUTHOR

Don Duggan-Haas

Perspective

Box: Real life fire and brimstone

Among many stories of environmental degradation going on today, one of the more symbolic of apocalyptic "fire and brimstone" is the stunning late spring 2016 fires around Fort McMurray, Alberta. The site is the largest area for oil ("tar") sands development in the world. To mine the tar sands several hundred square miles of surface boreal bogs are removed for open-pit mining.

Fort McMurray is the town adjacent to the oil sands production facility (and production waste). Producing oil from tar sands is more energy intensive than other forms of oil production. That means it produces more greenhouse gases per barrel of oil than other means. And in an Earth system irony, it may be that the likelihood of drought-induced fires in the Canadian Rockies was increased by climate change associated with carbon emissions—less snowpack than typical and record setting temperatures of about 90 degrees F (32 C), low humidity, and high winds.

Production of oil from oil sands also produces another byproduct in huge quantities - sulfur. The largest pyramids in the world are not in Egypt or made of cut stone. They are near Fort McMurray and made of sulfur from tar sands development. Brimstone is a stone—sulfur—that forms at the brim of a volcano. Though some sulfur is sold for commercial use, in Fort McMurray, it accumulates much faster than it's used.

The two months of Fort McMurray fires was the costliest disaster in Canadian history, and forced the evacuation of 90,000 people, also the largest in Canadian history. The fires were associated with over 2400 burned structures, extensive burned forest, and weeks of halted oil sands production. The fire and brimstone together had the ingredients of a biblical apocalypse.

Fire near the Fort McMurray oil sands production facility.

generally well aligned with the consensus of scientists). Bill Nye is increasingly seen in the same light.

2. Use of Language and Perspective in Teaching Climate Change

Research shows that the impact of apocalyptic messages and dire warnings may not lead to the responses we might expect or that the messages are intended to create. Fear, for example, may influence people to stop doing something (stop smoking, for example), but it may be less effective than hoped at persuading people to take action.[4] Consistently bad news over time may lead people to lose hope, which can have the effect of causing people to give up, deciding their actions are likely to be ineffectual. Thus, while not sugar-coating the reality, it's important to celebrate successes where they occur. For example, alternative energy use has been growing exponentially, and the rate of growth of CO_2 emissions has been declining, so people should recognize that positive actions are making a difference.

Moreover, while apocalyptic approaches may motivate some to act to reduce **global warming's** impacts,[5] they may reduce acceptance of global warming in audiences already skeptical.[6] These latter audiences may see doom and gloom scenarios, with associated pictures of smoke stacks and industrial pollution, as propaganda rather than scientific information. Such audiences may respond better to consideration of personally relevant impacts on the economy and local communities, to attention to saving money through conserving energy. These approaches seek common ground and work toward goals at least in part outside a narrative of environmental alarm.

There is also a difference in how new information is integrated into pre-existing beliefs between those who accept or deny climate change. Those who are skeptical of global warming are more likely to change their beliefs in response to unexpected good news (for example, if temperature rise is less than predicted) and less likely to change their beliefs given unexpected bad news (if temperature rise is larger than expected). The converse is true for people who think that human-induced climate change is occurring.[7]

In sum, the lesson you teach or the materials you create will have different effects on different people. It's common for education about climate change to be effective for one audience and not merely ineffective for another, but anti-

global warming • *the current increase in the average temperature worldwide, caused by the buildup of greenhouse gases in the atmosphere. With the coming of the Industrial Age and exponential increases in human population, large amounts of gases have been released into the atmosphere (especially carbon dioxide) that give rise to global warming. The term CLIMATE CHANGE is preferred because warming contributes to other climatic changes such as precipitation and storm strength.*

---

[4] Tali Sharot's 2011 book The Optimism Bias: A Tour of the Irrationally Positive Brain explores the influence of positive versus negative emotions in outlook and decision-making. Pantheon Books: NY, 272 pp.

[5] Some environmental activism occurs not despite apocalyptic framing but because of it. See Veldman, Robin Globus. "Narrating the Environmental Apocalypse: How Imagining the End Facilitates Moral Reasoning Among Environmental Activists." Ethics & the Environment 17, no. 1 (2012): 1–23.

[6] A proposed explanation for why apocalyptic predictions diminish willingness to act on climate change is that such stories are perceived to be at odds with a world that is "...just, orderly and stable." See Feinberg M, and Willer R. "Apocalypse Soon? Dire Messages Reduce Belief in Global Warming by Contradicting Just-World Beliefs." Psychological Science 22, no. 1 (2011): 34–38.

[7] Sunstein, Cass R. and Bobadilla-Suarez, Sebastian and Lazzaro, Stephanie C. and Sharot, Tali, How People Update Beliefs about Climate Change: Good News and Bad News (September 2, 2016) https://ssrn.com/abstract=2821919.

---

greenhouse gas • a gas that absorbs and re-radiates energy in the form of heat; carbon dioxide, water vapor, and methane are examples.

---

chlorofluorocarbons • compounds of carbon, hydrogen, chlorine, and fluorine, usually ANTHROPOGENIC gases used as refrigerants or in aerosol cans. Released into the ATMOSPHERE, these compounds are GREENHOUSE GASES and are responsible for the OZONE HOLE.

---

stratospheric ozone • a region of OZONE gas in the STRATOSPHERE.

---

ultraviolet light • electromagnetic radiation in the part of the spectrum with wavelengths from 10 to 400 nanometers.

---

ozone hole • a region of ozone depletion in the STRATOSPHERE above Antarctica, caused by destruction of ozone from ANTHROPOGENIC chemicals released into the ATMOSPHERE.

---

glacier • a very large piece of ice that sits at least partially on land and moves under the force of gravity.

Perspective

effective other audiences. One class or program may include multiple audiences in the same crowd. How do we craft our instruction so that it maximizes the desired understandings, while *both* being true to the science and minimizing the pushback brought by what some might consider to be like false prophecies?

3. Hope and Optimism

At first blush, some of society's previous environmental parables may seem to have been false prophecies in the sense that these tales of apocalypse did not become fully fulfilled. One reason, of course, is that some of these issues were resolved because people did something about them.

As one relatively localized but well publicized example, certain rivers in the US caught fire a number of times in the 19th and 20th centuries, and they don't anymore. The most famous example is Cleveland's Cuyahoga, but it's far from the only example. Generally, the water in US rivers, lakes and streams, and the air we breathe, are much cleaner than was the case a few decades ago. The environment in many heavily industrialized areas is less polluted than it was half a century ago. Littering has declined substantially, and in many areas municipal solid waste disposal rates are substantially down because recycling rates are up.

A global atmospheric example, the most comparable we have to controlling **greenhouse gas** emissions, is reducing chemicals—especially coolants such as **chlorofluorocarbons** (CFCs)—that deplete **stratospheric ozone**.[8] The ozone layer absorbs **ultraviolet light** and thereby protects tissues of living organisms. In the 1980s it became established that the ozone concentration declined by over half its natural state during summers over Antarctica—this became known as the "**ozone hole**" (ozone also diminished in the Artic and in temperate latitudes, but not to the same degree). By the 1980s an international agreement was made to freeze and then phase out CFCs. Once regulations of CFCs were put into place, ozone concentrations began to stabilize, and at the time of this writing, the ozone hole over Antarctica is showing signs of healing. Environmental issues can and do improve.

How did we clean up our act in these cases? In these examples, we responded to the scientific projections that were coming true before our eyes. We created laws and agreements to regulate what we were putting into our waters and into our atmosphere, and we changed cultural norms regarding acceptable ways to treat the environment.

4. Apocalyptic Prophesies Versus Predictions of Climate Change

Are the apocalyptic prophesies of climate change coming true? Yes. In many respects the Earth is changing—in temperature, ice and **glacier** melt, storm frequency, and many other respects—in ways projected by climate scientists.

---

[8] Tropospheric (ground level) ozone is considered a form of pollution, forming from reactions between certain carbon compounds with nitrogen oxide. It can irritate lungs, especially if there are pre-existing conditions such as asthma.

But there are hopeful signs. US carbon emissions have declined; alternative energies, particularly **wind energy**, are increasing exponentially in the US and globally; and plans for new power plants, building designs, and transportation systems promise greatly improved efficiencies within coming decades. Many towns and cities, colleges and universities, and businesses have set ambitious low to zero carbon emissions goals within the coming decades. And there is such global awareness of climate change as a significant issue, that major treaties have been signed by a substantial fraction of world's nations.

There is also, however, considerable uncertainty.[9] Because of the nature of complex systems, it's challenging to quantify the degree or likelihood to which specific events (heat waves, droughts, floods, wildfires and so) can be attributed to climate change. And, though climate scientists can project within meaningful confidence intervals what will happen to global atmospheric temperatures, ice melt, and **sea level** rise given specific inputs (CO_2 and CH_4 levels, for example), there remain many uncertainties about what will happen to, for example, precipitation at very local scales, and to parts of the system such as individual species. This uncertainty arises both because the climate system is complicated and because we don't know how humans, at a planetary scale, are going to respond environmentally in the next 50 to 100 years.

Part of teaching climate change will be taking into account the strong possibility that the near future will hold some ongoing uncertainties and surprises. This is, after all, part of the nature of complex systems science. Almost certainly different parts of the climate system will change at different rates, either more slowly or more quickly than we expected, and these changes will be geographically varied. If some climate projections are, in the near-term, not as severe or as rapid as what we expected, that could be very good news—but such news might also add to complacency or skepticism even while climate change impacts continue. Apocalyptic projections of climate change are not inevitable, but as new information becomes available we need to be aware that the impacts of climate change are not binary, solved or world-ending: we will need to (and can) mitigate climate change, in many steps, over many years.

5. Reality Check: A Personal Perspective

Teaching about climate change can be horribly depressing work. It seems as though we are marching headlong into hellish times, and are not sufficiently rising to the challenge. This, to some degree, is the natural state of things. We have always lived in horrible times, if you choose to look at things that way. We've also always lived in marvelous times. Sometimes we can see that too, but reminders are helpful. When the situation becomes dire, as seems to be happening, we do have a history of rising to meet the ominous challenges. It is my hope we are in the process of doing that now.

To consider the concept of wonderful horrible times, I'll quickly step through five generations of my own family history. My great-grandfather, Adgate Loomis, was born December 4, 1843, in Lebanon, Connecticut and my great-

Reality Check

wind energy • *electrical energy derived from the mechanical energy of a TURBINE which moves due to the action of the wind.*

sea level • *global sea level is the average height of Earth's oceans. Local sea level is the height of the ocean as measured along the coast relative to a specific point on land.*

---

[9] Read more about uncertainty and motivation in Rutjens, Bastiaan T, Joop van der Pligt, and Frenk van Harreveld. "Regulating Psychological Threat: The Motivational Consequences of Threatening Contexts," 2012, 38–56.

Perspective

grandmother, his wife, Melissa "Minnie" Bridget Hardy, was born Dec. 13, 1847 in Hoskinsville, Ohio. Slavery was still firmly entrenched in the American South, and Adgate and his brother Lucius both fought for the Union Army, and Lucius died at the Andersonville Prison Camp. Clearly, these were horrible times.

The Civil War ended, and my great-grandfather marched in front of President Lincoln. Horrible times were not over, but the abomination that was slavery did come to an end. Adgate and Minnie married in 1871, and honeymooned in Niagara Falls. They went on to have five daughters and four sons, and were married for more than 50 years. The brood included twins - Ruth and Ralph, born in 1891. Ralph was my grandfather. I don't know if their life was wonderful, but it did have some wonderful outcomes.

My grandfather also saw the tragedy of war, serving in a machine gunners' unit in World War I. He also saw pestilence - helping to manage an impromptu hospital during the Spanish Flu epidemic. His twin, Ruth, died as a young woman. But, as these horrible things were going on, wonderful things were happening too. Nellie Brown, my grandmother, was the only woman in the University of Missouri's Rocky Mountain field camp. And Grandpa went on to earn a Master's degree in agricultural economics and then a divinity degree. As an extension agent, he was effective in helping bring an end to swine cholera. He married Nellie and they had four children, including twins of their own, Carolyn and Marilyn (my mother), who were born in 1931. And my grandparents were married for more than fifty years. Grandpa managed a dairy co-op and preached in several churches, and returned to Agricultural Extension work for the University of Missouri in 1936. And Grandma taught physical geography and more.

And Hitler rose to power in Europe, and the Japanese bombed Pearl Harbor, bringing the US into World War II. And my grandfather was fired from the Extension as, "The Extension didn't need any pacifists." A few years later, my father, Roger Haas, enlisted in the Navy, though, fortunately, the war was in its final year. These were horrible times. But the war ended, though my dad served until just before the Korean War began. My folks met at the University of Missouri, Dad attending on the GI Bill.

And Jim Crow was still festering in the south, and Joe McCarthy was feeding the Red Scare. And Rock-and-Roll was coming up, and life expectancy was growing. And the skies were black with smoke and smog and rivers caught fire. And my parents married and had six kids, beginning with my brother in 1952 and ending with me in 1963, just a few months before President Kennedy was killed. And Dad worked on technologies to see people through the forests of Southeast Asia, and my brothers worried about (but were not called for) the draft. And Mom was a university librarian who wrote books about books. And Martin Luther King, Jr. and Bobby Kennedy were killed. And riots. And there was Woodstock and the Civil Rights Act, and the Environmental Protection Agency. They were wonderful horrible times. And Mom and Dad were married for more than 50 years.

And Richard Nixon and Kent State. And Free Love. And disco. And the lakes and rivers got cleaner and the bald eagle came back. And, eventually, I married Katy Duggan and we had two wonderful kids, Kiana born in 2001, just a few months before September 11, and Nellie in 2004 as the country grew more and more mired in America's longest war.

All along, we worried about the fate of our children in these turbulent times, whatever time it happened to be. All along, horrible things were happening that looked like the end of the world. And each time it looked like the end of the world we did things to make it not be the end of the world. And, ok, it never really looked like the end of the world, though it may have looked like the end of civilization.

Yes, horrible things are happening now—I first wrote this in 2016, in the aftermath of a series of horrible shootings, and it looked to be an unending series of horrible shootings. But violent crime is actually at its lowest level in decades, which is pretty wonderful. And, 2016 was the hottest year on record,[10] which brought unprecedented droughts and floods and fires to various parts of North America, which is pretty horrible. And my daughters are kind, hardworking, smart, happy, engaged in things that make the world a better place, and beautiful. And hopefully, your kids are too, and so are you.

There are horrible things in the world. When the horror becomes clear to enough people, we do something about it to make it less horrible. Let's do that now. And celebrate the wonderful things too.

6. Science Teaching Toward a Sustainable World

While plenty has gone horribly wrong in the world and with civilization, both the world and civilization live on. The world will go on for a very, very long time - likely much longer than civilization. Earth is about 4.5 billion years old. Civilization is about 10,000 years old. At time scales that humans can easily understand, civilization will likely last quite a while too. Though it stands a good chance of getting pretty awful in various ways, times, and places in the future, if we act wisely, we have the capacity to reduce the potential horrible outcomes a great deal.

Each case that moved from horrible to less horrible involved people taking action to make things better. Ultimately, people made coalitions of institutions and organizations that helped us collectively behave responsibly. That means people assumed responsibility or were held responsible for the problems we faced, and they changed course. History shows that action is required to make things better and that, in numerous instances involving the environment, people have improved the environment through scientific understanding, education, and action. Perhaps the Onceler's repentance in *The Lorax* says it best: "*Unless someone like you cares a whole awful lot, nothing's going to get better. It's not.*"

We will need to use numerous strategies make changes to mitigate climate change, some of which will be social and political. But at the core must be basic public understanding of the science of Earth systems, and of climate in

---

[10] 2016 was the warmest year for average global temperature, 0.94 degrees C above the 20th century average (https://www.ncdc.noaa.gov/sotc/global/201613).

11 Perspective

Science Teaching

particular, in order to facilitate good decision-making. No one is more important than teachers to help future generations understand Earth's systems, and to help students work with each other toward stewardship of the Earth's future climate.

Resources

Books With Apocalyptic Rhetoric

If you don't have familiarity with the stories of Genesis and Revelation, start at the source. The Holy Bible, "King James Version." Texas: National Publishing Company, 2000. http://www.biblesfree.org/ruth.html.

Carson, Rachel. Silent Spring. Houghton Mifflin Harcourt, 2002. The classic book that is thought by many to be the start of the environmental revolution that led to the Clean Air and Clean Water Acts, and the founding of the Environmental Protection Agency. https://books.google.com/books?hl=en&lr=&id=HeR1I0V0r54C&oi=fnd&pg=PR8&dq=silent+spring&ots=1taaXokV5z&sig=JgF_fxI2s7DHQEfyjxpI4TU1IYQ.

Seuss. The Lorax. New York: Random House, 1971. The classic children's book.

Books That Address Some Problems With Apocalyptic Rhetoric

Davis, Kenneth C. Don't Know Much about the Bible: Everything You Need to Know about the Good Book But Never Learned. Harper Collins, 2009. Reading the Bible has challenges. This book offers a good overview of every book in the Bible with some interpretation and a bit of a sense of humor.

Olson, Randy. Don't Be Such a Scientist: Talking Substance in an Age of Style. Washington, DC: Island Press, 2009. Scientists are notorious for speaking above the heads of their audiences or being too dry in their communication style. Whether you're a scientist, a science teacher, or just someone who wants to be more clear and engaging in talking about science, this book is helpful.

Romm, Joseph J. Language Intelligence: Lessons on Persuasion from Jesus, Shakespeare, Lincoln, and Lady Gaga. CreateSpace, 2012. A thoughtful, helpful and amusing look at how to engage an audience in your writing and speaking.

Online Resources

You can find more information about stratospheric ozone at NASA's website "Ozone Hold Watch": https://ozonewatch.gsfc.nasa.gov.

Climate Change 101 with Bill Nye | National Geographic: https://www.youtube.com/watch?v=EtW2rrLHs08.

Bill Nye's Global Meltdown Climate Change Documentary, National Geographic Explorer https://www.youtube.com/watch?v=wmrsbY3MCZs.

Perspective

The Climate Reality Project, https://www.algore.com/project/the-climate-reality-project, Al Gore

The Canadian news site, Global News, has a regularly updated page on Fort McMurray wildfires and the ongoing issues associated with the most expensive disaster and largest evacuation in Canadian history: http://globalnews.ca/tag/fort-mcmurray-wildfire/.

Chapter 12:
Frequently Asked Questions About Climate Change

1. Is there consensus among climate scientists that global warming is occurring and that humans are the cause?

Yes. Multiple studies published in peer-reviewed scientific journals[1] show that 97 percent or more of actively publishing climate scientists agree: climate-warming trends over the past century are extremely likely due to human activities. In addition, most of the leading scientific organizations worldwide have issued public statements endorsing this position; two hundred scientific societies from 76 countries concur.[2] Consider the statement of a leading US scientific society, the American Geophysical Union:

"The Earth's climate is now clearly out of balance and is warming. Many components of the climate system—including the temperatures of the **atmosphere**, *land and ocean, the extent of* **sea ice** *and* **mountain glaciers**, *the* **sea level**, *the distribution of precipitation, and the length of seasons— are now changing at rates and in patterns that are not natural and are best explained by the increased atmospheric abundances of* **greenhouse gases** *and* **aerosols** *generated by human activity during the 20th century." (Adopted December 2003, Revised and Reaffirmed December 2007.)[3]*

---

[1] A recent synthesis of consensus estimates was published by J. Cook et al: "Consensus on consensus: a synthesis of consensus estimates on human-caused global warming," in Environmental Research Letters, Volume 11, Number 4, 048002 (http://iopscience.iop.org/1748-9326/11/4/048002), doi:10.1088/1748-9326/11/4/048002.

[2] For a list of these organizations see https://www.opr.ca.gov/s_listoforganizations.php.

[3] Statements from many professional organizations can be found here: http://www.ucsusa.org/global_warming/science_and_impacts/science/scientific-consensus-on.html#.WPEdBFPyu-4.

atmosphere • *the layer of gases that surrounds a planet.*

sea ice • *frozen seawater at the surface of the ocean.*

mountain glacier • *a glacier found in high mountains, often spanning across multiple peaks.*

sea level • *global sea level is the average height of Earth's oceans. Local sea level is the height of the ocean as measured along the coast relative to a specific point on land.*

greenhouse gas • *a gas that absorbs and re-radiates energy in the form of heat; carbon dioxide, water vapor, and methane are examples.*

CHAPTER AUTHORS

Alexandra F. Moore

and authors of

A Very Short Guide to Climate Change

Frequently Asked Questions

aerosol • *the suspension of very fine solid or liquid particles in a gas.*

Younger Dryas • *an abrupt shift in the Northern Hemisphere from a warm to a cold climate and then an abrupt shift back again, occurring over about 1,200 years starting around 13,000 years ago. The shift back to a warmer climate occurred with a 10°C (18°F) rise in temperature over only a decade.*

2. If geology tells us that the Earth's climate has changed in the past, why should we be concerned that it is changing now?

We are concerned about the *rate* of change. Consider the change in global climate that marked the end of the last ice age. During the 6000 year interval of rapid post-glacial global warming (about 17,000 to 11,000 years ago), Earth's average temperature increased 8°C. During that same interval, sea level rose by 80 meters (262 feet), and the atmospheric CO_2 concentration increased by 70 ppm (from 190 to 260 ppm).[4] Contrast these rates—which are an extreme example of natural change—with that of recent decades. At the current rate of global temperature increase (+0.02 °C/year[5]), a change of 8°C will take only 400 years, over 10 times faster than average post-glacial warming. Or consider that while a post-glacial increase of 70 ppm took 6000 years, the current atmospheric CO_2 concentration jumped 70 ppm in just 38 years, from 1979 to its current level of 407 ppm (April, 2017).[6]

The concern of such high rates of change is that in many respects both natural ecosystems and human populations would not be able to keep pace with the change. More specifically, most species of organisms are adapted to a particular set of temperatures, food resources, chemical environments, and ecological interactions that develop over hundreds of thousands of years; if these species cannot quickly extend their geographic ranges into similar environments, they may go extinct. There *have* been rare intervals of natural climate change as fast or faster than the 6000 year interval of post-glacial global warming, such as a localized cooling and rewarming event at the very end of that interval (the **Younger Dryas**) and at the Paleocene-Eocene Thermal Maximum, but high rates of extinction have been attributed to such events. And humans, while remarkably adaptable culturally, live within many constraints of infrastructure, available food and shelter, financial resources, and national boundaries. Thus even taking human ingenuity into account, large populations of people will not likely be able to easily relocate to find alternative resources.

Over the past billion years, of course, the Earth has experienced climates that were much warmer than those of today, as well as much colder periods. While many organisms and, theoretically, humans could survive in these more extreme global climates, the climate would not be generally hospitable. In the mid-Cretaceous period, for example, average global temperatures were as much as 9°C (16°F) warmer than today, and sea level was about 100 meters (328 feet) higher than today, covering large tracts of the continent. More importantly, humans have built a global civilization around the relatively stable climate conditions of the past 10,000 years. Even if species extinctions were not greatly increased, and even if humans in developed countries were insulated from changes going on elsewhere, there are vast parts of the world where millions of

[4] Data from Vostok ice core and Barbados corals.

[5] These and many other data, visualizations, plots, etc. can be found at climate.nasa.gov/vital-signs.

[6] Data from the Scripps Institute CO_2 program.

people are much more sensitively connected to their environment and cannot readily move or otherwise adapt in a short span of time.

See Chapter 4: Climate Change Through Earth History for more information on past climates.

anthropogenic • *made by humans, or resulting from human activity.*

3. How can we be sure that changes going on now are not just part of natural climate variation?

There are three major reasons why most climate scientists are convinced that the current warming is not due to natural processes:

a) We know that greenhouse gases are accumulating in the atmosphere at levels that have not been experienced in over 20 million years.

b) The pattern of the observed warming fits the pattern that we would expect from warming caused by the buildup of greenhouse gases. That is, almost all areas of the planet are warming; the Earth's surface and lower atmosphere are warming; the upper atmosphere is cooling; and the temperature changes are greatest in the Arctic during winter.

c) The warming is much more rapid than most of the natural variations we have seen in the past. The past century of warming cannot be explained without factoring in **anthropogenic** influences. Only by including the net effect of human-made greenhouse gases and aerosols can the observed changes be reproduced to match the actual record.

See Chapter 5: Evidence and Causes of Recent Climate Change for more detail on the causes of current climate change.

There are no known sources of natural variation that would give rise to changes as rapid as those observed in global temperature over the past 150 years. There is, however, a human-induced cause (increased CO_2) that not only fits the variation extremely well, but has long been expected to give rise to such change based on basic physical principles. We know the amount of CO_2 that humans release to the atmosphere, and analysis of the chemistry of the CO_2 identifies it unequivocally as anthropogenic. Over the last million years, the current atmospheric changes are unprecedented.

Could current change just be unusually extreme variation that we do not yet understand? While all phenomena are open to new explanations, and scientists must always be ready to consider other options, scientists do not favor or give equal weight to random or unknown variation if another known explanation fits

carbon-14 • *an isotope of carbon often used in dating materials.*

fossil fuel • *a non-renewable, carbon-based fuel source like OIL, NATURAL GAS, or COAL, developed from the preserved organic remains of fossil organisms.*

coal • *a rock formed from ancient plant matter that can be burned as fuel. Since coal is formed from fossilized plant remains it is considered a FOSSIL FUEL.*

oil • *a naturally occurring, flammable liquid found in geologic formations beneath the Earth's surface and consisting primarily of hydrocarbons. Oil, also called PETROLEUM, is a fossil fuel, formed when large masses of dead organisms (usually algae or plankton) are buried underneath sediments and subjected to intense heat and pressure.*

natural gas • *a hydrocarbon gas mixture composed primarily of methane (CH_4), but also small quantites of hydrocarbons such as ethane and propane. See also FOSSIL FUEL.*

the available data. Some explanations fit available evidence much better than others, and it would be inappropriate to act as if every explanation, no matter how unlikely, should receive equal treatment.

4. How do we know the increase in CO_2 since the 1800s is from human activities?

There are several lines of evidence that indicate an anthropogenic source for the increase in CO_2. One of the most compelling is the decrease in the radiocarbon (**carbon-14**) content of the atmosphere from 1850 to 1950 that correlates well with the increase in CO_2. Carbon-14 is not found in **fossil fuels**, so burning fossil fuels increases CO_2 but dilutes the carbon-14 in the atmosphere. Since **coal**, **oil** and **natural gas** are valuable commodities there are quite good records of their use over the last 200 years. The dilution of carbon-14 is exactly what one would predict given the known history of fossil fuel consumption. And there is no other plausible source of the increased CO_2 that can explain the dilution of the carbon-14. After 1950 the carbon-14 budget of the atmosphere was perturbed by nuclear weapons testing, which generated large quantities of carbon-14, masking the subsequent dilution. However, a similar calculation can be carried out for carbon-13 to the present day, and this too is consistent with a fossil fuel source for the increased CO_2.

See Chapter 5: Evidence and Causes of Recent Climate Change for more detail on the causes of current climate change.

5. Correlation is not proof of causation. Although temperature and CO_2 are correlated, how do we know that CO_2 is the cause of the current warming?

For any given scientific problem, scientists look at the sum of observable evidence and formulate hypotheses that can explain this evidence. We make predictions and design experiments to confirm, modify, or contradict these hypotheses, and then modify hypotheses as new information becomes available. In the case of anthropogenic CO_2-driven global warming, we have a hypothesis (first articulated over 100 years ago) that is based on well-established laws of physics, is consistent with extremely large quantities of observations and data, both contemporary and historical, and is supported by both conceptually simple and very sophisticated and refined global climate models that can successfully reproduce the climate's behavior over the last century. The confluence these many forms of independent evidence provide very strong confidence that CO_2 is the cause of current warming.

6. There was discussion of a warming hiatus at the beginning of the 21st century. Is this pause real, and what is the current status?

There has not been a warming "pause" in the early 21st century. Annual temperatures have a lot of natural variation from year to year—climate is defined as a long-term average (thirty years or more) for this reason. If an observer examines only the data across a very short time frame, for example, a few years or a single decade, then the long-term trend may be difficult to discern. An analogy might be trying to discern the change from winter to summer by observing just a week of weather in late March; given the natural day-to-day variation, the trend may not be obvious without at least a few weeks of data, and preferably all the data from January to July. In *Figure 12.1* the years from 2000-2010 show variability of around 0.5°C (the anomaly above the long term average temperature). Yet when that decade is viewed in the context of decades before and after, it is clear that the data from the 2000s are part of a long-term upward trend.

The argument for a "hiatus" was in no small part based on picking a very unusually warm year (1998) as a starting point. Relative to that year alone, following years looked less unusual. Further, there was no hiatus in other observations related to global warming. For example, sea level continued to rise through the 2000-2010 interval. Conclusions should always be drawn on all available data—not a subset. The first decade of the 21st century was much warmer than the long-term baseline, and the subsequent years show a continued warming trend.

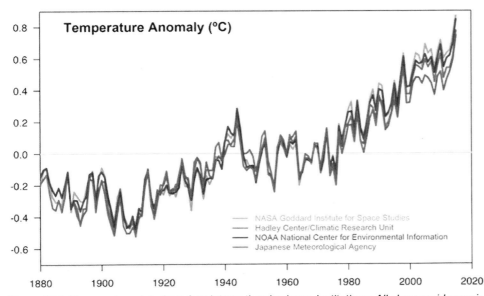

Figure 12.1: Temperature data from four international science institutions. All show rapid warming in the past few decades and that the last decade has been the warmest on record. Data sources: NASA's Goddard Institute for Space Studies, NOAA National Climatic Data Center, Met Office Hadley Centre/Climatic Research Unit and the Japanese Meteorological Agency. (See Teacher-Friendly Guide website for a full color version.)

permafrost • *a layer of soil below the surface that remains frozen all year round. Its thickness can range from tens of centimeters (inches) to a few meters (yards). Permafrost is typically defined as any soil that has remained at a temperature below the freezing point of water for at least two years.*

ocean acidification • *the increasing acidity, or lowered pH, of ocean waters, caused by absorption of atmospheric carbon dioxide.*

7. Why would global warming necessarily be bad for humans? Are people who are arguing that global warming is happening being alarmists?

It is true that some places with cold climates could see benefits from global warming. These positive effects include longer growing seasons and greater agricultural productivity in high-latitude countries like Canada and Russia, smaller winter heating bills, and fewer hassles with icy roads. However, there will also almost certainly be a larger number of more significant negative consequences. For example, high latitude ecosystems—such as the Arctic and Antarctic—will change dramatically, leading to reduction or extinction of many species. As **permafrost** melts, buildings and roads built on it will sink, tilt, or collapse entirely. This phenomenon is already observed. Droughts and severe weather events such as floods and tropical storms are predicted to become stronger and more frequent. Rising sea level will be difficult to deal with along densely-populated low-lying coastlines like those in Louisiana and Bangladesh and on coral atolls, and poorer countries will be disproportionately affected. Insect-vectored human diseases will spread into areas in which they were formerly not a problem. Domestic and agricultural water supplies are projected to decrease. **Ocean acidification** will further endanger already-threatened coral reefs that form the ecological base for other marine life.

Increasing temperatures also mean that climates (and the ecosystems associated with them) will shift poleward. Poisonous or ecologically aggressive insects and plants that thrive in warmer climates will be able to migrate as temperatures increase. Pest species will have more reproductive cycles as temperatures increase. We already see agricultural and forest pest species undergoing a population expansion that has creates increased agricultural damage.

We should be alarmed. Climate change will have serious impacts on humans, including health, agriculture, land use, and water availability. These are not science fiction. Our current lifestyle, including the ability to feed a large number of people, move vast quantities of goods large distances quickly, and live in the wide range of environments that we do, revolves around a stable climate system. Realistic worst-case scenarios of climate change could very plausibly lead to massive disruption of modern lifestyles, the global economy, and even national security.

See Chapter 9: Climate Change Adaptation for more on the impacts of climate change and strategies for adapting.

8. Won't new technologies and "green energy" get us out of this?

We are already in the process of designing and deploying technologies that produce or use energy that do not contribute to global warming. Many countries and US states have adopted climate and fossil-fuel reduction targets and timelines. We are working to engineer effective ways to sequester the carbon that we are currently emitting and store it below ground. We continue to employ available energy-efficient technologies. It is important to recognize, however, that even the most fast-paced of these technological solutions will take decades, at best, to make a significant difference. Meanwhile, it is important for all stakeholders to work to make the problem as small as possible. Smaller problems are less expensive and much easier to solve.

See Chapter 7: Climate Change Mitigation and Chapter 8: Geoengineering for more on technological solutions.

9. We have trouble forecasting the local weather for next week with reasonable accuracy; how can we predict the climate over the next 100 years?

Although weather and climate are complex systems, that does not mean that they are entirely unpredictable. The unpredictable character of complex systems arises from their sensitivity to changes in the conditions that control their development. Weather is a highly complex mix of events that happen in a particular locality on any particular day, including small changes in rainfall, temperature, humidity, and other factors that can cause weather to vary. These changes are under continual observation, and, since current conditions are the starting point for forecasting future conditions, these observations are used to update weather predictions in real time. This is why tomorrow's weather forecast is more accurate than next week's.

Climate is the longer-term generalization about a region's weather—the average of decades of weather patterns in a region. Although weather changes rapidly on human timescales, climate changes more slowly. And just like weather forecasting, current observations are input to climate models to make them more robust. Accurate prediction is a matter of choosing the right timescale—days in the case of weather, and decades to centuries in the case of climate, using every available observation to update the predictions. As an example, we can predict with a high degree of confidence that in Chicago January 2020 will be colder on average than July 2020, and that the *average* Chicago temperature that year will be higher than that of Dallas—that's climate. But we can't predict for these places what the temperature will be, or whether it will rain or snow, on any given day during those months. That's weather, and cannot be predicted that far in advance.

10. A lot of climate predictions depend on computer models. How much can we trust such models?

Numerical models (General Circulation Models or GCMs), representing physical processes in the atmosphere, ocean, cryosphere and land surface, are the most advanced tools currently available for simulating the response of the global climate system to increasing greenhouse gas concentrations. GCMs are based on equations of fluid motion, and are the subjects of intense research and continued improvement. Global GCMs often contain smaller-scale regional models nested within them for better resolution and accuracy. Hundreds of individual parameters provide the input to a GCM; these include, for example, air temperature and pressure at various elevations, ocean temperature and pressure at multiple depths, horizontal and vertical velocities (e.g., winds and currents), radiation at short, medium and long wavelengths, land surface processes such as evaporation and transpiration, land and sea surface albedo (reflectivity), cloud cover, and elevation. Thus GCMs are used to model a variety of different processes at different scales. In order to validate a model and its predictions for the future, the model is run for past climates to test its ability to reconstruct the events that we already know. If a GCM predicts the past (which the best models do well), they provide similarly robust predictions for the future. Models designed two decades ago have proved to be good predictors of the climate that we are currently experiencing.

However, it's important to realize that the basic features of climate change were successfully calculated in the 1890s by the famous Swedish chemist Svante Arrhenius, and in the 1930s by the British scientist Guy Callendar, well before the computer age. Simple models such as those that can be done without even an electronic calculator, somewhat more sophisticated ones that can be run on a laptop, and much more complex GCM models that must be run on large computer clusters all give similar overall results. The reason that many climate scientists use GCMs is not because they are the only way to model climate change, but because they give more detail and insight into the ways that climate processes change in response to increases in greenhouse gas emissions.

See *Box 6.2* in Chapter 6: US Regional Climates Current and Future for an analogy that describes a climate model.

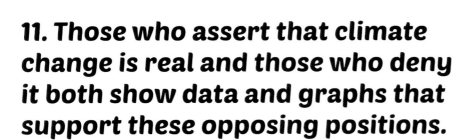
11. Those who assert that climate change is real and those who deny it both show data and graphs that support these opposing positions. How is this possible?

In order for a scientific hypothesis to become accepted idea it must pass a very important hurdle: the idea must be the best explanation for *all* of the available data and observations. Human-caused global warming currently meets that criterion. In the last decade there have been several high-profile instances in which climate change deniers have presented only partial data sets in order to support their opposing beliefs. This practice is called "cherry-picking," and is not part of an honest scientific endeavor. For example, GCMs model hundreds of climate parameters and some of these parameters are known better than others. Thus some parameters have larger uncertainties while others are much more certain. Some climate change skeptics have selected the least certain parameters, and have withheld (or deleted) the uncertainty margins, to show how "poorly" they match observations. This is not good science.

Consider a sports analogy. Think of a football team—not all players are equally skilled. Would you assess that team's chances for a championship based on the performance of only one relatively mediocre player? Not likely, because it's the overall performance of all the individuals working as a team that results in the team's performance. Analysis of all the players and their interactions, or, for a climate model, all the climate parameters, will produce the most accurate predictions.

A second method that uses real data in order to create a false impression is manipulation of the scale on a graph. As discussed in the "warming hiatus" question above (Question 6), showing data over a very short time frame can be misleading. Similarly, using a vertical scale to either magnify or suppress a trend can also be misleading. For example, the temperature data plotted on the two graphs in *Figure 12.2* is exactly the same (the same data from Question 5), but the scale has been expanded in the right-hand graph to compress the data and make the temperature increase appear non-existent. This procedure has been used by some who deny the existence or significance of climate change to give an impression of "no problem."

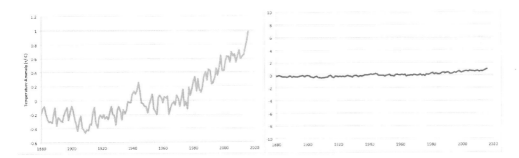

Figure 12.2. Historical temperature observations plotted on different scales.

Frequently Asked Questions

sunspot cycles · an 11-year cycle over which the number of SUNSPOTS varies, associated with a cyclical variation in the Sun's magnetic field.

12. Couldn't the sun be responsible for the observed recent climate changes?

The sun plays a central role in determining how warm our planet is. The issue today is how much solar changes have contributed to the recent warming, and what that tells us about future climate. The current scientific consensus is that changes in the energy output from the sun do not successfully account for the current warming trend. Eleven-year **sunspot cycles** have been consistently recorded, but these have risen and fallen as expected, never increasing their net output of energy. Nor do other solar outputs correlate with the warming trend. So for the period for which we have direct, observable records, the Earth has warmed dramatically even though there has been no corresponding rise in any kind of solar activity.

13. Aren't human CO_2 emissions too tiny to matter?

The important issue here is one of balance. CO_2 is part of the Earth's **carbon cycle**. When we take humans out of the equation and consider only natural processes, the carbon cycle runs in approximate balance on human time scales. In a balanced carbon cycle, CO_2 inputs to the atmosphere equal CO_2 outputs. Humans disrupt that balance. Human carbon emissions are currently 9 billion tons per year (1 billion tons = 1 Gigaton = 1 Gt).[7] This is a small number compared to the annual 120 Gt of carbon released to the atmosphere via decomposition and plant respiration. However, plants also remove 120 Gt/year via photosynthesis. The natural cycle of CO_2 is balanced, with uptake by plants and the oceans equal to release. Human emissions have no compensating removal process. Thus, the largest fraction of the 9 Gt that we add to the atmosphere stays in the atmosphere, with a substantial fraction of the rest absorbed into the surface ocean, increasing ocean acidity. Without a human effort to sequester (remove) atmospheric carbon to balance our input, we will continue to see increasing levels of atmospheric CO_2 and ocean acidity.

Some people have compared human carbon inputs to volcanic carbon emissions, saying that human emissions are less than volcanic emissions. This is untrue. All volcanoes, worldwide, emit an average of about 50 Mt of carbon per year. This is less than 1% of anthropogenic emissions.

The 9 Gt of annual anthropogenic input is enough to push atmospheric CO_2 concentrations to extremely high levels. Ice cores show that carbon dioxide levels in the atmosphere stayed between 260 and 280 parts per million for the past 10,000 years. This stability tells us that CO_2 sources and sinks have been very close to balanced over that long time span. CO_2 began to exceed that range during the Industrial Revolution, about 1850. Since them CO_2 has

---

[7] You may see references elsewhere (including Chapter 8 of this Guide) to global annual emissions of around 32 Gt. This figure is for CO_2, not carbon. One Gt of carbon corresponds to 3.667 Gt of CO_2, so 9 Gt of carbon emitted annually corresponds to 33 Gt of CO_2 emitted annually.

risen dramatically. In the past decade CO_2 levels have risen to 407ppm. The last time atmospheric CO_2 reached 400 ppm was 3.6 million years ago during the Pliocene epoch.[8] At that time Arctic summer temperatures averaged 60°F (15.5°C), 14 degrees warmer than present, and there was little to no year-round Arctic sea ice or Northern Hemisphere glaciers. Anthropogenic additions of CO_2 are creating conditions that Earth has not experienced for millions of years.

14. Why does CO_2 matter so much if it isn't the most important greenhouse gas?

The **greenhouse effect**—created by gases that absorb long wavelength radiation—currently keeps our planet 20° to 30°C warmer than it would be otherwise. This is essential for life on our planet to thrive. Global warming is the rise in temperature caused by an increase in the levels of greenhouse gases. Water vapor is the most important contributor to the greenhouse effect. Approximately 50% of the greenhouse effect is due to water vapor, with another 25% due to clouds and 20% due to CO_2, with other gases accounting for the remainder.

See Chapter 3: What is Climate? for more detail on the greenhouse effect.

So why are climate scientists not more worried about water vapor than about CO_2? The answer has to do with how long greenhouse gases persist in the atmosphere. Excess CO_2 accumulates, warming the atmosphere, which raises water vapor levels and causes further warming. The rapid turnover of water vapor, through evaporation and precipitation, means that even if human activity was directly adding or removing significant amounts of water vapor (which it is not), there would be no slow build-up of water vapor as is happening with CO_2. The level of water vapor in the atmosphere is determined mainly by temperature, and any excess is rapidly lost. The level of CO_2 is determined by the balance between sources and sinks, and it would take hundreds of years for it to return to pre-industrial levels even if all emissions ceased tomorrow. To put this another way, there is no limit to how much rain can fall, but there is a limit to how much extra CO_2 that the oceans and other sinks can soak up.

Carbon dioxide is not the only greenhouse gas emitted by humans. Many greenhouse gases, such as **methane** (CH_4), are far more powerful than CO_2 in terms of infrared absorption per molecule. However, the overall quantities and impacts of these other gases are smaller than those of CO_2; methane has a shorter residence time in the atmosphere, eventually oxidizing to CO_2. Even allowing for the relative strength of the effects, CO_2 is still responsible for 60% of the additional warming caused by all the greenhouse gases emitted as a result of human activity.

greenhouse effect • the influence of GREENHOUSE GAS molecules in the Earth's atmosphere to retain heat (infrared radiation) radiating from the Earth's surface that would otherwise escape into space.

methane • CH_4, a greenhouse gas formed from organic matter under heat and pressure from burial and from fermentation of organic matter by bacteria in low oxygen settings, including the digestion of animals.

---

[8] To learn more about the last time CO_2 levels were this high on Earth, see the article "Ice-Free Arctic in Pliocene, Last Time CO_2 Levels above 400 PPM" in Scientific American: https://www.scientificamerican.com/article/ice-free-arctic-in-pliocene-last-time-co2-levels-above-400ppm/.

ice core • *a large cylinder of ice extracted from an ice sheet or glacier, such as is found in Antarctica, Greenland, or on very high mountains worldwide. Chemical analysis of the ice and air bubbles can reveal information about the climate at the time the ice formed, as can materials such as dust or pollen found in the ice.*

glacial-interglacial cycle • *an alternation between times in Earth's history when continental ICE SHEETS grow and advance toward lower latitudes (GLACIALS), and times when the climate is warmer and ice sheets melt back (INTERGLACIALS).*

Milankovich cycles • *cyclical changes in the amount of heat received from the Sun, associated with how the Earth's orbit, tilt, and wobble alter its position with respect to the Sun. These changes affect the global climate, most notably alterations of glacial and interglacial intervals.*

15. Some ice cores show that CO₂ increases lag behind temperature rises. Doesn't this disprove the link to global warming?

The Antarctic **ice core** record of the past 800,000 years has provided a record of CO_2 and temperature data showing a close correlation in a series of 100,000 year **glacial-interglacial cycles**. During spans of several thousand years during transitions from glacials to interglacials there have been periods during which temperatures warmed and CO_2 rose relatively quickly; previous research indicated that warming events preceded CO_2 increases by roughly 800 years. This led some people to argue that CO_2 could not have been important for climate, as climate appeared to warm before the influence of increased CO_2. There are two important phenomena here. First, changes in the Earth's orbit (**Milankovich cyles**) provide modest changes in total global insolation that drive glacial-interglacial cycles, including the initial trigger that starts warming at the peak of each glacial advance. Second, temperature and CO_2 are an example of a positive feedback loop that occurs at many times scales and throughout glacial-interglacial cycles, amplifying the warming trend: as climate warms, CO_2 is released from the oceans and carbon-rich soils; in turn, as CO_2 increases, climate warms.

> See Chapter 3: What is Climate? for more detail on the carbon cycle and on Milankovich cycles. See Chapter 4: Climate Change Through Earth History for more about glacial-interglacial cycles.

It is also important to note that in the last few years the dating of ice cores that contain the CO_2 record has improved. It is relatively straightforward to measure the amount of CO_2 trapped in ice cores, and to estimate changes in the temperature recorded in the ice core, but dating the *age* when the CO_2 was trapped is not. The uncertainties in the early estimates were more than 600 years. New dating techniques have shown that there is no statistically significant difference between the timing of temperature increases and CO_2 increases. At some points during deglaciations, temperature appears to lead CO_2, but at others CO_2 increases appear to precede warming. This is an outcome of the feedback connections between the carbon cycle and climate system.[9]

[9] A technical discussion of this point is found here: F. Parrenin et al. (2013). Synchronous Change of Atmospheric CO2 and Antarctic Temperature During the Last Deglacial Warming. Science 01 Mar 2013: Vol. 339, Issue 6123, pp. 1060-1063. DOI: 10.1126/science.1226368.

16. Climate websites refer to both the IPCC and, more recently, the NIPCC. What is the difference between these two organizations?

The Intergovernmental Panel on Climate Change (IPCC) was created by the United Nations in 1988 to review scientific conclusions on climate change that have already passed peer review and been published in the scientific literature. The IPCC includes thousands of climate scientists and is open to all member countries of the United Nations and the World Meteorological Organization. The IPCC publishes periodic reports on the state of global climate (1990, 1995, 2001, 2007 and 2014). These assessment reports involve more than 500 lead authors and 2000 reviewers from more than 100 participating nations, and cite >9000 published scientific literature sources. The 2014 Report makes the following conclusions:

"Warming of the climate system is unequivocal, and since the 1950s, many of the observed changes are unprecedented over decades to millennia. The atmosphere and ocean have warmed, the amounts of snow and ice have diminished, and sea level has risen….

Human influence on the climate system is clear, and recent anthropogenic emissions of greenhouse gases are the highest in history. Recent climate changes have had widespread impacts on human and natural systems."[10]

The IPCC reports been criticized by the NIPCC. The "Nongovernmental International Panel on Climate Change" is sponsored by the Heartland Institute, a US-based conservative think tank best known for fighting government regulation of the tobacco and fossil fuel industries. Heartland has campaigned to downplay threats posed by second-hand smoke, acid rain, and ozone depletion, as well as against the Endangered Species Act. The Heartland NIPCC also issues periodic reports, timed to coincide with the release of IPCC assessment reports and formatted to look like them. NIPCC reports are authored by fewer than 50 individuals and the most recent report cites only 72 papers, mostly written by the NIPCC authors.[11]

---

[10] See the IPCC Summary for Policymakers here: https://www.ipcc.ch/pdf/assessment-report/ar5/syr/AR5_SYR_FINAL_SPM.pdf.

[11] Learn more about debunking the report at: https://ncse.com/files/nipcc.pdf.

17. Is climate change too big or too far along to be stopped?

It's possible to greatly slow down and diminish potential future climate change.

Human societies have developed under the rubric of certain climate patterns and have always depended on climate-dependent natural resources. For example, in the western US most residents rely on winter snow pack to store water that arrives in the winter for delivery in the summer when their demands are highest. Because significant climate change would alter accustomed climate patterns and regional natural resources (some natural systems will be irreversibly damaged by global warming), it could pose disruptions to socioeconomic systems around the world. These disruptions would be worse where global warming worsens existing conflicts over scarce resources and where the funding or capacity for preparing for or adapting to these changes is lacking. Many people agree that global warming is likely to have worse consequences for those with the least resources and therefore least able to adapt—the economically or politically vulnerable, for example.

"Stopping" anthropogenic global warming completely is now widely viewed as impossible in the short-term. There is, however, still time to minimize it, and there are things that we can do. Global warming *is* reversible in the long-term, at least in the sense that we could, eventually, bring global greenhouse gas emissions, the "human" part of climate change, back down. The issue here is a matter of how long we can wait. The sooner we reduce emissions, the better.

Even if we were to stop fossil fuel burning altogether and immediately, temperatures would almost certainly continue to rise because of the additional CO_2 already in the atmosphere. Carbon dioxide concentrations would eventually start to decline, but it would take much longer for them to return to preindustrial levels than they did to build up. This means that even in this extreme "best case" scenario, we still need to expect some level of climate change and to prepare accordingly.

> See Chapter 7: Climate Change Mitigation and Chapter 9: Climate Change Adaptation for more information on strategies to respond to climate change.

18. What can be done by the average citizen?

The actions of individuals are where everything begins. We can, as individuals, reduce our reliance on fossil fuels in transportation, home heating and lighting, and consumption of goods. We can look for a lower emission vehicle when it's time for a new car. We can utilize public transportation. We can install energy-efficient appliances in our homes and businesses. We may be able to switch to alternative energy systems for home heating and electricity (*Figure 12.3*), or join a renewable energy co-op. We can make choices as consumers that

Figure 12.3: Aerial view of a solar farm near Austin, Texas.

minimize climate impact. For example, buying food in season and grown locally reduces the emissions that result from transporting food long distances. Beyond reducing our own emissions we can offset the emissions we cannot eliminate by supporting alternative energy technologies and reforestation efforts. Some corporations are beginning to act to offset their contributions to global warming. This is voluntary in the US, but mandatory in Europe. An individual might also think about the way a corporation is addressing global warming before making investment choices.

Individuals can work collaboratively to support communities and collective actions. Transportation, energy use, and other policies at the local, state, and federal levels will all influence greenhouse gas emissions. We can work for broad societal change, voting with our wallets when we make climate-friendly purchases, and at the ballot box when we choose representatives who will champion climate-neutral policies. Every step that we take—as an individual, as a community, or as a nation—to reduce our climate impact is a step that makes the problem a little smaller, a little less difficult. This is *enormously* important.

Shifting the world's economy away from its dependence on fossil fuels is the single step that would do the most to reduce anthropogenic climate change. This is also a huge challenge that will not be accomplished by any one change. It will require actions big and small by individuals, corporations, and governments around the world. Although people sometimes feel that nothing that they do matters, the only thing that *does* matter is what people do.

Glossary

ablation	the loss of snow and ice from a GLACIER or ICE SHEET by melting, evaporation, sublimation (a phase transition from solid directly to gas), iceberg calving, and other processes.
adaptation	in the context of climate change, action taken to prepare for unavoidable climate changes that are currently happening or are projected to happen in the future.
aerobic	involving free oxygen.
aerosol	the suspension of very fine solid or liquid particles in a gas.
albedo	the fraction of solar energy that a surface reflects back into space.
ammonoid	a group of extinct cephalopods belonging to the Phylum Mollusca, and possessing a spiraling, tightly-coiled shell characterized by ridges, or septa.
anthropogenic	made by humans, or resulting from human activity.
aquifer	a water-bearing formation of gravel, permeable rock, or sand that is capable of providing water, in usable quantities, to springs or wells.
arthropod	an invertebrate animal, belonding to the Phylum Arthropoda, and possessing an external skeleton (exoskeleton), body segments, and jointed appendages. Arthropods include crustaceans, arachnids, and insects, and there are over a million described arthropod species living today. Trilobites are a major group of extinct arthropods.
atmosphere	the layer of gases that surrounds a planet.
availability heuristic	the reliance on immediate examples rather than information grounded in extensive data or research, when looking for explanations.

Glossary

backfire effect	an effect that causes beliefs to become stronger rather than weaker when they are challenged with conflicting evidence. The backfire effect is in part a response to IDENTITY PROTECTIVE COGNITION, the STATUS QUO BIAS, and allegiance to community norms, each of which are powerful forces that resist change.
bacteria	single-celled microorganisms with cell membranes but without organelles or a nucleus.
banded iron formations	geologic formations comprised of layers of PRECAMBRIAN, iron-rich, sedimentary rock.
basalt	an extrusive igneous rock, and the most common rock type on the surface of the Earth. It forms the upper surface of all oceanic plates, and is the principal rock of ocean/seafloor ridges, oceanic islands, and high-volume continental eruptions. Basalt is fine-grained and mostly dark-colored, although it often weathers to reds and browns because of its high iron content.
biomass energy	energy produced by burning plants, wastes, or their derivatives.
biosphere	all organisms, both living and non-living, on Earth.
bolide	an extraterrestrial object of any composition that forms a large crater upon impact with the Earth. In astronomy, bolides are bright meteors (also known as fireballs) that explode as they pass through the Earth's atmosphere.
brownout	a situation where available electric power is limited but not eliminated.
Cambrian	a geologic time period lasting from 541 to 485 million years ago. During the Cambrian, multicellular marine organisms became increasingly diverse, as did their mineralized fossils. The Cambrian is part of the PALEOZOIC Era.
carbon cycle	the exchange and recycling of carbon between the geosphere, hydrosphere, atmosphere, and biosphere.

Glossary

carbon sink	a system or part of a system which absorbs carbon.
carbon-14	an isotope of carbon often used in dating materials.
Carboniferous	a geologic time period that extends from 359 to 299 million years ago. It is divided into two subperiods, the Mississippian and the Pennsylvanian. By the Carboniferous, terrestrial life had become well established.
Cenozoic	the geologic time period spanning from 66 million years ago to the present. The Cenozoic is also known as the age of mammals, since extinction of the large reptiles at the end of the MESOZOIC allowed mammals to diversify. The Cenozoic includes the Paleogene, Neogene, and Quaternary periods.
chemical weathering	the breaking down of rock through chemical processes.
chlorofluorocarbons	compounds of carbon, hydrogen, chlorine, and fluorine, usually ANTHROPOGENIC gases used as refrigerants or in aerosol cans. Released into the ATMOSPHERE, these compounds are GREENHOUSE GASES and are responsible for the OZONE HOLE.
climate	a description of both the average weather conditions (temperature, precipitation, wind, etc.) and the extremes that a region experiences.
climate change	the current increase in the average surface temperature worldwide, caused by the buildup of greenhouse gases in the atmosphere, and the related changes to other aspects of climate such as precipitation patterns and storm strength. See also GLOBAL WARMING.
climate change adaptation	actions taken to prepare for climate changes that are occurring or will occur in the future.
climate change mitigation	actions taken to limit or eliminate emissions of greenhouse gases in order to reduce future climate warming.
climate gradient	changes in climate across a distance.

Glossary

climate model	a computer-generated simulation of the Earth's climate system, projected through time.
climate normal	thirty-year averages of variables such as daily temperature, rainfall, snowfall, and frost and freeze dates that can be compared with thirty-year averages of these variables from other time periods.
cloud	a visible aggregation of condensed water vapor in the atmosphere.
coal	a rock formed from ancient plant matter that can be burned as fuel. Since coal is formed from fossilized plant remains it is considered a FOSSIL FUEL.
co-benefit	sometimes called multiple benefit, is an improvement or positive outcome from an action that was not the primary one intended. For example, a person might choose to use a highly energy-efficient appliance in order to reduce energy use and thus carbon emissions, and saving money might be a co-benefit of this choice.
cognitive bias	a holding on to incorrect thinking even in the presence of contrary information, because of beliefs or points of view one has.
combined heat and power	an approach that uses a single fuel source to generate both electricity and usable heat. Combined heat and power systems are typically located near where the energy is consumed, and they use the heat which is wasted in traditional electrical power generation processes.
condensation nuclei	suspended particles in the air which can serve as "seeds" for water molecules to attach to, in the first step in the formation of clouds. See also NUCLEATION SITES.
confirmation bias	the tendency to seek out information that agrees with one's existing prior opinions, and to ignore established evidence that might conflict with those opinions. See also MYSIDE BIAS.
Continental Divide	a ridge of high land on a continent, which separates regions where water flows to oceans or seas on different sides of the continent.

convection	movement of a fluid, such as air or water, resulting from gravitational force on the fluid. Warmer, less dense matter rises and cooler, more dense matter sinks, producing heat transfer.
convection cell	a zone where warm, less dense air or water rises and cool, more dense air or water sinks, creating a repetitive pattern of motion.
Coriolis effect	the apparent deflection of air masses in the atmosphere, which are moving relative to the rotating reference frame of the Earth.
Coriolis force	a force acting on objects (e.g., air masses in the atmosphere) that are moving relative to a rotating reference frame (e.g., the Earth)
Cretaceous	a geologic time period spanning from 144 to 66 million years ago. It is the youngest period of the MESOZOIC. The end of the Cretaceous bore witness to the MASS EXTINCTION event that resulted in the demise of the DINOSAURS.
cryosphere	the part of Earth's surface where water exists in solid form. This includes all major forms of ice, such as SEA ICE, GLACIERS, ICE SHEETS and permafrost.
current	directional movement of a fluid mass
cycad	a palm-like, terrestrial seed plant (tree) belonging to the Class Cycadopsida, and characterized by a woody trunk, a crown of stiff evergreen leaves, seeds without protective coatings, and no flowers. Cycads were very common in the MESOZOIC, but are much reduced in diversity today, restricted to the tropical and subtropical regions of the planet.
deciduous plants	plants which lose their leaves, typically in autumn, and regrow them the following spring.
Devonian	a geologic time period spanning from 419 to 359 million years ago. The Devonian is also called the "age of fishes" due to the diversity of fish that radiated during this time. On land, seed-bearing plants appeared and terrestrial arthropods became established. The Devonian is part of the Paleozoic.

Glossary

dinosaur	a member of a group of terrestrial reptiles with a common ancestor and thus certain anatomical similarities, including long ankle bones and erect limbs. Most species of the large reptile groups, including the dinosaurs, disappeared at or before the MASS EXTINCTION at the end of the CRETACEOUS.
drought	a long period of unusually low rainfall, resulting in lack of water for plants, animals, and people.
duration	the length of time an event or activity lasts.
eccentricity	the shape of Earth's orbit around the sun, which varies in the shape of an ellipse on a 100,000-year cycle
ecosystem services	the numerous benefits that healthy ecosystems provide to people, such as food, medicine sources, raw materials, erosion control, waste decomposition, filtering pollutants out of air and water, and recreation opportunities.
El Niño	also called the El Niño – Southern Oscillation (ENSO); is represented by fluctuating temperatures and air pressures in the tropical Pacific Ocean. During an El Niño event, the eastern Pacific experiences warmer water and higher air pressure than the western Pacific, changing rainfall patterns, eastern Pacific upwelling, and weather variables globally. ENSO events typically occur every 3 to 7 years.
energy balance	a state in which the energy coming in to a system equals the energy going out.
energy conservation	an approach to processes and activities that results in using less energy, on scales ranging from individual to industrial to national and global.
energy efficiency	methods which enable machines to perform functions while minimizing energy loss or using less energy than previously.
Eocene	a geologic time interval extending from 56 to 33 million years ago. The Eocene is the second epoch of the Cenozoic era.
equilibrium	a state of balance in opposing forces, amounts, or rates.

esker	a sinuous, elongated ridge of sand and gravel. Most eskers formed within ice-walled tunnels carved by streams flowing beneath a glacier. After the ice melted away, the stream deposits remained as long winding ridges. Eskers are sometimes mined for their well-sorted sand and gravel.
evapotranspiration	a combination of evaporation of liquid water on plant leaves and in the soil around the plant and transpiration, the transfer of water from a plant's roots to its leaves and then to water vapor in the air. Evapotranspiration cools the air because it takes heat from the air to convert liquid water to water vapor.
feedback	the response of a system to some change that either balances/opposes or reinforces/enhances the change that is applied to a system. Balancing feedback (sometimes called negative feedback) tends to push a system toward stability; reinforcing feedback (sometimes called positive feedback) tends to push a system towards extremes.
feedback loop	a repeating process where some of the output of a system becomes input as well.
feldspar	an extremely common group of rock-forming minerals found in igneous, metamorphic, and sedimentary rocks. There are two groups of feldspar: alkali feldspar (which ranges from potassium-rich to sodium-rich) and plagioclase feldspar (which ranges from sodium-rich to calcium-rich). Potassium feldspars of the alkali group are commonly seen as pink crystals in igneous and metamorphic rocks, or pink grains in sedimentary rocks. Plagioclase feldspars are more abundant than the alkali feldspars, ranging in color from light to dark. Feldspars are commercially used in ceramics and scouring powders.
fission	the process of bombarding atomic nuclei with neutrons, splitting the nuclei into those of lighter elements and more neutrons, and also resulting in the release of energy.
floodplain	the land around a river that is prone to flooding. This area can be grassy, but the sediments under the surface are usually deposits from previous floods.

Glossary

flue gas separation	a process which uses a liquid solvent to chemically remove CO_2 molecules from a gas as the molecules make their way through a flue.
forcing	a change that has a directional impact on what is being changed (e.g., a solar forcing on the Earth directly impacts the Earth's heat absorption).
fossil fuel	a non-renewable, carbon-based fuel source like OIL, NATURAL GAS, or COAL, developed from the preserved organic remains of fossil organisms.
geoengineering	a large-scale technological effort to change the Earth's climate, typically either by removing carbon dioxide from the atmosphere or by blocking incoming solar radiation.
geosphere	the solid portion of the Earth
geothermal energy	heat energy found below the surface of the Earth.
ginkgo	a terrestrial tree belonging to the plant division Ginkgophyta, and characterized by broad fan-shaped leaves, large seeds without protective coatings, and no flowers. Ginkgos were very common and diverse in the Mesozoic, but today only one species exists, *Ginkgo biloba*.
glacial	a time in Earth's history when a cold climate leads to the advance of GLACIERS and ICE SHEETS. See also INTERGLACIAL.
glacial-interglacial cycle	an alternation between times in Earth's history when continental ICE SHEETS grow and advance toward lower latitudes (GLACIALS), and times when the climate is warmer and ice sheets melt back (INTERGLACIALS).
glacier	a very large piece of ice that sits at least partially on land and moves under the force of gravity.

Glossary

global warming	the current increase in the average temperature worldwide, caused by the buildup of greenhouse gases in the atmosphere. With the coming of the Industrial Age and exponential increases in human population, large amounts of gases have been released into the atmosphere (especially carbon dioxide) that give rise to global warming. The term CLIMATE CHANGE is preferred because warming contributes to other climatic changes such as precipitation and storm strength.
Goldilocks Principle	the idea that the temperature on Earth is not too hot and not too cold, but "just right" for life as we know it to exist.
Gondwana	the supercontinent of the Southern Hemisphere, composed of Africa, Australia, India, and South America. It combined with the North American continent to form PANGAEA during the late PALEOZOIC.
gradient	a change, either increasing or decreasing, in the magnitude of a quantity over space or time.
green infrastructure	structures that use plants, soil, and other natural features to perform functions such as providing shade, absorbing heat, blocking wind, or absorbing and filtering stormwater.
greenhouse effect	the influence of greenhouse gas molecules in the Earth's atmosphere to retain heat (infrared radiation) radiating from the Earth's surface that would otherwise escape into space.
greenhouse gas	a gas that absorbs and re-radiates energy in the form of heat; carbon dioxide, water vapor, and methane are examples.
Gulf Stream	a current in the Atlantic Ocean which transports warm water from the Gulf of Mexico along North America's East Coast, then across the Atlantic, where it splits into two streams, one traveling to Northern Europe and one to West Africa.
gypsum	a soft, sulfate mineral that is widely mined for its use as fertilizer and as a constituent of plaster. Alabaster, a fine-grained light colored variety of gypsum, has been used for sculpture making by many cultures since ancient times.

Glossary

gyre	large- (i.e., global-) scale rotating masses of ocean water.
heat island	an urban area which experiences higher temperatures than do surrounding rural areas as a result of pollution, pavement, and the surfaces of buildings magnifying localized heating.
heat wave	a prolonged period of extremely high air temperatures.
Heinrich events	periods during the last 100,000 years when large volumes of freshwater entered the ocean from icebergs which broke off glaciers and ice sheets in the Arctic and floated into the North Atlantic Ocean. This release of freshwater changed ocean circulation because freshwater and seawater have different densities.
Holocene	the most recent portion of the QUATERNARY, beginning about 11,700 years ago and continuing to the present. It is the most recent (and current) interglacial, an interval of glacial retreat. The Holocene also encompasses the global growth and impact of the human species.
horsetail	a terrestrial plant belonging to the Family Equisetaceae in the plant division Pteridophyta, and characterized by hollow, jointed stems with reduced, unbranched leaves at the nodes.
hurricane	a rapidly rotating storm system with heavy winds, a low-pressure center, and a spiral arrangement of thunderstorms. These storm systems tend to form over the tropical ocean, and are classified as hurricanes, typhoons, or cyclones (depending on their location in the world) once winds have reached 199 kilometers per hours (74 miles per hour). See also TROPICAL CYCLONE.
hydropower	electric power derived from the kinetic energy of falling or moving water.
hydrosphere	all of the water on Earth.

Glossary

ice core	a large cylinder of ice extracted from an ice sheet or glacier, such as is found in Antarctica, Greenland, or on very high mountains worldwide. Chemical analysis of the ice and air bubbles can reveal information about the climate at the time the ice formed, as can materials such as dust or pollen found in the ice.
ice sheet	a mass of glacial ice that covers part of a continent and has an area greater than 50,000 square kilometers (19,000 square miles).
iceberg	a large chunk of ice, generally ranging in height from 1 to 75 meters (3 to 246 feet) above sea level, that has broken off of an ice sheet or glacier and floats freely in open water.
identity-protective cognition	a way of thinking that drives us to select the evidence that is consistent with the worldview of our social groups, sometimes leading us to believe certain things that are demonstrably false.
infrared	electromagnetic radiation in the part of the spectrum with wavelengths from 750 nanometers to 1 millimeter. People sense infrared radiation as heat.
inland sea	a shallow sea covering the central area of a continent during periods of high sea level. An inland sea is located on continental crust, while other seas are located on oceanic crust.
insolation	the amount of solar radiation reaching the Earth.
interglacial	a time in Earth's history between GLACIAL advances; there have been about 50 glacial advances and interglacials in the past 2.5 million years.
ionizing radiation	high-energy electromagnetic energy which can cause ionization in the material through which it passes, for example, x-rays and gamma rays.
IPCC	the Intergovernmental Panel on Climate Change, a large, international group of climate scientists working to understand climate change and to present reliable climate data and information to policy-makers and the public at large.

Glossary

iron oxide minerals	a range of minerals containing chemical compounds of iron and oxygen.
irradiance	the intensity of radiated energy received, for example, by the Earth from the sun.
isotope	a form of a chemical element that contains a specific number of neutrons. For example, the isotope of carbon with six neutrons is known as carbon-12 (^{12}C) and the isotope of carbon with eight neutrons is carbon-14 (^{14}C). All isotopes of an element contain the same number of protons.
jet stream	a fast-flowing, narrow air current found in the ATMOSPHERE. The polar jet stream is found at an altitude of 7–12 kilometers (23,000–39,000 feet), and the air within can travel as fast as 160 kph (100 mph). Jet streams are created by a combination of the Earth's rotation and atmospheric heating.
Jurassic	the geologic time period lasting from 201 to 145 million years ago. During the Jurassic, dinosaurs dominated the landscape and the first birds appeared. The Jurassic is the middle period of the MESOZOIC.
kettle	a depression formed where a large, isolated block of ice became separated from the retreating ICE SHEET. The ice becomes buried by sediment; when it melts, it leaves a shallow depression in the landscape that often persists as a small lake.
Köppen system	a commonly used system of climate categorization developed by Russian climatologist Wladimir Köppen. It is based on the kinds of vegetation that areas sustain, and defines 12 climate types: rainforest, MONSOON, tropical SAVANNA, humid subtropical, humid continental, oceanic, Mediterranean, STEPPE, subarctic, TUNDRA, polar ice cap, and desert. Updated by Rudolf Geiger, it has been refined to five groups each with two to four subgroups.
lag	a period of time between events, such as between the incidence of solar radiation and a certain amount of warming of the Earth.
lake effect snow	snowfall caused by the movement of cold weather systems over a relatively warm lake, in which an air mass picks up water from the lake and deposits it in the form of snow across an adjacent land mass.

leaf margin analysis	a PROXY method for estimating past temperatures using known relationships between the shape of leaf margins (smooth or toothed) and temperature and humidity.
leeward	the side of a mountain range or other high landmass which is facing away from the direction the wind is coming. For example, if a wind is coming from the West, the leeward side of a mountain range is the eastern side.
life cycle analysis	a way of determining the total environmental impact of a product, including all steps from beginning (extraction of raw materials) to end (disposal, recycling, or reuse) and quantifying all inputs and outputs.
limestone	a sedimentary rock composed of calcium carbonate ($CaCO_3$). Most limestones are formed by the deposition and consolidation of the skeletons of marine invertebrates; a few originate in chemical precipitation from solution.
linear	a mathematical relationship where a variable is directly proportional to another variable.
Little Ice Age	a relatively modest cooling (less than 1° C) of the Northern Hemisphere in the 16th–19th centuries.
loess	very fine-grained, wind-blown sediment, usually rock flour left behind by the grinding action of flowing GLACIERS.
logical fallacy	incorrect reasoning due to faulty logic.
magma	molten rock located below the surface of the Earth.
magnetic field	a conceptualization of the strength and direction of the magnetic force at a distance from an object.
magnitude	the size of a quantity.
mantle	the layer of the Earth between the crust and core. It consists of solid silicate rocks that, over long intervals of time, flow like a highly viscous liquid. Convection currents within the mantle drive the motion of plate tectonics.

m

Glossary

Marinoan glaciation	a time in Earth's history, around 640 to 635 million years ago, when the entire planet may have been covered in ice.
mass extinction	the extinction (loss of the last living member of a species) of a large percentage of the Earth's species over a relatively short span of geologic time.
Medieval Warm Period	a period of warm climate in the North Atlantic region during approximately the years 950 to 1100.
Mesozoic	a geologic time era that spans from 252 to 66 million years ago. This era is also called the "age of reptiles" since dinosaurs and other reptiles dominated both marine and terrestrial ecosystems. During this time, the last of the Earth's major supercontinents, PANGAEA, formed and later broke up, producing the Earth's current geography.
methane	CH_4, a greenhouse gas formed from organic matter under heat and pressure from burial and from fermentation of organic matter by bacteria in low oxygen settings, including the digestion of animals.
metric ton	a unit of weight equivalent to a mass of 1,000 kilograms. It is sometimes called a British tonne.
microwave radiation	electromagnetic radiation in the part of the spectrum with wavelengths from about 0.1 to 100 centimeters.
mid-Atlantic ridge	a ridge on the floor of the Atlantic Ocean generally running North-South at the boundary of tectonic plates, where these plates are moving apart.
Milankovitch cycles	cyclical changes in the amount of heat received from the sun, associated with how the Earth's orbit, tilt, and wobble alter its position with respect to the sun. These changes affect the global climate, most notably alterations of glacial and interglacial intervals.
Miocene	fourth geologic epoch of the Cenozoic era, extending from 23 to 5 million years ago.
monsoon	a seasonal wind pattern in the Indian Ocean and South Asia which reverses direction between southwesterly and northeasterly, creating a wet season in summer and a dry season in winter.

mountain glacier	a glacier found in high mountains, often spanning across multiple peaks.
myside bias	the tendency to seek out information that agrees with one's existing prior opinions, and to ignore established evidence that might conflict with those opinions. See also CONFIRMATION BIAS.
natural gas	a hydrocarbon gas mixture composed primarily of methane (CH_4), but also small quantites of hydrocarbons such as ethane and propane. See also FOSSIL FUEL.
near-surface	near the surface of the Earth; typically within a few meters above the surface.
non-linear	a mathematical relationship where a variable is not directly proportional to another variable.
Nor'easter	a storm, often severe, along the U.S. East coast which forms when warm air from the Atlantic Ocean meets cold air from the north and west.
nucleation site	suspended particles in the air which can serve as "seeds" for water molecules to attach to, in the first step in the formation of clouds. See also CONDENSATION NUCLEI.
nuisance flooding	flooding which leads to inconveniences such as road closures and overflowing storm drains, but which does not cause severe damage.
obliquity	the tilt of the Earth on its orbital axis, which can range from 22–24° from vertical, and changes periodically on a roughly 40,000-year cycle
ocean	the large, saline body of water that covers most of the Earth's surface.
ocean acidification	the increasing acidity, or lowered pH, of ocean waters, caused by absorption of atmospheric carbon dioxide.
ocean circulation	global-scale patterns of water movement throughout the world's oceans.

Glossary

oil	a naturally occurring, flammable liquid found in geologic formations beneath the Earth's surface and consisting primarily of hydrocarbons. Oil, also called PETROLEUM, is a fossil fuel, formed when large masses of dead organisms (usually algae or plankton) are buried underneath sediments and subjected to intense heat and pressure.
Oligocene	third geologic time epoch of the Cenozoic era, spanning from about 34 to 23 million years ago.
Ordovician	a geologic time period spanning from 485 to 443 million years ago. During the Ordovician, invertebrates dominated the oceans and fish began to diversify.
organic matter	decomposed remains of plants, animals, and their wastes.
oxy-fuel combustion	burning a fuel in pure or enriched oxygen instead of in air.
ozone	a molecule (O_3) found in the STRATOSPHERE which absorbs ultraviolet light. When found near the surface of the Earth, ozone is considered a pollutant because it is a component of smog and can cause lung irritation.
ozone hole	a region of ozone depletion in the STRATOSPHERE above Antarctica, caused by destruction of ozone from ANTHROPOGENIC chemicals released into the ATMOSPHERE.
Paleocene	first geologic time interval of the Cenozoic era, spanning from about 66 to 56 million years ago.
Paleozoic	a geologic time era that extends from 541 to 252 million years ago. Fossil evidence shows that during this time period, life evolved in the oceans and gradually colonized the land.
palynology	the study of modern and fossil pollen, spores, and other microscopic plant matter.

Pangaea	a supercontinent, meaning "all Earth," which formed over 300 million years ago and lasted for almost 150 million years, during which all of the Earth's continents were joined in a giant supercontinent. Pangaea eventually rifted apart and separated into the continents in their current configuration.
peat	an accumulation of partially decayed plant matter. Under sufficient heat and pressure, it will turn into lignite COAL over geologic periods of time.
permafrost	a layer of soil below the surface that remains frozen all year round. Its thickness can range from tens of centimeters (inches) to a few meters (yards). Permafrost is typically defined as any soil that has remained at a temperature below the freezing point of water for at least two years.
Permian	the geologic time period lasting from 299 to 252 million years ago. During the Permian, the world's landmass was combined into the supercontinent PANGAEA. The Permian is the last period of the PALEOZOIC. It ended with the largest mass extinction in Earth's history, which wiped out 70% of terrestrial animal species and 90% of all marine animal species.
petroleum	a naturally occurring, flammable liquid found in geologic formations beneath the Earth's surface and consisting primarily of hydrocarbons. Petroleum, also called OIL, is a fossil fuel, formed when large masses of dead organisms (usually algae or plankton) are buried underneath sediments and subjected to intense heat and pressure.
Phanerozoic	a geologic eon representing the entirety of geological history after the PRECAMBRIAN, from 541 million years ago to the present.
photosynthesis	a chemical process in plants and other organisms which converts light energy and carbon dioxide into chemical energy (sugars that provide fuel) and oxygen.
physical weathering	the breaking down of rock through physical processes such as wind and water erosion and cracking from expansion of freezing water.

Glossary

phytoplankton	one-celled photosynthetic algae that float near the surface of bodies of both marine and freshwater.
Pleistocene	an epoch of the QUATERNARY period, lasting from 2.5 million to about 11,700 years ago. During the Pleistocene, continental ice sheets advanced south and retreated north several dozen times.
Pliocene	fifth geologic epoch of the Cenozoic era, extending from roughly 5 to 2.5 million years ago.
post-consumer	created after use by a consumer, and not involving production of any new material.
potential energy	the energy stored within an object or system, due to its position (gravitational potential energy), charge (electric potential), or other characteristics.
Precambrian	a geologic time interval that spans from the formation of Earth (4.6 billion years ago) to the beginning of the CAMBRIAN (541 million years ago). Relatively little is known about this time period since very few fossils or unaltered rocks have survived. What few clues exist indicate that life first appeared on the planet as long as 3.9 billion years ago in the form of single-celled organisms.
precession	commonly called "wobble," because it is the small variation in the direction of Earth's axis as it points relative to the fixed stars in the solar system. Because of precession, the point in Earth's orbit when the Northern Hemisphere is angled toward the sun changes over a cycle of approximately 20,000 years.
pre-combustion	taking place before burning.
pre-consumer	created before being used by a consumer. For example, pre-consumer recycled items are recycled before they have been used.
protists	a diverse group of single-celled eukaryotes (organisms with complex cells containing a nucleus and organelles).
proxy	an alternative to direct measurements of climate variables; data from sources like tree rings, lichens, and pollen are used to infer climate information.

pterosaur	extinct flying reptiles with wingspans of up to 15 meters (49 feet). They lived during the same time as the dinosaurs.
pyroclastic flow	the rapid flow of lava, ash, and gases resulting from an explosive volcanic eruption.
pyrolysis	a method of decomposing organic material by heating it at high temperatures in the absence of oxygen.
Quaternary	a geologic time period that extends from 2.6 million years ago to the present. This period is largely defined by the periodic advance and retreat of continental glaciers. The Quaternary is part of the CENOZOIC.
radiation	emission of electromagnetic energy from an object.
rain gauge	an instrument used to measure precipitation by collecting rainfall.
rain shadow	an area on one side of a mountain that experiences little rainfall.
rare earth metal	one of a group of seventeen chemical elements with similar properties and often found together in the Earth. Rare earth metals include the fifteen lanthanides, scandium, and yttrium.
relative humidity	the ratio of the water vapor density in the air to the maximum water vapor density possible in the air at a given temperature and pressure (the saturation water vapor density).
relief	the amount of elevation and slope change in a region.
remote sensing	a method of scientific investigation that uses instruments on satellites or aircraft to make measurements of the Earth's surface. It is particularly useful for studying areas that are large in extent, difficult to access on the ground or ocean, and in some cases for areas that are dark for much of the winter.

Glossary

renewable	able to be naturally replenished on a short time scale. While FOSSIL FUELS come from natural sources (the fossilized remains of plants and animals), they are not renewable on human time scales because they take many millions of years to form.
response	the result of a change (see FORCING).
rift basin	a topographic depression caused by subsidence within a rift (a break or crack in the Earth's crust); the basin, since it is at a relatively low elevation, usually contains freshwater bodies such as rivers and lakes.
rock weathering	the breaking down of solid rock into small particles. See CHEMICAL WEATHERING and PHYSICAL WEATHERING.
Rodinia	a supercontinent that contained most or all of Earth's landmass, between 1.1 billion and 750 million years ago, during the PRECAMBRIAN. Geologists are not sure of the exact size and shape of Rodinia. It was analogous to but not the same supercontinent as PANGAEA, which formed several hundred million years later during the PERMIAN.
Sankey Diagram	a diagram that depicts flows of any kind, where the width of each flow pictured is based on its quantity.
savanna	a grassland in tropical or subtropical regions.
sea ice	frozen seawater at the surface of the ocean.
sea level	global sea level is the average height of Earth's oceans. Local sea level is the height of the ocean as measured along the coast relative to a specific point on land.
seafloor spreading	the formation of new crust around an oceanic ridge when two adjacent oceanic plates move in opposite directions and lava erupts from between them, hardens, and then the new material moves apart.
sediment	grains of broken rock, crystals, skeletal fragments, and ORGANIC MATTER.
severe weather	dangerous weather events that can cause harm to life and property.

Silurian	a geologic time period spanning from 443 to 419 million years ago. During the Silurian, jawed and bony fish diversified, and life first began to appear on land.
snowpack	snow accumulated over time, often in mountainous areas that have a long cold season. When snowpack melts it feeds streams and rivers.
soil	the accumulation of natural materials that collect on Earth's surface above the bedrock.
solar energy	electrical or thermal energy derived from the sun's radiation, either through collection and conversion via photovoltaic cells, or through passive solar heating.
solar flare	a sudden release of energy near the sun's surface which appears very bright from the Earth.
solar flux	the rate of flow of solar energy across an area such as the surface of the Earth.
solar radiation	electromagnetic energy emitted by the sun.
solution aversion	the idea that claims (such as the influence of climate change) might be rejected because the implication of accepting those claims would be accepting solutions that require sweeping (and therefore challenging) changes to the systems and cultures in which one lives and works.
status quo bias	an emotional bias and a preference for the current state of affairs.
steppe	a large, flat, dry grassland area.
storm surge	a large volume of ocean water pushed onto land by offshore winds during a storm.
stratosphere	the second layer above the Earth's surface in the ATMOSPHERE. The stratosphere reaches to about 50 kilometers (30 miles) above the Earth's surface.
stratospheric ozone	a region of OZONE gas in the STRATOSPHERE.

Glossary

Sturtian glaciation	a time in Earth's history, around 717 to 660 million years ago, when the entire planet may have been covered in ice.
sunk-cost fallacy	the tendency to pour resources into a system in part to justify the resources already used.
sunspot	dark areas on the surface of the sun that are cooler than surrounding regions. Sunspots typically last from a few days to a few months. SOLAR FLARES can erupt from sunspots.
sunspot cycle	an 11-year cycle over which the number of SUNSPOTS varies, associated with a cyclical variation in the sun's magnetic field.
system	a combination of interacting parts whose interaction creates behaviors that might not occur if each part were isolated.
tar sand	a mixture of clay, sand, water, and bitumen, a thick oil that can be extracted and refined into liquid oil.
tectonic plate	a section of the Earth's lithosphere that moves along the surface of the Earth. The scientific theory of plate tectonics is that Earth's crust consists of a series of 7 or 8 large plates and numerous small ones. Plate tectonics are responsible for the distribution of the Earth's continents, for the uplift and position of mountain ranges, and for many other features of the Earth's surface.
temperature anomaly	the difference in temperature relative to a reference time period.
thermal expansion	the increase in size or extent of a material as it warms.
thermal flux	the rate of flow of thermal energy across an area such as the surface of the Earth.
thermal radiation	the emission of electromagnetic radiation from all materials, from the motion of charged particles.
threshold	a magnitude of a quantity beyond which the behavior of a system changes or a phenomenon occurs. See also TIPPING POINT.

thunderstorm	a storm characterized by thunder and lightning, and also typically with heavy rain and high winds.
tidal flood	a flood occurring during high tides.
tipping point	an event after which the behavior of a system changes or a phenomenon occurs. See also THRESHOLD.
tornado	a vertical funnel-shaped storm with a visible horizontal rotation.
trace gases	gases whose volume makes up less than 1% of the Earth's atmosphere.
trade wind	persistent, large-scale winds in the tropical oceans which blow from the northeast in the Northern Hemisphere and from the southeast in the Southern hemisphere.
Triassic	a geologic time period that spans from 252 to 201 million years ago. During this period, DINOSAURS, PTEROSAURS, and the first mammals appear and begin to diversify.
tropical cyclone	a rapidly rotating storm system with heavy winds, a low-pressure center, and a spiral arrangement of thunderstorms. These storm systems tend to form over the tropical ocean, and are classified as HURRICANES, typhoons, or cyclones (depending on their location in the world) once winds have reached 199 kilometers per hours (74 miles per hour).
troposphere	the layer of the ATMOSPHERE extending from the Earth's surface to about 7 to 20 kilometers (4 to 12 miles) above the surface. The height of the troposphere depends upon latitude and season.
tundra	a region and climate zone with frozen ground (PERMAFROST) and no trees.

Glossary

turbine	a machine that converts rotational mechanical energy into to electrical energy. In its simplest form, a turbine consists of a shaft with a rotor with blades on one end and an electric generator on the other end. Water, wind, or steam pushes the blades and causes the rotor to rotate. Inside the generator, a coil of metal wire sits inside a large magnet. When the shaft rotates it spins the metal coil in a magnetic field, producing electric current by induction.
turbulence	irregular or chaotic movement of a fluid such as air or water.
ultraviolet light	electromagnetic radiation in the part of the spectrum with wavelengths from 10 to 400 nanometers.
urban heat island effect	a phenomenon in which an urban area experiences higher temperatures than do surrounding rural areas as a result of pollution, pavement, and the surfaces of buildings magnifying localized heating.
vertebrate	an animal with a backbone, such as fishes, amphibians, reptiles, birds, and mammals.
visible light	electromagnetic radiation in the part of the spectrum with wavelengths from about 400 to 750 nanometers.
volcanic sulfates	sulfate molecules in the atmosphere formed from chemical reactions with sulfur dioxide released in volcanic eruptions.
wastewater	water that has been used in residential or commercial activities and which needs to be treated before being released back into the environment.
weather	fluctuations in variables such as temperature, rainfall, snowfall, and wind that last hours, days, or up to two weeks.
Western Interior Seaway	an INLAND SEA which divided North America in two along a North-South axis during the mid and late CRETACEOUS.
wetland	land region where the soil is covered or saturated with water, either for part or all of the year.

wind energy	electrical energy derived from the mechanical energy of a TURBINE which moves due to the action of the wind.
windward	the side of a mountain range or other high landmass which is facing toward the direction the wind is coming. For example, if a wind is coming from the West, the windward side of a mountain range is the western side.
Younger Dryas	an abrupt shift in the Northern Hemisphere from a warm to a cold climate and then an abrupt shift back again, occurring over about 1,200 years starting around 13,000 years ago. The shift back to a warmer climate occurred with a 10°C (18°F) rise in temperature over only a decade.

Acknowledgments

This book drew substantially from related recent PRI publications. These included the climate chapters of each of the seven regional *Teacher-Friendly Guides™ to Earth Science* (all seven chapters authored by Ingrid Zabel with co-authors Richard Kissel, Gary Lewis, Alexandra Moore, Judy Parrish, Andrielle Swaby, and Alex Wall) and the book *Climate Change Past, Present, and Future: A Very Short Guide* (by Warren Allmon, Trisha Smrecak, and Robert Ross).

We are grateful to all those who contributed a climate change big idea, listed in Chapter 2, in the form of an answer to the question "What should everyone know about climate change?"

Thank you to Jon Hendricks, PRI Director of Publications, for creating the page layout of this Guide and help with page proof editing.

Thank you to Andrielle Swaby, whose work as editor of the regional series of *Teacher-Friendly Guides to Earth Science* was foundational for this Guide, for example development of portions of the glossary, prior work on photocredits, and general advice on layout. Andrielle also created the chapter icon graphics for this book. Thanks also to Paula Mikkelsen, who developed the layout for recent versions of the *Teacher-Friendly Guides to Earth Science* upon which this Guide is based, and who co-developed parts of the glossary with Andrielle.

We are grateful to the following individuals, each of whom reviewed one or more chapters of The *Teacher-Friendly Guide™ to Climate Change*: Warren Allmon (chapters 1 to 9), Ben Brown-Steiner (3, 7, and 9), Alex Burrows (3), Art DeGaetano (3), Lou Derry (12); Heidi Lux (2), Carlie Pietsch (4), and Crystal Theesfeld (2, 5); and Gang Chen and Phoebe Cohen for feedback on specific points of chapter 4. We benefitted greatly from their insight and expertise.

Early conception of this book benefitted from feedback from an advisory panel meeting at PRI in October 2015 that included Toby Ault, Mike Breed, Ben Brown-Steiner, Fred Leff, Curt Lindy, Jennifer Mahoney, Karen Moshier, and Becky Remis.

The choice of content of the Guide has been influenced by discussions with Joe Henderson and Seamus McGraw, by presentations at the Tompkins County Climate Protection Initiative, and by our co-hosts of the Teaching Controversial Issues workshops at Geological Society of America annual conferences: Minda Berbeco, Glenn Dolphin, Tanya Furman, Laura Guertin, Richard Kissell, Scott Mandia, Mark Nielsen, and Peg Steffen.

Thank you to Natalie Mahowald, Cornell University Department of Earth and Atmospheric Sciences (EAS), for involving PRI in the Broader Impacts component of her National Science Foundation grant AGS 1049033, which paid for initial development of this Guide. This project also benefitted from related funding for PRI's climate change education program, including grants from the Park Foundation (Ithaca, NY) and an NSF grant (AGS-1349605) to Gang Chen, Cornell EAS (now UCLA Atmospheric and Oceanic Sciences). This book also benefitted indirectly from work done by Ingrid Zabel for the New York Climate Change Science Clearinghouse, through a grant from the NYS Energy Research and Development Authority to Art DeGaetano of Cornell University (EAS).

Figure Credits

Creative Commons enables the sharing and reuse of media through a variety of free copyright licenses. The Creative Commons licenses used by images in this publication can be found at the following URLs:

CC0 1.0 Universal Public Domain Dedication: https://creativecommons.org/publicdomain/zero/1.0/deed.en
CC Public Domain: https://commons.wikimedia.org/wiki/Commons:Licensing#Material_in_the_public_domain
CC Attribution 2.0 Generic: https://creativecommons.org/licenses/by/2.0/deed.en
CC Attribution-NoDerivs 2.0 Generic [CC BY-ND 2.0]: https://creativecommons.org/licenses/by-nd/2.0/
CC Attribution 2.5 Generic: https://creativecommons.org/licenses/by/2.5/deed.en
CC by SA 3.0: http://creativecommons.org/licenses/by-sa/3.0/
CC-BY-SA-4.0: https://creativecommons.org/licenses/by-sa/4.0/

Chapter 1: Introduction

Box 1.1a: "Wars," [CC Attribution 2.5 Generic] via Wikimedia Commons
Box 1.1b: "Fortunate4now," [CC0 1.0 Universal Public Domain Dedication] via Wikimedia Commons
1.1: NASA
1.2: Robert Ross, adapted from Figure 8 in Peterson, Garry; Allen, Craig R.; and Holling, C. S., 1998, Ecological Resilience, Biodiversity, and Scale, Ecosystems 1998 1(1): 6–18 (http://digitalcommons.unl.edu/cgi/viewcontent.cgi?article=1003&context=ncfwrustaff)
1.3: Aerial photograph (left) from the Cornell University Library Digital Collections New York Aerial Photographs from 1938. Satellite photograph (right) screenshot from Google Maps, retrieved May 2014.

Chapter 2: What Should Everyone Understand About Climate Change and Energy?

2.1: Paul Price, incorporating illustration of temperature reconstructions compiled by Jos Hagelaars.
2.2: Don Duggan-Haas

Chapter 3: What is Climate?

3.1: Climate Change Past, Present & Future: A Very Short Guide, Warren D. Allmon, Trisha A. Smrecak, and Robert M. Ross, Paleontological Research Institution, 2010.
3.2: Ingrid Zabel
3.3: U.S. Drought Monitor, NOAA Climate.gov, https://www.climate.gov/maps-data/data-snapshots/usdroughtmonitor-weekly-ndmc-2016-09-06?theme=Drought
3.4: Wade Greenberg-Brand
3.5: Climate Change Past, Present & Future: A Very Short Guide, Warren D. Allmon, Trisha A. Smrecak, and Robert M. Ross, Paleontological Research Institution, 2010.
3.6: NOAA

Figure Credits

3.7: Climate Change Past, Present & Future: A Very Short Guide, Warren D. Allmon, Trisha A. Smrecak, and Robert M. Ross, Paleontological Research Institution, 2010.

3.8: Modified after a graph produced by Robert A. Rohde for Global Warming Art.com. Figure found in Climate Change Past, Present & Future: A Very Short Guide, Warren D. Allmon, Trisha A. Smrecak, and Robert M. Ross, Paleontological Research Institution, 2010.

3.9: Climate Change Past, Present & Future: A Very Short Guide, Warren D. Allmon, Trisha A. Smrecak, and Robert M. Ross, Paleontological Research Institution, 2010.

3.10: Map by US Geological Survey. Figure found in Climate Change Past, Present & Future: A Very Short Guide, Warren D. Allmon, Trisha A. Smrecak, and Robert M. Ross, Paleontological Research Institution, 2010.

Chapter 4: Past Climates

4.1: Jane Picconi

4.2: Graeme Churchard [CC Attribution 2.0 Generic] via Wikimedia Commons

4.3: Adapted from image by John Goodge, USGS

4.4: Adapted from Wikipedia

4.5: Jim Houghton

4.6: Robert Rohde [CC-BY-SA-3.0] via Wikimedia Commons

4.7: Adapted from image by Ron Blakey, NAU Geology

4.8: Adapted from image by Ron Blakey, NAU Geology

Box 4.3: Figure A: Fossil palm frond and alligator photographs by Paleontological Research Institution. Benthic foraminifera photographs by United States Geological Survey. Pollen grain photographs by Dartmouth University.

Box 4.3: Figure B: Photographs by Warren Allmon (top left and right), Alejandra Gandolfo (lower left), and Judith Nagel-Myers (lower right).

4.9: Pangaea Box: Wade Greenberg-Brand, adapted from image by USGS

4.10: Kevin Walsh [CC-BY-2.0] via Flickr

4.11: Dirk Van de Velde [CC-BY-2.0] via Flickr

4.12: Adapted from image by Ron Blakey, NAU Geology

4.13: Wade Greenberg-Brand, adapted from image by William A. Cobban and Kevin C. McKinney, USGS

4.14: A), B), and D) James St. John [CC-BY-2.0] via Flickr; C) Didier Descouens [CC-BY-SA-4.0] via Wikimedia Commons

4.15: Modified after a graph produced by Robert A. Rohde for Global Warming Art.com

4.16: Wade Greenberg-Brand, adapted from image by Lisiecki, L.E. and Rayno, M.E. (2005), A Pliocene–Pleistocene stack of 57 globally distributed benthic $\delta18O$ records, Paleoceanography, 20, PA1003, doi:10.1029/2004PA001071

4.17: Wade Greenberg-Brand, adapted from data by NOAA

4.18: Jim Houghton

4.19: Jim Houghton

4.20: Modified after a graph produced by Robert A. Rohde for Global Warming Art.com

Box 4.7: Photograph by Warren Allmon

4.21: Modified after a graph on page 58 of W.S. Broecker, *Fossil Fuel, CO₂, and the Angry Climate Beast* (2003), Eldigio Press, Palisades, NY, 112 pp.

Figure Credits

4.22: Wade Greenberg-Brand, adapted from image by Illinois State Geological Survey

4.23: Modified after a graph produced by Robert A. Rohde for Global Warming Art.com.

Box 4.8 Fig A: Clinton Steeds [CC Attribution 2.0 Generic] via Wikimedia Commons

Box 4.8 Fig B: Warren Allmon

4.24: Modified after Mann, M.E., R.S. Bradley, and M.K. Hughes (1998), Global-scale temperature patterns and climate forcings over the past six centuries, Nature, 392: 779-787.

Chapter 5: Evidence and Causes of Recent Climate Change

5.1: Data from NASA Goddard Institute for Space Studies (GISS), http://climate.nasa.gov/vital-signs/global-temperature/

5.2: NOAA

5.3: NOAA, http://climate.nasa.gov/vital-signs/carbon-dioxide/

Box 5.1: Figure adapted from an image from NASA's Imagine the Universe

Box 5.2: NOAA National Centers for Environmental Information

5.4: NASA, http://climate.nasa.gov/vital-signs/land-ice/

5.5: MODIS images from NASA's Terra satellite, http://earthobservatory.nasa.gov/Features/WorldOfChange/larsenb.php

5.6: NASA EarthObservatory, http://earthobservatory.nasa.gov/Features/WorldOfChange/sea_ice.php

5.7: NASA, https://sealevel.nasa.gov/

5.8: NOAA Tides and Currents, Sea Level Trends, https://tidesandcurrents.noaa.gov/sltrends/sltrends.html

Box 5.4: Ingrid Zabel

5.9: Third National Climate Assessment (2014); data from Boden, T., G. Marland, and R. Andres (2012): Global, regional, and national fossil-fuel CO_2 emissions. Carbon Dioxide Information Analysis Center, Oak Ridge National Laboratory, US Department of Energy, Oak Ridge, Tenn., USA

Chapter 6: US Regional Climates Current and Future

Box 6.1: Wade Greenberg-Brand, adapted from figures by NOAA and Grieser et al., 2006, World Map of the Köppen-Geiger climate classification updated, Meteorologische Zeitschrift, 15: 259-263.

6.1: US Climate Atlas, National Centers for Environmental Information, https://www.ncdc.noaa.gov/climateatlas/

Box 6.3: NASA Earth Observatory, https://www.nasa.gov/topics/earth/features/heat-island-sprawl.html

6.2: US Third National Climate Assessment (2014). Original source: updated from Global Climate Change Impacts in the United States (2009); Thomas R. Karl, Jerry Melillo, and Thomas C. Peterson, eds., US Global Change Research Program.

6.3: Northeast Regional Climate Center, http://www.nrcc.cornell.edu/

6.4: NOAA Tides and Currents, Sea Level Trends, https://tidesandcurrents.noaa.gov/sltrends/sltrends.html

6.5: Adapted from US Third National Climate Assessment (2014). Original source: Kenneth Kunkel, Cooperative Institute for Climate and Satellites - NC.

6.6: NOAA Coastal Flood Exposure Mapper

Figure Credits

6.7: US Third National Climate Assessment (2014). Original source: updated from Kunkel et al. (2013), Regional Climate Trends and Scenarios for the U.S. National Climate Assessment: Part 3. Climate of the Midwest U.S. NOAA Technical Report NESDIS 142-3.

Box 6.4: USDA, http://planthardiness.ars.usda.gov/PHZMWeb/

6.8: NOAA Coastal Flood Exposure Mapper

6.9: Adapted from Scenarios for Climate Assessment and Adaptation, US Global Change Research Program

6.10: Wade Greenberg-Brand

6.11: US Geological Survey

6.12: Tom Hiett, reproduced with permission

6.13: US Third National Climate Assessment (2014)

6.14: US Third National Climate Assessment (2014)

6.15: US Bureau of Land Reclamation

6.16: Adapted from Scenarios for Climate Assessment and Adaptation, US Global Change Research Program

6.17: Adapted from Scenarios for Climate Assessment and Adaptation, US Global Change Research Program

6.18: Global Climate Change Impacts in the United States 2009 Report. Original source: Petersen, A., Anticipating Sea Level Rise Response in Puget Sound In School of Marine Affairs. Vol. Master of Marine Affairs. Seattle Washington: University of Washington, Seattle, 2007.

6.19: NOAA

6.20: Adapted from Giambelluca, T.W., X. Shuai, M.L. Barnes, R.J. Alliss, R.J. Longman, T. Miura, Q. Chen, A.G. Frazier, R.G. Mudd, L. Cuo, and A.D. Businger. 2014. Evapotranspiration of Hawai'i. Final report submitted to the U.S. Army Corps of Engineers—Honolulu District, and the Commission on Water Resource Management, State of Hawai'i.

6.21: Adapted from Giambelluca, T.W., Q. Chen, A.G. Frazier, J.P. Price, Y.-L. Chen, P.-S. Chu, J.K. Eischeid, and D.M. Delparte, 2013: Online Rainfall Atlas of Hawai'i. Bull. Amer. Meteor. Soc. 94, 313-316, doi: 10.1175/BAMS-D-11-00228.1

6.22: Adapted from Scenarios for Climate Assessment and Adaptation, US Global Change Research Program

6.23: Adapted from Scenarios for Climate Assessment and Adaptation, US Global Change Research Program

6.24: US Third National Climate Assessment (2014). Adapted from orignal source: Stewart et al. (2013), Regional Climate Trends and Scenarios for the U.S. National Climate Assessment: Part 7. Climate of Alaska. NOAA Technical Report NESDIS 142-7.

Chapter 7: Climate Change Mitigation

7.1: Adapted from image with permission from Carbon Mitigation Initiative, Princeton University

7.2: Adapted from image with permission from Carbon Mitigation Initiative, Princeton University

7.3: US Energy Information Administration (eia.gov)

7.4: US Energy Information Administration (eia.gov)

7.5: National Energy Education Development Project

7.6: United States Bureau of Reclamation [Public Domain] via Wikimedia Commons

Figure Credits

7.7: Winchell Joshua, U.S. Fish and Wildlife Service [Public Domain] via Wikimedia Commons

7.8: National Energy Education Development Project

7.9: Nancy Arazon, US EPA [Public Domain] via Wikimedia Commons

7.10: Raysonho [CC0 1.0 Universal Public Domain Dedication] via Wikimedia Commons

7.11: National Energy Education Development Project

7.12: US EPA

7.13: Geoffrey Coates, used with permission

7.14: Erwin Cole, USDA Natural Resources Conservation Service [Public Domain] via Wikimedia Commons

7.15: US EPA [Public Domain] via Wikimedia Commons

Box 7.7: Energy Guide Label from US Federal Trade Commission

Chapter 8: Geoengineering

8.1: Alexandra Moore

8.2: NASA Earth Observatory, Nov. 9, 2009, [Public Domain] via Wikimedia Commons

8.3: NOAA, Prof. Gordon T. Taylor, Stony Brook University, 1983 [Public Domain] via Wikimedia Commons

8.4: NASA Earth Observatory, Jeff Schmaltz, MODIS Rapid Response Team

8.5: D. Harlow, USGS [Public Domain] via Wikimedia Commons

8.6: NASA Earth Observations

Chapter 9: Climate Change Adaptation

9.1: "B137" [CC0 1.0 Universal Public Domain Dedication] via Wikimedia Commons

9.2: US Fish and Wildlife Service [CC Attribution 2.0 Generic] via Wikimedia Commons

9.3: "Juliancolton" [Public domain] via Wikimedia Commons

9.4: Airman 1st Class Rustie Kramer [Public domain] http://www.jba.af.mil/News/Photos/igphoto/2001635627/

9.5: US Third National Climate Assessment (2014). Original source: updated from Global Climate Change Impacts in the United States (2009); Thomas R. Karl, Jerry Melillo, and Thomas C. Peterson, eds., US Global Change Research Program.

9.6: Clarion Associates/EPA [Public Domain] via Wikimedia Commons

9.7: US EPA [Public Domain] via Wikimedia Commons

9.8: Yonah Walter/FEMA [Public Domain] via Wikimedia Commons

Chapter 10: Obstacles to Addressing Climate Change

10.1: *Kathy Sierra https://1wv60g2kc56t1i45ld1gqzj3-wpengine.netdna-ssl.com/wp-content/uploads/2015/02/big-frickin-wall-graphic_459x267.jpg*

Chapter 11: Perspective

Box 11.1: PremierofAlberta [CC BY-ND 2.0] via Flickr

Figure Credits

Chapter 12: Frequently Asked Questions About Climate Change

12.1: NASA Global Climate Change: Vital Signs of the Planet
12.2: NASA Goddard Institute for Space Sciences
12.3: "The tdog" [CC0 1.0 Universal Public Domain Dedication] via Wikimedia Commons

Icons

Chapter 2 Icon: Lloyd Humphreys, the Noun Project
Chapter 4 Icon: Natalka Dmitrova, Vecteezy
Chapter 10 Icon: Freepik, www.flaticon.com